To Sue Keay
in appreciation of
the very friendly and
super support for
yourself [illegible] Benchmark
team throughout the
[illegible] congress
A bit of light reading now
for your relief

Victor [illegible]

2/10/2008

RAMBLINGS OF A PERIPATETIC PAEDIATRICIAN

Previous books by author

Developing and diseased muscle. A histochemical study

The Floppy Infant

Muscle biopsy. A modern approach (with MH Brooke)

Muscle disorders in childhood

A colour atlas of muscle disorders in childhood

Gestational age of the newborn: a clinical manual
(with LMS Dubowitz)

The neurological assessment of the preterm and full-term newborn infant
(with LMS Dubowitz)

A colour atlas of brain lesions in the newborn
(with LS de Vries, LMS Dubowitz and J Pennock)

RAMBLINGS OF A PERIPATETIC PAEDIATRICIAN

Victor Dubowitz

The Memoir Club

First published in 2005 by
The Memoir Club
Stanhope Old Hall
Stanhope
Weardale
County Durham

British Library Cataloguing in Publication Data.
A catalogue record for this book is available from the British Library

ISBN: 1 84104 115 7

Typeset by TW Typesetting, Plymouth, Devon
Printed by CPI Bath

Contents

For Lilly

Preface

This is not an autobiography; rather a journey into a career in paediatrics that has spanned some 50 years, the past 47 years of which have been devoted to muscular dystrophy and other neuromuscular disorders. My career has been a somewhat unconventional one, often going off unpredictably at tangents rather than following a preset course. Following an original intention of going into general practice in South Africa, after seeing a bit of the world, I unexpectedly channeled into muscle research and paediatrics and have been there ever since. I have always followed the principle of doing what you really enjoy, rather than climbing the ladder.

After resisting the repeated overtures from the Memoir Club for a number of years, I hatched the idea of doing something pictorial, in the way of a photo-medical odyssey, given my dual passion for photography and travel. This was stimulated particularly after I had some requests to purchase some of the photographs I had on display in *Children around the world*, part of a retrospective of my publications and my artwork organised by the librarian at the Royal Postgraduate Medical School at the time of my official retirement in 1996. This gradually crystallised and I started adding snippets of specific memoirs to accompany the pictures.

The title came to me early on and ramblings just seemed to encompass my parallel interests in teaching and travel. I have always liked the word peripatetic and often use it, although I nearly dropped it a few years ago, after my clinical secretary transposed my dictation to a colleague, 'I have just returned from one of my peripatetic lecture visits to Bologna,' as '. . . one of my very pathetic lecture visits . . .'

I was at a loss for a definition of peripatetic when a friend recently asked me what exactly it meant. I looked it up in the thesaurus, which gave as synonyms itinerant, nomadic, travelling, drifting, rootless, roving. That seemed to say it all. However, I was much more taken with the description I recently came across in the *Popular Oxford Dictionary*.

> **pĕrĭpatĕ'tĭc. 1.** (*P*~) *a.* & *n.* Aristotelian [f. Aristotle's custom of walking while teaching]. **2.** *a.* (~**ally**). Going from place to place on one's business, itinerant. [F or L f. Gk (*pateō* walk)]

I was beginning to feel quite comfortable with the general flow and content, until I consulted my four sons for their opinion, and the youngest, the architect, photographer, artist, arranged to meet me in London en route from Glasgow to Milan, for a discussion. This turned into an in-depth interrogation on my objectives in writing the book, my intended audience and my main theme. He sent me back to the drawing board to sort this all out before going further. I felt completely drained and demoralised but took up the challenge. Having decided the one consistent thread through the book was my continuing interest in muscle diseases, I considered changing the title to *Muscles on the move*. But I had become too attached to my peripatetic rambling, and the possibility of a subtitle seemed to stretch an already fairly long title. I was also keen to retain a broad base rather than too narrow a focus.

Dan also strongly advised me against any thought of colour illustrations of my photography unless I could work directly with the printers, based on his own experience of doing a series of books based on his photography of neglected buildings of architectural importance. I accordingly decided to stick to black and white instead, which I have always liked since my early days of dabbling in a darkroom. Lil then came to the rescue with an offer to convert all colour prints and digital images to digital black and white, which would then be ready for the typesetter to simply drop into the text. Lil was feeling very confident after a course on *Photoshop* she had attended with Pat Clough and some additional personal tuition by him. This saved a considerable cost. But she soon realised the immensity of the task and realised she had undoubtedly bitten off a lot more than she could comfortably chew. However, given her innate tenacity, resoluteness and commitment to completing any task she tackles, she persisted and some 200 pictures later, most of which she has assembled into composite plates, the light finally appeared at the end of the tunnel and we are on normal talking terms again. If there are any of my close friends and colleagues who feel aggrieved at not being included, I hasten to assure them it was almost certainly Lil rejecting the poor quality of my low resolution digital images, rather than their importance or standing which led to their exclusion, and I shall be happy to share with them my favourites in Lil's reject album.

In addition to her major contribution with the illustrations, Lil has also been a tower of strength in encouraging me to continue the project, which started in a modest way and just continued to grow and grow. I am also very grateful to a number of friends for constructive advice on the inclusion of various topics in the text, and in particular Fernando Tomé, Alan Emery, Kati Vamos, Jane Duncan and Sylvia Caveney, and to Simon Stern for his expertise in relation to the visual presentation of the material. I also appreciate the helpful discussions with Sheila Seacroft, my designated editor with the Memoir Club. I am also most grateful to TW Typesetting for their meticulous care in the placing of all the illustrations and for completing the typesetting in record time.

1

Roots

I was born and grew up in a small country town called Beaufort West, in the semi-desert, sheep-farming, Great Karroo in the Cape Province in South Africa, which nobody seemed to have heard of until Chris Barnard, the pioneer heart transplant surgeon, said that he came from there as well.

The town was on the main road and rail route between Cape Town and Johannesburg, some 300 miles north of Cape Town, and a popular stopover for motorists. The main road, Donkin Street, ran north/south through the town and was just a mile in length, with the town jail at the northern end, and a park of mainly eucalyptus trees, the plantation, with a cluster of swings for children, at the south. The main street was lined on either side by pear trees and flowing furrows for residents to irrigate their gardens with water from the local dam at the north end of the town.

In parallel with the main street were New Street to the west and Bird Street to the east, intersected by many cross streets, the central one being Church Street, with the landmark Dutch Reformed church on the corner of Donkin and Church Streets. The town's first traffic light was installed at this intersection in the 1950s. My parents had a general dealer's store in New Street, just north of Church Street, and we lived in an adjacent house.

The community was mainly a farming one, and the predominant language of the 5000 white inhabitants of the town was Afrikaans, as was that of the Coloured, mixed race, community who lived in a separate township on the edge of the town. The Africans, who numbered some 3000, lived in a separate area, the 'location' as it was then called, just south of the town, and spoke their own Xhosa language as well as English and Afrikaans, which were the two official languages of the country and taught in parallel in all schools.

In parallel with many other country towns in South Africa of comparable size, Beaufort West had a thriving Jewish community, with its own synagogue and all-purpose rabbi, who officiated at all the religious services, was the tutor of the children at the cheder classes, equivalent to Sunday school, and also responsible for the ritual slaughter of chickens by the traditional kosher techniques, which he did locally in the backyard of his residence adjacent to the synagogue. I have vivid memories of taking a chicken from our chicken run for slaughter. During my schooldays in the 1930s there were about 20 Jewish families, most of whom owned general stores, including four Dubowitz families.

The Jewish community integrated well with the local Afrikaner community, although in parallel with the rise of National Socialism in Europe, even in this small country town there were already in the 1930s and early years of the Second World War (1939–45) two active right wing movements. One was a pro-Nazi, anti-semitic greyshirt movement, headed not by an Afrikaner but by an Englishman, a local hotelkeeper. Perhaps he had been an admirer of Moseley. The second was an extreme right wing element of Afrikaners, the *Ossewa Brandwag*, literally 'Guards of the Ox Wagons', who were rabidly anti-British and pro-German. The Afrikaners had never forgiven the British for the atrocities against their women and children in their newly invented concentration camps in the 1899–1902 Boer war, which seemed to have become imprinted through successive generations. But for the diplomacy and statesmanship of General Smuts at the outbreak of the war in September 1939, which narrowly won over the parliament, South Africa would certainly have remained 'neutral' with a strong pro-German bias. Although South Africa was pretty remote from the ravages of war in Europe, the volunteers for the South African army played a decisive role in routing Rommel in the North African campaign and subsequently in Italy.

Beaufort West also had the dubious honour of having as its member of parliament for many years Eric Louw, who was one of the most vindictive and outspoken anti-Semites in parliament and lost no opportunity of blaming the Jews for all the ills in the world. He had served as a Nationalist Party member of parliament for Beaufort West from the 1930s right through the war years and became minister of foreign affairs when the Nationalists came to power in 1947. He was indeed so firmly entrenched as the parliamentary representative for Beaufort West, that it was remarked that even if Jesus Christ stood for the United Party against Eric Louw, he would have no chance.

Grandparents and roots

My grandparents on both sides of my family had emigrated from Lithuania at the turn of the century, as a direct result of the Russian pogroms and repressive measures against the Jews in the villages and towns throughout Lithuania after the assassination of Czar Alexander II in 1881. I do not know the exact circumstances of my paternal grandfather, born in a small village in Lithuania called Pasvetin (now Pasvitinys) in 1874, coming out on his own on a ship to South Africa in the 1890s. It is possible that like many before and after him, he embarked from a port such as Memel (now Kleipeda) in Lithuania, bound for Southampton and then took any available liner which might be heading for South Africa or North America or South America, as chance would have it. Once one member of a family established roots in a new country he would then save up to bring other members of the family out, and this was certainly the case of the Dubowitzes from Lithuania right into the ensuing decades, with the shipping records of the Union Castle line listing whole families joining a husband or father in a specific town.

Once my grandfather, Nathan Dubowitz, reached Cape Town he headed, like many others, for the hinterland, ending up as *smouses* (itinerant peddlers) in remote country towns, amongst the local farming communities. Several contemporary Dubowitzes ended up in small towns in the eastern Cape Province, such as Aberdeen and Jansenville, even smaller than Beaufort West. My grandfather settled in Aberdeen.

With an acute shortage of female companions in these remote country environs, my grandfather fell in love with a young Afrikaner girl, who, to the undoubted dismay of her strictly orthodox Dutch Reformed Calvinist family, not only married him but went through the full ritual of conversion to Judaism, and perhaps less surprisingly remained the most strictly observant Jew in our whole extended family.

My grandmother was born in Aberdeen in October 1879, and baptised at the local Dutch Reformed Church in May 1880. She was converted to Judaism and had a Jewish wedding in 1904. I have a copy of the original marriage certificate (*ketubah*). I presume they must have had a civil wedding in 1900 or 1901, given my father was born in Aberdeen in 1903, and his older brother in 1902!

My grandmother's family name was Claassen, and it was of interest that recently one of the present generation compiled a family tree of the Claassen family, which went back several centuries to their Dutch forbears. He was now keen to complete a large black hole in the family tree, referred to as the 'Claassen Jode' (the Claassen Jews). It transpires that my grandmother's grandmother was a small girl at the time of the Great Trek, and was with the Piet Retief contingent at the battle of Blood River in 1836, which was the victorious battle of revenge for a Voortrekker party seeking negotiation with the Zulu chief Dingaan who had been massacred. The family name on her mother's side was van Vuuren, a well known extreme right wing ultra-orthodox group, who were called '*doppers*', as they were the custodians of the moral integrity of the church. My grandmother had certainly brought down the line a very strong and dominant personality, who had strong views on all matters, and I was a regular visitor on a Sunday morning for a cup of well-brewed tea and a good dose of her views on current events and her general philosophy on life. I am relieved to add that the pendulum of political orientation has swung right across to the other side.

There was certainly also a longevity gene in her family as both she and her mother before her lived to 93 and she died suddenly in her bath one morning, having had her full faculties to the end and still baking her own bread each week. Her daughter, Annie, also lived till 92 and was reciting large tracts of Shakespeare at her 90th birthday celebration.

Nathan Dubowitz acquired two farms, Pitfontein in the Aberdeen area and Kroonplaas south of Beaufort West. He died in 1932 and bequeathed Pitfontein to my father and his sister Annie, who sold it during the great depression in the 1930s, and Kroonplaas to Jack, who continued to farm it into the late 1930s. I still recall visits to it over weekends in my schooldays. I also recall my father often mentioning they had sold Pitfontein for a song during the depression of the 1930s, each time the current farmer used to come and visit us to do some shopping and to bring us a huge basket of oranges from the farm.

My paternal grandparents, Nathan and Esther, resplendent in ostrich feather hat. c. 1910

ק״ק תקות ישראל
פארטעליזאבעט

אסתר בת אברהם אב״נו

Left. Dutch Reformed Church in Aberdeen, Eastern Cape Province, where Esther was baptised in 1880

Right. Jewish Ketubah (marriage certificate) 1904

My sister in pram and myself with my cousin Simeon (left) on his father Jack's farm Kroonplaas near Beaufort West c. 1934

My grandfather Nathan with a sheep, 1920s

My grandfather moved to Beaufort West in 1913 and established a general dealer's business in Plantation Street in the southern end of the town, just off Donkin Street, opposite the plantation, and the family lived in an adjacent house. They were commonly called general dealers and produce merchants as they also dealt in bones and hides. This activity probably dated from the activities as a *smous* in remote farm areas where they would also barter essential materials required by the farmers in return for hides or wool. All three of their sons as well as their daughter subsequently remained in the town and had individual shops.

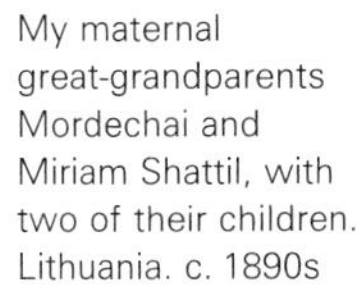

My maternal great-grandparents Mordechai and Miriam Shattil, with two of their children. Lithuania. c. 1890s

Maternal family

My mother's family, Schattel or Shattil, came from a large town to the west of Lithuania called Telz in Yiddish and now Telsiai in Lithuanian, where she was born in 1903, the third of six siblings. It was well known worldwide for its Yeshiva of Jewish rabbinical study. The family owned a corn mill and were apparently quite well off. My great-grandparents, Mordechai and Miriam, had nine children. Three brothers, including my grandfather Victor, emigrated to Rhodesia around 1910, and a fourth headed for the USA.

My grandfather contracted severe malaria with blackwater fever and was advised he would not survive unless he left Rhodesia. So he packed up with his wife and six small children and settled in Heidelberg Cape, where the Heidelberg Hotel he owned still stands. He died not long after of his malaria and my grandmother later transferred with her youngest daughter Minnie to the Kingsley Hotel in Muizenberg, a popular holiday resort on the Indian Ocean side of the Cape Peninsula, frequented in the summer holiday period in December and January by a large influx of holidaymakers, mainly from Johannesburg, and where we also spent many of our summer vacations. I still remember the enthusiasm of my sister and myself to have our photos taken with the lions, in a photographic studio on the beach front.

My maternal grandparents Victor and Bela Schattel, and their two eldest children Leo and Fanny, taken in Lithuania 1890s

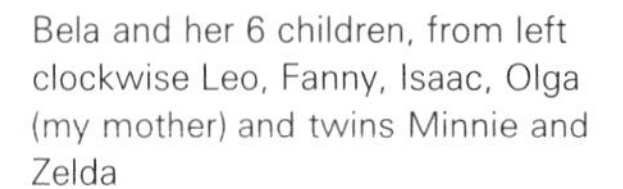

Bela and her 6 children, from left clockwise Leo, Fanny, Isaac, Olga (my mother) and twins Minnie and Zelda

Heidelberg Hotel, Heidelberg, Cape 1920

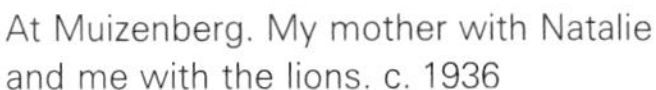

At Muizenberg. My mother with Natalie and me with the lions. c. 1936

With my father on Muizenberg beach 1942

My parents

Around the time of his marriage in 1930, my father opened a general dealer shop in New Street and also dealt actively in hides and bones, which he used to buy from the locals and then sell to wholesale merchants, whose commercial traveller used to visit at regular intervals to buy the stock. My father seemed very happy in his running of the business and always had a very friendly and outgoing personality. In addition to a number of regular customers amongst the farming community he also had a large number from amongst the railway personnel and amongst the local Coloured and African community. We always lived in the house adjoining the property. I know that at one time in the late 1940s my father was offered the purchase of one of the local garages, which had the franchise for Chevrolet and Buick cars, but he was reluctant to change his horizons or his lifestyle, and was content to continue in his current capacity, even though he was aware that there might be considerably more wealth in the other opportunities. My mother also actively helped in the

Portrait of my father as store manager of his father's shop, Beaufort West,1920s

My father's shop in New Street, Beaufort West, 1950s

My parents Charley and Olga at their wedding in 1930

Family photograph in 1944 at my barmitzvah (13 years) with Natalie and Leslie day-to-day running of the shop, but that did not detract her from smothering my younger sister and myself with unstinting love and affection.

Although my father never got involved in any local politics, such as serving on the local council, he always liked to refer to himself as the 'mayor of New Street'. He was very gregarious by nature and regularly frequented the pubs attached to the various local hotels to meet up with various friends for a drink. He was particularly partial to his whisky.

Looking back, I think my father served an important role model for me. I was always conscious of his friendly personality and interest in people, and his spontaneous and natural generosity. He always seemed to enjoy giving much more than receiving. He seemed to have a simple philosophy that life is for living, and money is for spending, within affordable limits. He also had a credo for independence and not depending on the charity of others. I still have a very vivid recollection of the one occasion when I accompanied him to Cape Town and Muizenberg, at the age of about 11 or 12, and had him all to myself for a few days.

My siblings

My sister, Natalie, was 18 months younger. We grew up close to each other, but also seemed to get into frequent pitched battles with each other, and I clearly recall that if there were any question of apportioning blame, my sister always got the sympathy of my father, whilst I got that of my mother. Where verbal discipline failed, there was always the threat of physical discipline, either with a leather strap or the slipper, which might entail one or two strokes on the buttocks, if the threat itself were not sufficient. This was part of the normal practice of the day, and I think we accepted it without any recrimination or rancour, much as physical punishment was part of the norm at school as well. I do think discipline is important for the growing child, but a clear distinction needs to be drawn between what is reasonable parental control, and what becomes physical or psychological abuse of the child.

Natalie also embarked on a medical career at Cape Town University but forsook it for matrimony early on in her career. She settled in the town of Wellington some 40 miles north of

Cape Town and continued to fire on all cylinders, with interest in various activities including politics. She stood as a councillor for the local town council and managed to unseat one of the elders of the town. This had an immediate and somewhat dramatic sequel. In the main Cape Town news bulletin of the South African Broadcasting Corporation at lunchtime that day, the announcer made a serious and potentially libellous slip of the tongue, and instead of announcing that she was the first woman councillor in Wellington, announced that she was the first Coloured woman councillor in Wellington. The regional manager of SABC instantly realised they were in dire danger of a major lawsuit for defamation of character, given the sharp divides of the apartheid system, so he got straight into his car and arrived unexpectedly and unannounced on her doorstep a couple of hours later. He expressed profuse apologies on behalf of the Corporation, and assured her that the subsequent news services would carry a correction and public apology and this would also follow in writing.

She emigrated to Sydney, Australia, in 1985 with her youngest son, Mark, then aged 12, whom she had acquired in the same year as a son-in-law for her eldest daughter. She established a health store in the historical Strand Arcade in downtown Sydney, and not knowing the difference between Vitamins A and C, she attended lectures at the School of Natural Therapies, and soon had clients from all the corners of the world. She retired after 14 years and still keeps in contact with clients in Europe and Japan.

Her daughter and older son followed her to Australia a few years later, and finally also the youngest son, Ivor, a dentist in practice in London for some years. Living in Sydney was certainly a far cry for her from the small country towns of Beaufort West or Wellington and gave her ample opportunity to indulge her passions for symphonic music, opera, ballet, reading, gardening, walking and lastly children. In her retirement she has started minding children professionally, and feels she could have been quite content as a super nanny. Although we have run neck on neck in totting up nine grandchildren, she has always been several lengths ahead of me, with hers ranging from 28 down to six years, when we had all but left the starting line.

We have maintained contact and still meet up for family celebrations from time to time, but the distance has rather isolated her from the rest of the family.

My brother Leslie, born some 13 years after me, was still in infancy when I left for university. He grew up essentially as an only child in our household, as my sister also left a couple of years later. Les was an enthusiastic letter writer and we kept up a regular correspondence once he learnt to write, and he was constantly reprimanding me for my tardy responses. However, we only got to know each other more intimately in our adult life. He also completed a career in medicine at UCT. After an initial period of specialisation in obstetrics, including some residency posts in London, he returned to family practice, initially in Cape Town and eventually in the United States, after emigrating permanently. For many years he has been director of the emergency room services of the Good Samaritan Hospital in Pottsville, Pennsylvania, a coal mining town made famous by the writings of John O'Hara. He has also had an interest in industrial medicine and been the director of the industrial medicine department of the Good Samaritan regional medical centre and consultant to the Alcoa aluminium company in the area. The proximity of Pottsville to New York, Philadelphia and Washington, has enabled me to take in a slight detour on many of my academic visits, although he would chastise me that it is not often enough. We both also tend to gravitate readily across the Atlantic pond for family celebrations on either side. Both his daughters have followed academic careers, Tamara in public health in the field of social epidemiology and Nadine in internal medicine. Both got their doctorates in 2005.

The great flood of 1941

One of my most vivid memories of my childhood is the great flood of 1941, an episode which remains imprinted in my mind, and I can relive as if it happened yesterday. On Sunday morning 6 April 1941, at 8 o'clock in the morning, neighbours came rushing into our house to alert us that the Gamka (which means dry) river, which ran parallel to New Street about 50 yards away, was in flood following torrential rain in the nearby Nieweveld mountains and was about to burst its banks behind our house as a result of impaction of floating trees against the bridge in Church Street, which ran at right-angles to New Street.

We rapidly dressed and rushed across the road to our neighbour who was on higher ground. Soon after we got there

With Les and Natalie at Tamara's batmitzvah, Pottsville PA, September 1987

Tamara (centre) on passing her DSc, Harvard, with husband Jay Aaronson, and sister Nadine who graduated MD, Brown University the floodwaters started rushing through our house; a really terrifying experience. We then had to move further away into the main street which ran parallel to New Street, and eventually reached my father's brother Jack's house at the bottom end of Donkin Street, and stayed with him for several months until our home and the adjoining shop were refurbished.

We had just under six feet of water in our house and the garage and other outbuildings retained the muddy high-water mark on the garage wall after the repainting of the rest the property.

This was a most unusual incident as Beaufort West lies in a large arid area called the Great Karroo, which is semi-desert and averages around ten inches of rain per year, which usually falls in the hot, dry summer in a series of spectacular thunderstorms. The brown arid desert then comes to life within weeks, with a tremendous show of wild flowers. The hardy Karroo bush shrub is able to withstand the harsh conditions and is very effective in sustaining the sheep, the main farming activity of the region

Early childhood in Beaufort West

I have a few very clear memories of my early childhood. One was the annual fancy dress competition which was held in the Lyric Hall in the north end of the town, when my mother always arranged for my sister and myself to have special costumes made by the nuns of the local roman catholic church, who had a special facility for this. I can still picture the year I was dressed up as a lobster and another as a chef and my sister as a fairy. It always seemed important to get a prize and we were very disappointed if we did not. But miraculously one of the many travelling salesmen who used to visit my father's store on behalf of various wholesalers in Cape Town, a Mr Winokur, stood out above all the rest as he always brought a present for my sister and myself, which in some ways compensated for missing out at the fancy dress party. Natalie has a clear recollection of the fancy dress party in the Lyric Hall in Beaufort West, when she was a fairy and I a chef, and also of receiving as a prize a doll's china tea set in the shape of elephants, which she still has. She also recalls my flood of tears at not having qualified for a prize, for which I have a total, possibly selective, amnesia.

Natalie as a fairy and me as a chef at annual fancy dress competition in the Lyric Hall, Beaufort West.

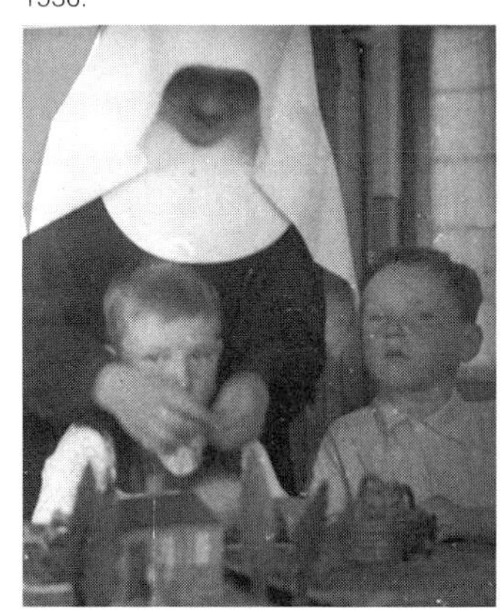

St Joseph's kindergarten, sub A class, with Alan Karabus, Beaufort West, 1936.

I also had a birthday party each year for about half a dozen of my close friends and I can recall having had a mock pipe which features in one of these birthday parties of which I have a picture.

Schooling

The schooling in those days was divided into three phases, infant school from the age of five or six comprising sub A, sub B and standard 1, then primary school, standard 2 to 6, and high school for standard 7 to 10. The provincial junior certificate examination was at the end of standard 8 and the senior certificate standard 10. For my kindergarten years I went to a local private school run by the nuns, which was of a high standard. Alan Karabus, born four days after me, also went there and we remained very close friends, as well as academic rivals throughout our school-days. I also had numerous friends across the various religious and cultural divides. On the other hand, there was no social contact at all with the black or coloured children, who were barred from the local schools and churches, and had separate schools under the longstanding traditional divide of apartheid, which dated back to the early days after the establishment of the Union of South Africa in 1910. The predominant language in a country area like Beaufort West was Afrikaans, but everybody was bilingual, up to a point, as one had to do both English and Afrikaans as compulsory subjects all the way through matriculation.

Threat and fear of childhood diseases

Whilst still at primary school, one of my classmates, Peter de Klerk, took ill with croup, a common respiratory disorder. He died two days later, aged 11 years. I still recall my grief and writing a personal note to attach to a wreath. I also recall the fear one had in those days of common illnesses, which were potentially fatal, such as diphtheria. My younger cousin Natie very nearly died of it around the age of five and was saved by an emergency tracheostomy, with a tube inserted in his windpipe. I cannot recall if it was literally done on the kitchen table. He carried a very obvious scar on the front of his neck for the rest of his life. Another cousin in Beaufort West also contracted diphtheria a couple of years later, at a similar age, and was in a delirium, and I recall his mother telling me that he kept asking when the hearse was coming to collect him.

Another scourge was whooping cough (pertussis), which my sister and I certainly had, and I guess a large number of young children too. Measles was practically universal and apart from the prolonged period of abject misery often accompanying it, left many children with chronic lung disease, and carried a significant mortality. Another feared disease, which claimed its young victims in each epidemic, was poliomyelitis. There was already availability of diphtheria and pertussis vaccines at that time, but probably a low uptake. On the other hand smallpox immunisation was obligatory by law, and lead to the total eradication of this awful disease in South Africa, and a few years ago worldwide.

It is very easy to become complacent after the virtual eradication of these childhood diseases by the introduction of effective vaccines. They could very easily re-emerge in a community which never experienced them, if the repeated public anxiety about dangers of immunisation, fuelled by the media, leads to a drop in immunisation generally and a loss of the herd immunity.

Hobbies

Some of my childhood hobbies were undoubtedly inspired by my grandmother. These included breeding chickens, collecting succulent plants for my rockery, and growing vegetables such as carrots, beans and mealies (maize). I had a particular passion from early childhood for collecting stamps. This initially was any stamps worldwide, then concentrating on the British Commonwealth and particularly the current reign of King George VI. The Stanley Gibbons Catalogue was the bible of stamp collectors in those days. Later I specialised in South African stamps and used to collect all the different printings of the lower denominations, which one identified by the plate numbers of the printing in the margins at one corner. I also had a particular interest in looking for errors in individual stamps on a sheet, which one reported to the philatelic society. The more significant printing errors were listed in the specialised catalogue of the South African stamps. I still recall collecting large numbers of the regular two pence postage stamps, which were reduced in size in the war years to economise on paper, and looking out for particular small aberrations in individual stamps. Looking back I think this obsession of my youth was a good grounding for my eagle eye in proof reading in later years, and also in picking up minor abnormalities in clinical practice. Through the philatelic societies I also acquired some interesting pen pals in my high school years in Canada and the USA, and it was interesting not only exchanging new issues of stamps, but also current news and views. One experiment I found of interest as well was to post an airletter to a fictitious address in New York or other international city and when it eventually came back to the sender listed on the back, to try and track the route it had followed through its three or six month course from the various postmarks.

High school

Once I got to High School, I had a special passion for mathematics, and also chemistry, and built up a mini-laboratory at home of a range of different chemicals for doing experiments, in a large wooden packing case, to which I added a padlock. I recall an occasion I was doing some experiment in a test tube and asked my sister to smell the gas it generated. She had quite an unpleasant reaction, which lasted some hours and caused me considerable concern. I realised afterwards I must have generated chlorine gas in the experiment. I also had a particular interest in producing explosives, which went somewhat in the face of my rather pacifist temperament. Perhaps it was the big bang which impressed me. My favourite one was to half fill a Brasso polish tin with a screw-on cap, with a mixture of potassium chlorate and sulphur, and to make a hole in the side with a nail, in which I inserted a slow burning fuse of string soaked in potassium nitrate. The force of the rapidly burning mixture blew the tin apart with a tremendous bang, audible some distance away. Unfortunately on one occasion after I had lit the fuse, one of my mother's chickens came to investigate and promptly took off together with the Brasso tin, but fortunately survived.

Looking back on one's schooldays it was certainly a pretty basic education, with concentration on the obligatory subjects and on sport, and little else beside in the way of any cultural activities. Academically one might have thought there was very little hope of achieving much success in such a remote backwater, in competition with many of the prestigious schools in the main cities, such as SACS, Bishops, van Riebeeck, Christian Brothers. Yet my classmate, Alan Karabus, and I seemed to have established a competitive streak and apart from vying with each other for top position in the class, we made history for the school, by ending up in third and fourth places in the Cape Province senior certificate (matriculation) examination in 1947, and attaining the prestigious merit list of the top ten in the province. This attracted a merit award of some 50 pounds sterling, a small fortune in those days, for which I promptly opened a personal savings account, and also a university entrance scholarship of £50 per year for up to three years, subject to satisfactory performance.

Alan had a flair for history and literature, and went into Law, whereas I always had a special interest in mathematics and science and applied for both chemical engineering and medicine, and having been accepted for both at the University of Cape Town, opted for medicine. It was certainly not an easy task to decide on one's future career when matriculating at the somewhat tender age of 16, and not coming from an academic background or environment, and having no previous medics in my family.

The motto of our school was '*Facta non Verba*' (deeds not words) which we were always encouraged to follow. I think this credo has stayed with me throughout my career and I rarely talk about the things I am aspiring to do but rather get on with the task and talk about it after the completion.

Youth movements

At school we all were automatically in the cadet corps in the last four years of high school, and had a parade each Friday afternoon, resplendent with platoons, officers and a sergeant major. When reaching 18 years one had to register for compulsory military training but could get deferment when going to university. When I finished university my name went back on the list and to my relief I received a letter some time later from the Kommandant (commander) of the local *skietkommando* ('shooting commando') in Beaufort West that I had come up for military training but regretfully the *skietkommando* was full so that I could not be enrolled.

Reflecting the political divide, were the two major youth movements during my school years, the voortrekkers, an active youth group reminding the current generation of the Great Trek in the 1830s, when their Dutch forbears left the Cape Colony for the unknown north of the country to escape the British jurisdiction of the Cape Colony and the introduction of new laws such as the abolition of slavery. They became known as the 'voortrekkers', the people who were trekking forwards.

In parallel with the voortrekkers was a small boy scout troop, following the scout rules laid down by its founder, Lord Baden-Powell, and still swearing allegiance to God, the King and the country, and learning the ten scout rules. Our scout troop met every Friday evening in one of the local halls. The main excitement, apart from camping excursions and national scout jamborees, was pursuing proficiency badges, which one sewed on one's sleeve, for activities such as cycling, first aid and camping. I full remember my mother's extreme anxiety at seeing her young teenager setting off on his own hiking to the mountains some five miles north of the town to camp for two nights at the 'waterfall', a popular weekend picnic spot, particularly on the rare occasions after a summer thunderstorm when water was actually flowing and one could swim in the natural pool below.

Searching for roots. Lithuania, May 1995

One thing that I could never understand was why these immigrants from Eastern Europe, who had made such long journeys to unknown countries with languages they did not speak or understand, did not stay in the big cities where they landed but rather dispersed into the remote countryside. This finally became patently clear to me a few years ago when I managed to trace my paternal roots during a visit to Lithuania to the small town of Pasvetin, now Pasvetiniz, in the north of the country some 100 miles north of the well known towns of Paneves (now Panevezys) and Shavel (now Siailiai).

My expert guide, arranged with the kind help of Rachel Kostanian at the Jewish Museum in Vilnius, was Regina Kopilevich, a physicist by training, but now a professional archivist and genealogist, with the excellent taxi service of Regina's sister, Dina, a pharmacologist by profession, doing a bit of moonlighting in her spare time to supplement her meagre income. Paneves is quite a big town, and like many others in Lithuania, noted for the bulldozing of its Jewish cemetery by the Russians, who used the broken up tombstones as building material in the construction of a theatre, many of the Hebrew inscriptions still being visible on fragments of the granite. Rather ironic that the Germans destroyed the people and the Russian liberators destroyed the tombstones.

Driving from Paneves towards Pasvetin, you could easily imagine yourself driving to Beaufort West. The countryside is pretty flat and the roads pretty straight. You enter Pasvetin on an untarred road and are immediately struck that it is a very small village, in a very rural setting, surrounded by farms.

The main street one comes in on ends after a couple of hundred yards in the small square, with the church on the northern side. There were a few brick houses around the square, possibly inhabited originally by the Jews of the town, whereas most buildings, as in most Lithuanian towns, are of wood. The population before the Second World War was about a thousand, with about a hundred Jews. There had been a wooden synagogue pre-war, but a couple of days before the German invasion in 1941 there was a massive fire in the town, started accidentally by some schoolchildren, which destroyed several buildings, including the synagogue.

Beaufort West, South Africa, Donkin Street 1950s

Pasvitiniz, Lithuania, main street and church square 1995

My paternal great-grandparents Shimoin and Libshe in Lithuania, who died in 1913 and 1925

Their gravestones in Pasvitiniz cemetery (1995) with clear inscription in Hebrew, Shimoin son of Jacob Dubowitz and Libshe daughter of Kalman Dubowitz

Regina spoke to several of the townsfolk, most of whom were of post-war vintage, and had no recollection of the name Dubowitz. There was however still a Jewish Cemetery about a mile outside the town, which we then visited. It was unfenced and completely overgrown, but now protected since Lithuanian independence from the Russians, with a corresponding notice in Hebrew and Lithuanian.

Regina and I then wandered into the cemetery through the thick undergrowth and in the far side away form the road, we came across a few tombstones. Within minutes of starting to look a bit more closely at some of the fairly simple granite stones, Regina called out, 'mazeltov, it is a Dubowitz'.

And there it was, with clearly legible Hebrew lettering, Shimoin bar Jaakov (Shimoin son of Jacob) Dubowitz. So my father's older brother, Jack, was named after the paternal grandfather of his father, Nathan. It is a Jewish tradition to name a child after a deceased relative. A few stones away and Regina called out, 'Here's another one.' It was Libshe bat Kalman (Libshe (Libby/Lilly) daughter of Kalman (Charles) Dubowitz. So my father, Charley (Kalman) was named after his father's maternal grandfather. According to the Hebrew dates, Shimoin died in 1913 and Libshe in 1925. We were unable to find any other Dubowitzes amongst the remaining tombstones. Some were badly corroded by surface lichen and simple weathering and were essentially illegible. I arranged through my guide for the cemetery to be cleared and restored at my expense.

In our subsequent visit to the large town of Telz (Telsiai), we found a historic wind-operated corn mill, which I would like to believe may have been the one belonging to my forbears on my mother's side, but I guess that is unlikely. We could not find any tombstones of any Schattils in the local cemeteries but this may be because many of the cemeteries had been cleared by the Russians for public parks or sports fields.

Around many of these cities were the killing fields where the local Lithuanian militia, in cahoots with the Nazi occupiers, had congregated the local Jewish population and massacred them en masse. Our local guide, who is now the custodian of these designated national monuments, was the only survivor of his whole family because he had joined the Russian army early on in the war.

One of a series of life-size tree sculptures by Yossel Bunks, a holocaust survivor from Plunge (originally Plunyam), to mark the suffering of the local Jewish population, massacred in this forest by the Germans and local Lithuanians in the Second World War

Another survivor we met in the nearby city of Plunge, which used to be well known as Plunyam in Yiddish, was a gifted sculptor, Yossel Bunks, who had recorded in larger-than-life figures the grief and despair of the local Jewish population, by directly carving a grove of trees in the woods of Kishon, adjacent to one of the killing fields.

Investment in education

A remarkable feature of the Lithuanian immigrants of my grandparents' generation and carried on to the next generation was a tremendous work ethic and a determination to earn sufficient money in order to ensure that the next generation had a good education. They had a very firm philosophy that education was the only security for the future. Perhaps this was imprinted in the migrants who often lost all their possessions when having to flee harassment or persecution. A large cohort of the following generation thus made it into university, with a disproportionately large component going into Medicine. Somehow the traditional Yiddishe mama felt more proud to speak of 'my son the doctor', than of any other profession. But this may date back much further since in Jewish orthodox tradition the doctor is held in high veneration, only second to that of the rabbi. This generation of Jewish medical graduates in turn formed a large part of the exodus from South Africa in the turbulent 1960s and created a new Diaspora of South African Jewish émigrés to the United Kingdom and the United States, who filled a remarkable number of university positions in these two countries as well as further afield in Australia, Canada and New Zealand. One American colleague recently remarked that it was difficult to find a medical school in the United States that did not have at least one expatriate South African on its faculty.

Extended Dubowitz family

There was an extended branch of the Dubowitz family in the Eastern Cape Province around Port Elizabeth, comprising three cousins of my grandfather, Barney, Harry and Meyer, sons of Shimoin's brother Eliezer, who died in Pasvetin in 1892. Barney shortened his name to Dubb and his family were well known in Port Elizabeth, including Louis who was mayor for several years. A son of Louis, Allie Dubb, a renowned anthropologist, now living in Israel, visited me in London a few years ago after we made contact for the first time by correspondence. Harry Dubowitz settled in a small town called Jansenville, near Port Elizabeth, and according to the Union Castle shipping records brought his wife and four children out on the *Caernarvon Castle* in September 1927, including two-year-old Nathan, who was later to be a general practitioner in Cape Town, and whose son Howard, whom I know well, is a paediatrician in Washington DC with an academic attachment at the University of Maryland.

Asher Dubb, Professor of Medicine, University of Witwatersrand (Johannesburg), Senior Physician Baragwanath Hospital, philatelist, medical historian, revered physician and teacher, humanitarian. Died January 2005

Neville Dubow, architect, Professor of Fine Art, University of Cape Town

Nathan Finkelstein, Professor of Pharmacy, University of Cape Town

The third brother Meyer also shortened his name to Dubb. I met his son, Asher Dubb, for the first time in January 2003 at a combined congress in Cape Town of the British and South African neurological associations. He had qualified in medicine at Wits University a few years ahead of me in 1950, and had been Professor of Medicine and Consultant Physician at Baragwanath Hospital for more than 40 years. His lecture at the congress, entitled 'British neuroscientists. A philatelic tribute,' was extremely erudite as well as entertaining and beautifully illustrated with series of postage stamps worldwide depicting famous British neuroscientists, who had made important discoveries. It reflected his passion for philately as well as medical history. I was amazed how much we shared in our philosophy on life in general and also on clinical medicine.

A cousin of my father, Herman Dubowitz, who shortened his name to Dubow, had a well known dress shop in Wynberg, Cape Town. His son Neville Dubow, two years younger than me, trained in architecture and became professor of fine arts at Cape Town University. Nathan Finkelstein, son of my father's sister Annie, also grew up in Beaufort West, and became a foundation professor of pharmacy at the University of Cape Town.

Schattel (Schattil; Shattil) family

Apart from my mother's two brothers, Leo and Isaac, who stayed on in Rhodesia, and used to visit us in South Africa from time to time and also sent me letters and birthday gifts, I did not have any contact at all with the extended Shattil family. I was aware that her cousin Alex Schattil, whom I had not met, was well known as the Receiver of Revenue in Rhodesia and an author of authoritative books on taxation. In 1995 I had a telephone call out of the blue from Judith Stern in London, who was the granddaughter of Joseph Shattil, a brother of my grandfather. This was the day prior to my departure for Lithuania. She had contacted my sister in Australia, who gave her my telephone number.

Judith and I have met frequently since, particularly after they emigrated to San Francisco, and in 2000 I had a chance to meet for the first time several members of the extended Shattil clan, particularly the descendants of one of my grandfather's brothers,

Reunion of the Shattil family, San Francisco, October, 2000.

Julius Shattil, who emigrated from Rhodesia to the USA. Judith's grandfather, Joseph, the oldest of the seven Shattil brothers had been the trailblazer and the first to emigrate to Rhodesia to prospect for gold, and subsequently brought out three brothers, including my grandfather. One of the reasons for the confusion of the spelling of Shattil (Schattil; Schattel) was the suggestion of the bank manager in Bulawayo that Joe Shattil, change his name to Schattil to distinguish his signature from those of his brothers Jacob and Julius (also J. Shattil). The American branch of Julius retained the original Shattil, whereas my grandfather Victor at some point compounded it further with the spelling Schattel.

Olympic swimmer

There has never been any particular sporting prowess on either side of the family and the first international star was Sarah Poewe, daughter of Lorraine, and the granddaughter of my mother's youngest sister Minnie (Stoch). Sarah showed promise in swimming from an early age in South Africa and broke several junior and national records. At 17 she was placed 4th in the 100m breaststroke in the Sydney Olympics, and 5th at the Athens Olympics in 2004.

Sarah Poewe, daughter of my cousin Lorraine, granddaughter of Minnie Schattel.
South African breaststroke champion. Photograph at our home in London with all the medals she won at the world short course championships in London in 2000. She was placed 4th in the 100 metres breaststroke in the Sydney Olympics in 2000 and 5th in the Athens Olympics in 2004.

2

Cape Town

Going to university was a completely novel experience for me and for my family, as I had no contemporaries of my generation who were or had been at university. It was also a major transition for a 16-year-old moving from home to a big city for the first time and from the sheltered and somewhat formal educational system at school to an academic environment of relative freedom and independence.

The University of Cape Town has a commanding position on the slopes of Devil's Peak on the eastern side of Table Mountain, and there were two separate residences on campus for men and for women. I duly applied for men's residence, but was not successful and later realised it had an exclusivity for the old boy network, and public school applicants. I was offered a place at an alternative residence, College House, but as this was located in the city, some distance from the university, I declined it and opted for a local private residence in Rosebank called Rostrevor, run by a Mrs Zabow, and catering for some 25 residents. Many of us shared rooms, especially in the first year.

My roommate Sid Cywes from Paarl became a life-long friend. He stayed on in Cape Town after graduating, specialising in paediatric surgery and becoming head of the paediatric surgery unit at the Red Cross Hospital. He built up an international reputation for his innovative work in the field and also attracted conjoined ('Siamese') twins from the whole of Africa and held a world record for separating the greatest number. He later developed a special interest in horticulture and became rose king in South Africa and swept the boards each year with all the main prizes for his roses at the annual show. He subsequently switched his interest to disas, a magnificent indigenous member of the orchid family, growing in the wild on Table Mountain and elsewhere in South Africa and the official symbol of the Mountain Club of South Africa. Not only did he produce

At Rostrevor residence, 1948. Sid Cywes standing left, Mandfred Bloch right

prize-winning disas in his elaborate greenhouses, but also a large variety of new hybrids, by crossing various species, varying in colour and size and also season of blooming. In recent years he introduced a novel incentive for generous benefactors of the Red Cross Children's Hospital of naming a new disa after them.

All the university residences had an initiation process, which was pretty rigid and aimed at reducing the new boys to size. Thus for the first six months we had to wear a distinctive plain yellow tie, had to address all senior residents as 'sir', had to entertain the seniors with various theatrical activities from time to time and also had to be able to respond instantly with the definition of a 'new man' as 'the lowest of the low, lower than shark shit at the bottom of the ocean'. There were also day-to-day chores such as doing the wake-up calls in the morning, collecting the seniors' laundry and standing in line to collect tickets for intervarsity matches for the seniors. Whilst it was at times very irritating as a distraction from one's work schedule, overall we took it in good spirit. Although these initiation processes have steadily declined in more recent years, mainly as a result of an occasional accident in relation to more violent physical activities, and may in retrospect appear somewhat puerile, they did serve to engender a close friendship between the new students and subsequently also with the senior students.

There were also a number of traditional university activities that brought students together and a major one was the annual hospital rag, where large floats were prepared by groups of students, usually coming together to represent a residence or other grouping, and involving about a week of very intense all-night effort building the floats in time for the parade through the city on the Saturday and of course also extracting charitable funds from the public for support of the hospitals and various student voluntary health schemes in the poorer communities. As I recall we also went around the neighbourhood rattling collection boxes from door to door.

I always thought one was privileged in these activities to live in a university residence rather than at home, when one would miss out on the spirit of the occasion.

Another annual activity that riveted all the students was the annual rugby match between arch rivals Cape Town and Stellenbosch universities and alternated in venue between the two cities. This was a real gala occasion, and in addition to the match itself, the student supporters were segregated into two separate halves of the main stand and had a cheerleader in full regalia and university colours to conduct the singing of special songs for the occasion. In 1950 one of my medical classmates, Maurice Silbert, was cheerleader and a very dashing, efficient and spectacular one. He has been in general practice in Cape Town since we graduated.

Wednesday afternoons were traditionally free of any formal lectures so that students could give priority to any sporting activities. In addition to the various team sports, there were also more individual sports, which were advantageous for diversion and expenditure of energy during one's times of active study. Thus many medical students were keen on squash and in one's later more congested clinical years it remained a good outlet late at night or other times and one could always find a fellow student to join in. I never excelled at sport and as I realised I could not make it into any of the university rugby teams, I joined the hockey club, which at least assured me of a weekly match on Saturday afternoon in the third team and also an intervarsity match at that level. I also enjoyed the contact with students from other faculties.

The first year subjects comprised botany for six months and zoology, chemistry and physics for the full year. In many respects the chemistry and physics were an extension of the science we

University of Cape Town third Hockey team. I am third from right in back row

Annual intervarsity rugby match between UCT and Stellenbosch University
(I am at 3 o'clock leaning on railing)

did at school and the botany and zoology provided a good basis of biology, which I had not done at school. There were a number of matriculation subjects for admission to medical school, one of which was mathematics, which I think had been an alternative to biology in my school. The first year was a very competitive one as the annual intake was about twice the number of places available in the second year at medical school. So a large number bit the dust, and had to either repeat the year or if borderline in only one subject, that subject, or might transfer to a BSc course with a possibility of entering second year medicine after completion at the end of three years. So of the 200 or so first years only about 120 made it each year into second year.

The second year comprised anatomy and physiology and was a big leap into much more relevant medical subjects. There was no shortage of cadavers in those days, and we were divided into groups of around six or eight to work on the systematic dissection of the whole body, stage by stage. The physiology was also a broad coverage of the physiology of all systems and a basis for pathology, the main subject for the third year. I very much enjoyed both these subjects. As I still had some aspirations for pure science which needed working out of my system, I opted for a special opportunity of doing a concurrent BSc degree in one extra year, which entailed splitting away from the current class going into third year medicine, but spending the year on a second course in anatomy and physiology, as well as additional courses in biochemistry. It was not an easy decision to make, because it meant giving up the close association with one's current classmates and having to join a completely alien group a year later. Moreover, at the time it looked like a huge sacrifice losing a whole year of one's career at an early stage, and a year somehow looks an eternity at that time. But I was also conscious of the positive side of consolidating my interest in science and potentially also in research. I think my decision was the right one for me, and I had no cause to regret it. There were only two of us on this course, Lenny Anstey and myself. We also had some overlap with one of the candidates from the previous year, Whitey Thurlbeck.

It was a wonderful experience having essentially one-to-one tuition from one's teachers in these circumstances, somewhat comparable to the privileged tutorial system in Oxford and Cambridge. One of my personal problems that already became evident at that time, and more conspicuous under the circumstances, was the difficulty of getting on time to a particular appointment. This has remained with me throughout my career. I think there are basically two factors involved. Firstly I seem to have an innate aversion for being early, and as a result always try and fill in any spare time, virtual or real, with some additional activity. Secondly, I had already realised at that time that I was essentially a night owl and at my most lucid late at night, when I seemed to get a sort of second wind. As a result I was not at my best or most active in the morning. Lenny found a simple and most effective solution. He arranged with the lecturers to formally start our sessions 15 minutes later, but did not inform me of it. A few years later I had a somewhat salutary experience. It was the beginning of our fifth year term and the Professor of Obstetrics, James Louw, was giving his introductory lecture. He said there were a number of things he could not tolerate, the most important being people coming in late, and once he started no one would be allowed in. With split second timing I burst through the lecture room door, at the front of the lecture theatre. There was a spontaneous roar of laughter, which puzzled me, until I had the explanation afterwards.

Surprisingly though, I had no difficulty waking in the morning, whatever time I went to bed, and never used an alarm clock; I would just say to myself on going to sleep, I must be up at 6 or 7 tomorrow and my own biological clock would rouse me about five minutes ahead. I also seemed to be able to manage on very little sleep, with an average of five or six hours being ample. But to keep up with this cycle I often had a sudden need for a short sleep in the late afternoon and could totally recharge my batteries with a deep catnap for a half or a full hour.

An additional bonus of my year out for the medical BSc was that we were appointed as demonstrators in Anatomy and Physiology and provided tuition to the regular students for set sessions each week. I derived a great pleasure from teaching, and also looked upon it as one of the best ways of learning. My enthusiasm for teaching has continued ever since. But probably the most important bonus was the opportunity of doing some experimental studies, mainly under the direction of a very dynamic Dane in the physiology department, Otto Budtz-Olsen. Some of the experiments were very simple, others complex in construction. I clearly remember one study I got involved in with him, which I volunteered for in the January summer vacation after completing my BSc. This entailed trying to establish a bioassay for minute amounts of the nerve transmitter acetylcholine, which was thought to rise in the spinal fluid after head injury. The 'heart' of the clam (shellfish) is a very simple tubular structure, which will continue contracting rhythmically for up to 24 hours, when suspended in seawater in a test-tube, and can be anchored at each end. One can also easily set up a device for recording the contractions. I made the trip to Muizenberg beach to dig on the water's edge for the clams, and the neurosurgeons provided the cerebrospinal fluid from head injury patients.

It was quite remarkable that concentrations as low as one part in a million of acetylcholine could change the heart beat of the clam. Budtz-Olsen was certainly a most dynamic character, and a couple of years later he wrote the libretto of a medical opera which was put on by the students as a special Christmas show. The characters involved many well-known names in the medical world, such as Wasserman (who introduced a standard blood test for syphilis), and other household names.

The anatomy also had some more dynamic components with embryology and anthropology, and one of the senior lecturers 'Tubby' Singer had a special interest in anthropology and we used to go out with him and another senior lecturer, Dr Keen, on trips to Sandy Bay, a totally isolated beach with pristine white sand, between Hout Bay and Llandudno. As the only access was a three-mile hike over the sand dunes it was completely deserted in those days. In that area were a number of mounds which were kitchen middens of the Hottentot (*Khoi*) *strandloper* (beach walker) tribe, who inhabited the coastal area at the time Jan van Riebeeck landed at the Cape in 1652, These middens were burial grounds where numerous skeletons were unearthed for doing anthropomorphic measurements. Over the burials were closely packed large seashells, and in the topsoil of it was evidence of fire and cooking, a domestic activity. I was amazed to find some years later when I visited the National museum in Copenhagen a cross-sectional display of a Danish kitchen midden with exactly the same structure.

At that time I already had an eye for picking up interesting pieces of driftwood with unusual shapes, and one particular one protruding about four inches above the ground had a magnificent rotating tubular form about ten inches long below which I dug out and still have as a mounted natural figure 'supplication'. This was perhaps a prelude to my hobby in more recent years of sculpting stone or wood forms inspired by unusually shaped pebbles, especially flint stone, which I am always picking up when walking the dog.

Amongst my extramural activities, I already had an active interest at that time in the National Union of South African Students (NUSAS), which was boycotted by the Afrikaans speaking universities, such as Stellenbosch, and Pretoria, because of its liberal policies of having no constraint on membership on the grounds of colour or race. There was a subdivision on Research, in which I was active for a number of years, and which set up various projects. An ongoing one, which I personally got involved in, was the assessment of the frequency of tuberculosis in some of the African townships in urban areas, and we had somewhat grandiose plans of taking aerial photographs of the townships and then systematically working through the whole area, house by house.

In 1952 I went to the annual NUSAS congress in Pietermaritzburg, which was a unique experience for me in many ways. I motored up with Barry Lewis and Hackey Edelstein via my home town, Beaufort West, Bloemfontein, and Johannesburg, where we met up with Sydney Brenner, who was active in the NUSAS council and already firmly steeped in fundamental research at that time, even though completing his medical course, mainly to placate his mentors at Wits Medical School. He later moved to the renowned molecular genetics centre in Cambridge and was closely associated with Francis Crick, co-discoverer with James Watson of DNA, and later was a Nobel laureate himself. I am proud to claim the honour of having slept on the floor of his apartment in our student days en route to that NUSAS congress. I also gave my first conference presentation on the work of the research committee in Cape Town. The conference was very stimulating and as I recall, largely dominated by Philip Tobias and Sydney Brenner from Wits. Most nights a group of us slept in the open on Worlds View, on top of a nearby hill, watching the sunrise over the magnificent landscape of the valley of a thousand hills. This was undoubtedly enhanced at the time by my friendship with a fellow student from Cape Town, Sheila Macgregor, studying Social Sciences.

Another interesting activity of the students in the clinical years was to run a voluntary evening clinic in the poor areas and townships, under the supervision of a senior clinician. This provided a basic medical service for the local people and also dispensed basic medicines at no charge.

When I reached my clinical fourth year, I moved digs again to the Danilewitz family in Observatory, conveniently located near the medical school and Groote Schuur Hospital. Their son, Daniel, was a classmate of mine and another boarder was Jack Abrahamson, then a couple of years ahead of me in his final year. He was a keen mountaineer and I can still visualise Mr Danilewitz gazing in amazement as Jack practised his finger holds traversing the side of the garage hanging down from the flat roof, and repeatedly exclaiming 'such strong hands!'. Jack introduced me to mountains and I accompanied him and his climbing friends on many an enjoyable walk up Table Mountain. I still have a very vivid recollection of our weekend on the berg in April 1952 when we had a bird's-eye view of the fireworks on the foreshore celebrating the third centenary of the landing of Jan van Riebeeck in Table Bay in April 1652. I never attempted any rock faces as I had faithfully promised my mother when I left home that I would not go mountaineering. She was always grieved by the repeated reports of students getting lost on Table Mountain and ending at the bottom of a ravine, or coming off a rock face. My usual solo hikes were along the pipe track which one could

Weekend on Table Mountain with Jack Abrahamson during the tercentenary celebrations, 1952

traverse all the way from the medical school to the Kirstenbosch botanical gardens and it provided numerous spectacular views en route, and often also provided a relaxing environment to do some serious revision and reflection when getting too tense with preparing for examinations. Jack became a close friend and when we later met up in London, he was to have a very major influence on my life, thanks to the vagaries of his vintage car.

Clinical training in South Africa

The medical schools in South Africa had a long tradition of clinical teaching at the bedside, based on the British system. Many of our professors in the medical school were from Britain and particularly Scottish medical schools. At the Groote Schuur Hospital in Cape Town, associated with the university of Cape Town medical school, there was a very good system, which seemed to work very well. In addition to the two full-time Professors of Medicine (Forman and Brock), each of whom had a medical unit under their care, comprising a ward for whites and a ward for non-whites, within the traditional segregated system in the longstanding apartheid era, there were four more units run by senior clinicians, who also contributed substantially to the teaching programme and in addition had private practices outside the hospital. Then there were a group of senior consultants, who were in full-time private practice and did not have units in the hospital but had honorary contracts with the hospital, which gave them a priority for admitting their patients to the hospital and also a responsibility for clinical teaching of the medical students. They were a very motivated group, each of whom had a 'firm' with a small group of students attached. They did regular ward rounds with their tutorial group and in addition the students in their junior clinical (fourth) year, had to clerk and assess a series of patients and prepare a detailed written report on each, which they handed in to their tutor for appraisal and criticism and also a mark which contributed to the examination at the end of the year. This system worked very well for the students, who from an early stage were able to present and discuss their patients with the tutor and other students, and also for the tutors, who were in competition for the small number of 'firms' available, and in addition to enjoying their contribution to the teaching pro-

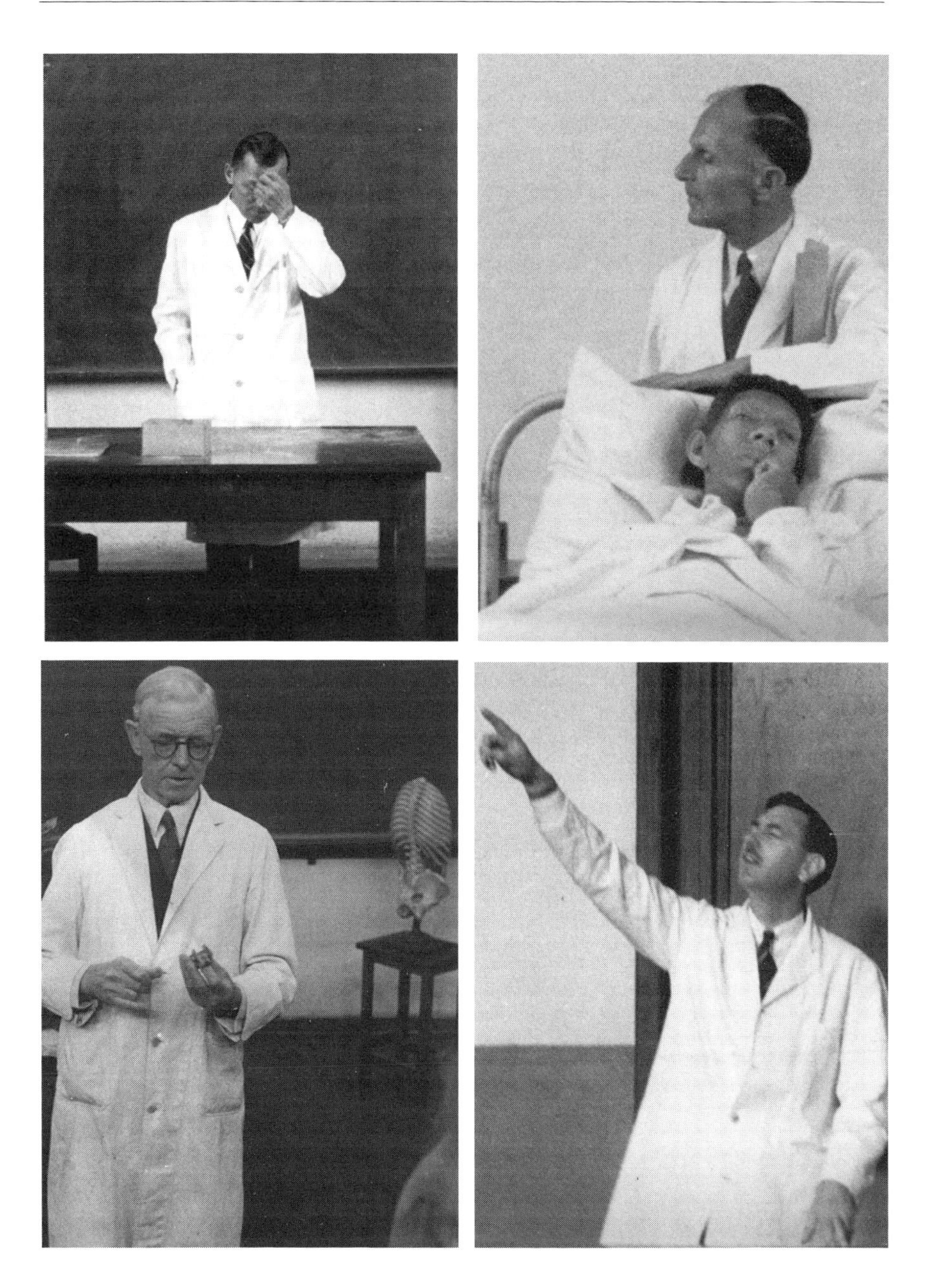

Four of my professors, clockwise from top left, Jannie Louw, Surgery: Frankie Forman, Medicine; James Louw, Obstetrics; Maxie Drennan, Anatomy gramme, also hoped that the students in their firm, mostly going into general practice, would in due course also refer their patients to the tutor for specialist advice. I can still recall the details of the very first patient I clerked and provided a detailed case report on for the scrutiny of my tutor. He was a 65-year-old man who had suffered a severe stroke, with severe compromise of his speech.

I think these tutors and also our main academic teachers inspired in us a particular passion for clinical medicine as well as for teaching and I have always enjoyed the opportunity of bedside teaching with students throughout my career. People often ask how come there are such a disproportionate number of South African doctors in medical schools around the globe. I think the answer is simply the high level of clinical teaching, with a passion for clinical medicine, and a sense of absolute commitment to one's profession.

Absurdities of apartheid

Thankfully apartheid is now a thing of the past and South Africa finally has a rainbow nation. There were always numerous absurdities within the system. In the medical profession there was of course little sign of apartheid at a personal academic level and certainly as medical students there was a free interaction between all students, irrespective of colour or creed. However, apartheid made it illegal to have any social interaction, so no black students could reside at the whites-only residences and medical residence of the university. By the same token, black medical students were prohibited from attending the grand round when white patients were discussed in the main lecture theatre and had to leave if a white patient were wheeled in. The same stringent rules also applied in the post mortem room. When one realises the all pervasive nature of the whole policy, which already had its roots in the 1930s with the passage of the Separate Areas Act through parliament, one begins to understand the mentality of the Nationalist member of parliament, who during a health debate probed the blood transfusion services on whether adequate precautions were taken to ensure that accidental mixing did not occur and could the Minister of Health clarify what the reaction and risks would be, if by chance, God forbid, a white man had a blood transfusion during an emergency from a black donor. He may well have had some vision of the poor white chap exploding in a puff of smoke. Chris Barnard was to settle all that with one blow some years later, when he did his first heart transplant with the donor heart from a young coloured woman to a white male recipient.

The legendary Frankie Forman

If one were to single out a person who probably, in his quiet unassuming way, contributed most to this clinical tradition, most Cape Town graduates of our era would immediately say Professor Frank ('Frankie') Forman, who stood out a good head and shoulders above anyone else in clinical acumen and encyclopaedic knowledge. He was basically a very gentle man, soft-spoken and almost self-effacing. He showed a remarkable respect and empathy for his patients and tried to communicate with them on their own level. He combined an encyclopaedic knowledge of clinical medicine with a remarkable bedside manner, and an innate ability to relate it directly to the patient.

Frankie had a phenomenal memory both for people and events and also for the world medical literature, which he read assiduously in the medical school library every Wednesday afternoon. There is the apocryphal story of Frankie doing his routine ward-round with his residents and listening to the medical history of a Cape Coloured lady with an unusual endocrine problem. 'Now where have I seen you before?' he asked her. 'Never doctor, I never seen doctor before.' Frankie reflected for a few moments. 'Now tell me, were you not in Groote Schuur Hospital about five years ago, on ward F4, I think the second or third bed on the left side . . .?' After a short silence, 'yes doctor, that's quite right. I remember now'.

Frankie had a quiet respect for his students, junior staff and residents, and seemed almost incapable of anger or criticism. There was the occasion that a rather anxious student was called down from the audience to examine the pulse of a patient. Frankie waited patiently for a few moments and then interjected, 'admittedly about 2% of the population may have the pulse on the ulnar side of the wrist, but as the vast majority are on the radial side – I would suggest you examine that side first.'

Frankie's teaching was entirely at the bedside. He never gave formal lectures and he was also criticised that he never published any papers or did any research, so his legacy might die with him. However, I think that his disciples provided the next generation who were our teachers, and we in turn have tried to carry on the tradition of clinical excellence, which he tried to instil.

The parallel professorial unit of Professor John Brock, whilst also aspiring to a high standard of clinical excellence, was the one that initiated research programmes into some of the common problems of the day, and helped to put the medical school and hospital on the international map.

Another interesting component of our training was in Obstetrics where we had hands-on experience during a residency in one of the obstetrical units. I spent a few weeks in the Peninsula Maternity Hospital in District 6, a very interesting area, where many of the early Jewish immigrants opened up businesses and where the population was largely comprised of Cape Coloured inhabitants. It was an area full of legend and character, and also criminal activity. Of special interest apart from the deliveries we officiated at together with the resident midwifery staff, were the home deliveries of many of the mothers having second or later infants with no problems with the first ones. One of the medical students would usually accompany one of the nurses on these calls. Much of the Cape Coloured humour emanated from District 6, as did many of the musical groups that made up the Coon Carnival on New Year's Day each year.

As the District 6 area is contiguous to the centre of Cape Town city, the Nationalist government in 1966 decided to declare it a white zone and razed it to the ground, moving all the residents to a remote new township at Mitchell's Plain south east of the peninsula, with the aim of rebuilding the area. There was such a protest from all communities that the area has remained derelict and deserted ever since and only in the last few years has an effort been made to start building new houses and bringing back some of the original residents. The Peninsula Maternity Hospital was one of the few buildings left standing.

The medical students at the Cape Town medical school had two literary publications, with an entirely student editorial board, as well as content. One was a newssheet, called *Cathartic*, produced at irregular intervals on behalf of the Medical Students Council (on which I served as secretary for several years), with items of topical interest, and the other a fairly serious well-

Vic Dubowitz

It was not without protest that Vic consented to tell me something about himself. He told me in no uncertain terms that he considered the Personalia column to be the worst form of flattery.

Born and schooled in Beaufort West, he obtained the distinction of having the 4th highest pass in the Cape Matriculation Examinations. He came to U C T in 1948 on an entrance scholarship and a departmental bursary, took his medical B.Sc degree in 1950, and is at present doing the final year of his medical studies.

Among his interests he has played an active part in NUSAS. For many years he served on the Local Research Council of this body and in 1952 he was appointed the Director of T.B. research. During the year 1952-53 he served as Secretary of the M.S.C. and has taken an active interest in the Visiting Lecturers Scheme, having organised the visits of Prof. Platt and Dr. Hunter, and is now busy making plans for the visits of Prof. Young this month and Prof. Boyd next month. He has been a keen member of the Retreat Students Clinic, and the Elsies River Clinic since is inception.

As for sporting activities, Vic has had varying interests - Rugby, Tennis and Hockey. His hobbies are even more varied. He has collected stamps since the age of 5, and is a member of the U.C.T. Philatelic Soc. He also collects coins, interesting pieces of wood, stones and succulents. He enjoys doing some carpentry, water colour painting and sketching, and is fond of hiking.

Vic has some very definite ideas on the clinical training of medical students and is convinced that it is the patient as a whole who is important and not the individual signs and symptoms. Since 4th year he has been violently opposed to the method of darting along to pick up the mid-diastolic rumble in the 3rd apex on the left, stopping on the way to feel for the spleen in the second abdomen and, en passant, catching a whiff of acetone in the 1st breath on the right on the way out.

It is impossible that a person who has played a part in so many student activities will go 'unmissed' when he leaves Medical School at the end of this year.

Mr. Maytham

Mr Maytham is a technician with whom very few students have come into contact, and this is indeed a pity, because he is a most affable man. He holds one of the most important positions on the technical staff of Medical School, namely that of chief technician of the department of Bacteriology. He is in charge of serology, routine bacteriology and the media kitchen.

Born and bred in this country, he joined the technical staff of the department in 1929, when an apprentice started off with a wage of £3 a month as compared with £25 to-day. There were three technicians in the department then, and now Mr Maytham has fourteen working under him. During his 25 years at Medical School, he has worked under Professor Campbell and Professor van den Ende, the present Dean.

Nowadays Technicians have to go through an intensive course, during which they are shifted around from one type of work to another, and on passing their examinations they are registered with the S.A. Medical and Dental Council. At present there exists

continued on p. 12.....

Profile of me in *Cathartic*, 'a journal of irregular habits', published by the Medical Students Council, 1954 produced journal produced annually, called *Inyanga*, which is a Xhosa word for healer or witchdoctor, and contained contributions in the form of scientific reviews of a particular topic, or case presentations. There was another student publication, *Sax Appeal*, produced each year at the time of the annual Hospital Rag, to collect funds for the medical activities in the poor areas of the population.

Scratching through some old files, I have come across a copy of *Cathartic* from 1954, my final year at medical school, in which I was profiled, together with a sketch by Jane Bain, which is still recognisable, and I note I was stressing the importance of a holistic approach to the total problem of the patient as an individual, rather than a single medical aspect of interest in relation to one organ or system. I also found a photograph of the editorial team working on the annual *Sax Appeal*.

Literary aspirations

I wrote three articles for *Inyanga* during my clinical years. The first was 'The beloved physician', a short biography of Sir James Mackenzie, a well-beloved and admired general practitioner in Britain, who had earned that title, and who also had an experimental and scientific bent and designed an instrument for recording a printout of the pulse wave at the wrist. He epitomised my hero in the role of the family physician, which was my own orientation at the time. The second was a detailed case report on an adult man with ulcerative colitis that I had clerked as a fourth year student and become very interested in the many facets of the condition from a pathogenesis as well as a treatment point of view. The third was a detailed review of a hereditary condition with excess iron storage in the tissues called haemachromatosis, which affected mainly males, supposedly because females could rid themselves of the excess iron in their monthly loss of blood by menstruation. My review included a female patient I had clerked on the ward as a final-year student. I also produced a fourth paper of a more scientific nature on the regenerative potential of the nervous system, a subject that had fascinated me since my extra year of physiology for my medical BSc when I had read the book of John Fulton, *Physiology of the Nervous System*, followed by a wide range of works related to the subject of neuronal regeneration, including the writings of the famous Spanish neuropathologist Ramon y Cajal, and the fascinating experimental studies on the octopus by JZ Young, a professor of anatomy at University College London. Those were the halcyon days before personal computers and even typing facilities, so I prepared my whole review paper by hand-written text and did not even make a photocopy of it. I handed it personally to the editor of *Inyanga*, Ted Allen, who was one year ahead of me. When I had heard no decision about it some two months later, as the publication date was approaching I asked him what he thought of my paper. 'What paper?' he responded. He denied having ever seen the manuscript. That was the end of that episode and I never managed to prepare a further draft of it. I guess one only has that sort of catastrophe once in a lifetime, after which one ensures that everything that is irreplaceable should at least be backed up by whatever means.

Visiting lecturer scheme

Cape Town university had an interesting visiting lecturer scheme whereby all students automatically contributed half-a-crown and each faculty could each year select its own visiting lecturer from abroad. We also had a reciprocal arrangement with Wits University in Johannesburg to share lecturers, so each visitor might spend perhaps an extra week at the other university. I was the representative of the medical students on the central committee, and it was an interesting experience soliciting suggestions from faculty professors and staff, and also having responsibility for organising local academic and social arrangements for the visitors. Amongst our visitors was Dr Donald Hunter from the London Hospital, a pioneer in industrial medicine and a very dynamic speaker and also clinical demonstrator and quite a showman. In later years I attended some of his outpatient clinics at the London Hospital as part of my postgraduate experience. Another was Professor Robert Platt, Professor of Medicine in Manchester, whom I met at the airport, with the unusual experience of a cello case coming down the steps of the aircraft, with a somewhat stocky person of about the same height behind it. It transpired he was a superb cello player, who almost made his career in music and had played with the

Hallé orchestra. He always took his cello with him (as a fare-paying passenger companion in the adjacent seat) and practised every day. Needless to say his first priority was to get a quartet together for some informal music. We didn't quite manage a quartet, but as I recall got together a trio with Eric Rosen, a classmate who had similarly nearly become a concert violinist, and a non-medical friend who was an enthusiastic pianist. So we ended up with an informal concert by the trio for the medical faculty. Professor Platt had been in Sheffield as a consultant physician in his earlier years and also covered the Children's Hospital. He was later to become President of the Royal College of Physicians and was an unexpected attendee at the opening lecture I gave at the national meeting of the Society of Physiotherapists in 1960. It's a small world.

Even senior medical students are still students at heart

Medical students were considered a bit more mature by the time they got to their clinical years, and not expected to get up to the same sort of pranks as the undergraduates in their first few years. However, there was a tendency to let off steam on special occasions, and fairly consistently after the annual final year dinner. This was just ahead of the final exams, when all the senior medical staff were guests of the final year medics and expected traditionally, after suitable lubrication with alcohol, to give some clues, usually very cryptic, on questions likely to appear in the final papers. In my own year, a delegation decided to pay a courtesy visit ('raid') after the dinner on the senior women's residence, 'Hibernia', located near to the medical school. But the warden was not at all amused and looked upon it as a criminal act of breaking and entering, and summoned the police and also turned a fire hose on the revellers, which was not all that considerate, given that the dinner was black tie. Fortunately he thought better of it and did not press criminal charges when the police came but, as I recall, reported the matter to the dean of the medical faculty, who managed to defuse the whole situation, but did send a fairly strong letter to the class representative.

It would have been a bit of a disaster if a cohort of newly qualified doctors had started their careers with a criminal record

Belly dancers' floor show at annual medical residence dance. From left Hackey Edelstein, myself, Eddie Shapiro, Gerry Rosendorf

Editorial board meeting of *Sax Appeal*, annual medical student magazine for the Hospital Rag to raise funds for hospital charity

of housebreaking or disturbing the peace, or possibly even worse if they trumped up some imaginary charges of 'intent'. Another group from medical residence decided to visit the zoo on the slopes of the mountain just south of the main university campus. Mysteriously the following morning there appeared in the enclosed quadrangle within the medical residence a crane sporting a medical residence tie around its neck and a mountain tortoise with the car registration number of the warden, Pat Smythe, on its back. The warden was not amused. He duly notified the zoo, who sent one of their keepers along to collect the animals. He shook his head in disbelief and muttered to the assembled crowd, with a crane under one arm and a tortoise under the other, 'Wonder how they got here?' 'Must have flown!' came a spontaneous retort. 'And what about the tortoise?' No comment. I guess there must be a law for the protection of endangered species safely protected in cages in zoos, so the budding medics were probably lucky to have escaped a second criminal charge to launch them into their careers.

One of the additional concessions the residents of the medical residence were allowed, in keeping with their seniority, was visitors to their rooms on Saturdays from 2 pm till 10 pm, which was totally taboo in those days in any of the other university residences. One of the records my girlfriend and I enjoyed most as background in this treasured time together was Bruch's violin concerto, which still brings back vivid memories of those halcyon days.

On the occasion of our annual medical residence dance, one of our fellow medical students, Susan Vidor, originally from Hungary, tutored a group of us final years in belly dancing, which resulted in a rather amusing floorshow at the dance.

Residency year

After graduating, there was a statutory requirement, based on the British system, of doing six-month residency posts in medicine and surgery, before one could be registered as a medical practitioner. The number of posts available at the Groote Schuur Hospital associated with the Cape Town medical school was limited and strongly competed for and filled by selection based mainly on the final year examination results. I was fortunate in getting one of the surgical posts to start with, associated with the Professorial firm of Professor Jannie Louw, who had a special interest in paediatric surgery, together with a six-week rotation in orthopaedics.

There are a number of experiences in my residency year that are firmly imprinted in my mind. During my initial six weeks orthopaedic residency, there was also one particular case that left a lasting impact on me. A 16-year-old girl had dived at the beach into shallow water, struck her head in the sand and ended up with a fracture/dislocation of the cervical spine and was completely paralysed from the neck down. The outlook looked absolutely dismal. Almost immediately after I admitted her Professor Allen, the head of orthopaedics, came to assess her and then phoned his brother who was head of neurosurgery in Johannesburg. He flew down the same evening for an emergency operation to remove the part of the vertebra impacting on the spinal cord in the hope that if one got in quickly enough some of the nerves might still be viable and able to recover. She survived the operation, which took several hours, and then had the neck firmly immobilised in a plaster cast. Miraculously, function started coming back gradually, starting in the finger tips and working towards the body, and also in the legs and after several months of active rehabilitation she eventually walked unaided out of the ward, with full return of bladder and bowel control. This seemed to me at the time, and even now, nothing short of miraculous.

As residents we had responsibility for reducing many of the common fractures, but occasionally we were also allowed some surgical experience under close supervision, and I still remember the thrill of being supervised by Teddy Sarkin in doing an open reduction of a fractured head of the radius bone of the forearm at the elbow end, with success. I also felt a great sense of responsibility when I was on emergency call one evening and had to provide a functional plaster cast for a man who had fractured his scaphoid bone in his wrist (the bone below the anatomical 'snuff box' at the base of the thumb), in order to still allow approximation of the thumb to individual fingers. I had a further trepidation when it turned out he was an oboe player in the Cape Town symphony orchestra, so it was particularly satisfying that after prolonged immobilisation to allow full healing of the fracture he was able to get back to his full functional prowess again.

During my surgical residency with Professor Jannie Louw we were not only expected to be on almost continuous duty to clerk all our admissions to the ward, but the professor also did a regular wardround on Sunday morning to review the progress of patients operated on in the major theatre session on Friday and to discuss any new admissions going on to the surgical list on Monday. A large amount of one's time was taken up wandering around the various wards of the hospital to see if there were any empty beds available into which one could admit the patients coming long distances, prior to their surgery.

On one occasion I had been given a special dispensation to absent myself from the Sunday morning round in order to attend a family celebration. I did however, ensure that through the Saturday night I clerked up all the patients being admitted for surgery on the Monday. I recall having had quite a busy load of new patients, many of whom came from far afield, including one farmer who was being admitted for a partial gastrectomy (removal of the stomach), for a duodenal ulcer, a popular operation in those days to reduce the acidity of the stomach and enable the ulcer to heal, before the modern era of effective drugs. He was my final patient and it was approaching somewhere around 4 in the morning. I carefully examined his abdomen and thought I was able to palpate a small firm lump on the back of the abdominal cavity. So I stuck my neck out and wrote under diagnosis at the end of my detailed case notes, '? Carcinoma of the pancreas (reconsider gastrectomy)' I also left a personal note for my senior resident (the surgical registrar) to review the case prior to surgery and to defer any operation on the stomach.

When I returned on Tuesday morning the surgical registrar informed me my diagnosis had been correct and both the patient, and the professor, were happy he still had his stomach intact and that they had been able to remove the malignant lump which was still fairly confined to the head of the pancreas.

A special experience whilst on this surgical residency was to have Chris Barnard as one of our registrars. He had come back to academic medicine after many years in general practice and was on the medical unit doing research on potential treatment of tuberculous meningitis. Whilst in midstream of his study,

2133

GROOTE SCHUUR HOSPITAL

FIRM: PROF.J.H.LOUW. H/S:Dr.Dubowitz. Registrar: Dr.Barnard. C.5.
PATIENT:

SUMMARY

DIAGNOSIS: Right Indirect Inguinal Hernia.

OPERATIVE: Hernioplasty. 20.6.55. 4.15 p.m. 40 mins.Ind.for Op: Right indirect inguinal hernia. Risk: Anaesthetist:Dr.Citron. Anaesthetic:Pent GOE. Surgeon:Dr.Dubowitz. Assistant:Dr.Barnard.

DESCRIPTION: Right suprainguinal incision. External oblique divided. Cord mobilised. Cremaster incised and sac defined and freed down to its neck. Sac opened and neck transfixed, ligated and cut. Lattice of continuous dermalon between conjoint tendon and reflected part of inguinal ligament. Continuous chromic catgut to external oblique. Interrupted dermalon to skin.

COURSE: Uneventful post-operative course. Up and about on 2nd day. No complications. Discharged 26.6.55. To come again 30.6.55 for removal of stitches and check-up.

Extract from facsimile of one of my case summaries during my surgical residency in 1955. Note under 'Operative', surgeon Dubowitz, assistant Barnard

streptomycin was discovered as an effective drug against tuberculosis. Chris not only abandoned his project, but also decided to switch from medicine to surgery as a discipline. As house officers it was also our responsibility to do the case summaries on all the patients for sending to the referring practitioners and to have in the case files. We occasionally had the opportunity of doing minor operations under supervision such as appendicectomy or hernias. I have eventually discarded my own copies which I had kept over the years (I never seem to be able to discard anything!), but have kept and treasured a few of them where the surgeon is listed as Dubowitz, and the assistant as Barnard.

After completing my surgical residency, I was fortunate to obtain a second six-month post at Groote Schuur Hospital on the medical unit under the combined care of Dr Helen Brown, a superb clinician and very practical and methodical, with both her feet firmly on the ground, and Dr WPU (Peter) Jackson, a graduate originally of Birmingham University (UK), who had a very active scientific mind, was very interested in endocrine and metabolic disorders, and had been a pioneer in the recognition of pre-diabetes, particularly in pregnant women. Much of the time he had his head in the clouds and his feet some way off the ground.

I recall one occasion when I admitted a 22-year-old young lady, who was a trainee nurse at one of the smaller Cape Town hospitals, with a somewhat bizarre cluster of features, including some clouding of her concentration and swinging of her blood pressure. I presented her in detail on our regular morning wardround with all the consultant and resident staff. Peter Jackson listened attentively to the story and thought she might fit in with a newly recognised condition of hyperaldosteronism (excess production of the hormone aldosterone), which had just been documented in the *Lancet* journal the previous week. Helen Brown then reflected on the whole presentation and asked if I had checked the blood barbiturate levels, as she had a suspicion she might have taken an overdose of barbiturate tablets. She proved to be right.

We were always extremely busy on the acute take days, going flat-out for long periods of time, often through the night. In those days it was also the responsibility of the resident clerking a

Sr Hamman (left) and senior nursing staff outside Ward A1, Groote Schuur Hospital, at Christmas, 1955. Décor courtesy house physicians Lanzkowsky and Dubowitz

patient to do the routine blood and urine examinations, in the 'side room' of the ward, which had basic facilities for this. It was always particularly satisfying as I can recall on special occasions to detect the characteristic white cells in a blood smear one had stained confirming one's clinical diagnosis of glandular fever, or finding the sugar in the urine of a suspected diabetic. What always sustained us through the night was the short breaks chatting to the on-duty nursing staff and enjoying the constant supply of toasted banana sandwiches.

The shack at Llandudno

It was in my final year that I first visited the shack at Llandudno that was to become very important to me. I contacted its owner, Ginger Townley Johnson, who suggested I contact Jenny Milligan, a staff nurse at Groote Schuur who was a regular visitor. I can still remember the obvious enthusiasm Jenny had for the place and particularly the people who frequented it, on the first occasion I went along to introduce myself to her. That was the beginning of my longstanding friendship with Ginger Johnson and his wide circle of friends, who not only came to the shack but also had a passion for going out into the hinterland to explore sites of Bushman paintings, which Ginger, who had a background as a draughtsman as well as cartoonist and artist, recorded in meticulous detail, subsequently producing a scholarly book on them. Ginger had lived in Llandudno all his life and the shack had been built by his father amongst the trees and rocks at the north end of the long white sandy beach. It served as a beach hut, but in addition it was dedicated to the nursing profession and any nurses had carte blanche to come and use it over weekends or to stay over during the week. It had an area alongside for doing barbecues ('*braais*') and a stream of running water alongside.

In those days there were only a handful of houses at Llandudno along the single road, and a small parking area for the public who were prepared to brave the icy water on the Atlantic side of the Cape peninsula to come out for the day on the beach.

There was a path for the most glorious walks along the totally deserted coastline to Oudeschip, where there was a natural pool amongst the rocks for swimming, and on to Sandy Bay, which

Ginger Johnson, cartoonist, Bushman rock art enthusiast, humanitarian, friend

WHAT ARE YOU DOING HERE ?
NAY MASTER, EK SOEK WERK!

Episode in North African Campaign in the Second World War. A Cape Coloured soldier found himself behind German lines and when challenged responded, in Afrikaans, with classical Capie humour 'I was just looking for work'

One of Ginger's dynamic cartoons of a participant in the annual 'Coon Carnival' in Cape Town on New Year's Day. (Now called the minstrel show in compliance with political correctness)

The shack at Llandudno, 1960

Paul Boonzaaier, artist, bohemian, eccentric, at his isolated house near Cape Point

Hyme Rabinowitz at his pottery at Eagle's Nest, Constantia

we had in those days entirely to ourselves. A real paradise. I already had some previous acquaintance with Sandy Bay from my earlier hikes with Tubby Singer across the sand dunes from the main road near Hout Bay in search of the *strandloper* kitchen middens.

Now that is all a thing of the past. The whole of Llandudno has been built up into a township by property developers, with tremendous escalation of property value, and has gradually extended around the mountainside towards Sandy Bay, now a short walk from the end of the road, which is now a nudist beach and crowded over weekends to a state of almost standing room only.

Ginger was a quite remarkable man. His family had originally come out from England and he had a passion for cricket. He was also a keen mountaineer and loved the outdoors. He had a magnetic personality with a wide range of very close and intimate friends, who almost formed a family circle, and I was very pleased to become part of it. There was a remarkable divergence of personalities and characters, each of whom contributed something unique to the group. Story-telling and relating personal experiences was the order of the day around the outside fire late into the night. Ginger had a particular empathy for the Cape Coloureds and used to do the most remarkable colour sketches each year of the individual characters in the dancing troupes who used to parade through the streets of Cape Town on New Year's day each year in the Coon Carnival. He also had the most remarkable stories which he had gleaned from talking with or overhearing them and committed many of these to cartoons, some of which he gave to me. There was something very unique and spontaneous about the Cape Coloured humour and some of them have been immortalised in his cartoons. He saw active service in the North African campaign as a stretcher-bearer. One of his cartoons was of a Coloured soldier, who found himself behind enemy lines and looking into the revolvers of a group of German soldiers. 'What are you doing here?' they shouted. 'I was just looking for work!' came the spontaneous response.

Amongst some of the close friendships I forged with the crowd were Hyme Rabinowitz, an accountant who subsequently gave up his profession to become a potter, and after a period of training with Bernard Leach in St Ives became one of the leading potters in South Africa. He is still happily potting away at over 80 in an idyllic location in Constantia. Percy Sieff was already forging a career in acting and was a great raconteur with a flood of stories and jokes he told to perfection. Paul Boonzaaier was an artist, brother of a famous South African artist, Gregoire, and always something of a character. A recluse and a bit of a vagabond he enjoyed the open air and in his later years built himself a small retreat near Cape Point and stayed as a hermit but always welcoming friends, until he died a few years later. Amongst the regulars at the shack already at that time were Marlene Noar, who later married Issy Pilowsky, and became a longstanding and very close friend, Jenny Milligan, Val Kenyon, Sheila MacGregor, Bugs Muldal and many others.

During my residency year at Groote Schuur I spent most of my free weekends either at the shack or going out on trips with Ginger to various parts of the country in search of Bushman paintings. Ginger would make personal contact with farmers in the area and very often there was an elderly Cape Coloured employee on the farm who had personal knowledge of the area and the location of the open cave rock faces with the Bushman paintings on.

These paintings were traditionally thought to date back a few hundred years, but recent carbon dating studies suggest they may go back a lot longer. One of the areas we explored was Boontjies Kloof, where there was a river with wonderful rock pools we used to swim in and where I later was able to take my own family. In recent years an entrepreneurial farmer has developed the area as a popular tourist attraction, the name has been changed to Boesman's Kloof, and visitors are taken in four-wheel drive vehicles to the rock faces with the paintings, which are now protected by suitable screens.

I had an amusing experience on one occasion at the shack. During my surgical residency about a week before Christmas, I did an appendicectomy on a sailor from a Norwegian whaling boat en route to the Antarctic. He was accompanied by a young Danish doctor, Jorgen Nicholson, who I invited to come along with me to the shack for the weekend. He took to the primitive conditions very well until it came to brushing his teeth in the morning and asked where he got water. I took him to the running stream. 'But what about the frogs?' He sounded really

A trip to the Citrusdal area, northwest Cape in search of Bushman rock paintings. From left Ginger, Sylvia, Rael Jaffe, Percy Sieff and myself

Percy Sieff interviewing some of the local Cape Coloured farm workers who knew the area well

Knowledgeable old man who guided us to the Bushman sites

Recording a series of Bushman rock paintings, Cedarberg area

concerned. I tried to reassure him that despite all the myths about frogs causing warts I was not really aware of any hazard and certainly visitors to the shack had been drinking the water with impunity. He was not convinced, and the next thing I found him sitting beside the stream, toothbrush in one hand, and a bottle of gin he had brought from the boat in the other, and rinsing his mouth with neat gin! I couldn't resist noting this in the logbook of the shack, appropriately illustrated with a gin bottle and attached toothbrush.

I have many happy memories of the shack and the many happy visits. We often slept on the adjacent area outside with wonderful clear starlit skies on warm summer nights. On the hot summer days the water was a very icy 15°C, but very refreshing and tolerable for longer periods once one adapted. In winter the water was much warmer, getting the warm gulf stream coming down from the northwest, rather than the cold Benguella current from the south in the summer. It was often very enjoyable to take a midnight swim after a pleasant barbecue and evening by the fireside, in a water temperature above that in the air. There was one occasion on a Saturday with some 13 people sleeping over inside and around the shack, when Uys Krige, the well known Afrikaans author, who was a regular visitor to the shack, pitched up at about two in the morning. It wasn't long before he had everybody awake and in conversation, and after acquainting himself with everybody, started animated discussions and story telling through most of the night.

As my residency year drew to a close I spent the New Year's weekend at the shack and also my last weekend, coming down on the Friday evening, 20 January 1955, and finding myself the sole occupant. A really memorable night. Had an early morning swim and then went off with Ginger's son Jeremy, who called by, for a walk to Sandy Bay for the day. I wrote the following farewell message in the shack's logbook on the Friday night.

> My last weekend . . .
> Alone I have come
> Down to the shack
> That has been, in the course of the year,
> A home, and a friend
> To which I might turn
> In moments of stress and turmoil and toil.

For what man needs
For the peace of his mind
Is escape from himself,
From his everyday life,
And return for a while
To the rhythm and song,
The soothing embrace of Nature herself.
And this I have done . . .
The night is supreme
The sky is clear, the air is pure
The moon is but half
Yet the light that it throws
Is sufficient to turn the untiring waves
Into shimmering bands
Of spectacular glow.
The frogs in the stream
Are all happy and gay
And joyfully recant as they croak on their way.
My soul companion, a bashful mouse
Who lives in this place –
Intelligent bloke –
Has seen fit to come out
And sniff of the air
And nibble a morsel
In a cupboard quite bare.

And as I sit
By the flickering light
Of a candle half dead
I think . . . and rejoice . . .
How lucky we are
To have in our midst,
In a world that is full
Of anger and strife
A man . . .
With goodness of heart
And pureness of soul
Whose pleasure is giving,
And bringing to others
The joys he has found
In the treasures of Nature
Which, if only one looks,
Are present all round.

And as I take leave
And bid farewell
To all of you
My heart is sad
For I shall miss this place
And the folks who come here
A happy family
A jovial clan
Lovers of Nature,
Lovers of Man.
Although I am far
wherever I be
I shall rejoice in the memories I hold
And my mind shall turn back
To my happiest days
Which I spent at the shack.

3

London

During my two-week vacation in my residency year in 1954, I took a trip by car with my classmate Hackey Edelstein and a non-medical friend Monty Silverman to the Kruger National Park in the north east Transvaal, and Cathedral Peak in the Drakensberg mountains en route to Durban, followed by a boat trip back to Cape Town on the regular Union Castle Line. During our stopover in Port Elizabeth, I met up with Charles Trey, another classmate and close friend from medical residence, who suggested we might go over to England together. I agreed to do so in April after completion of my year's residency and a two-month locum I had arranged to do in general practice in Beaufort West, in order to save some money for a possible trip, and also to get a flavour of general practice which was my intended career aim at that time, having decided one year in the constraints and bureaucracy of hospital practice was quite sufficient for a lifetime. In addition, two of my longstanding aspirations were to do a cruise up the Amazon as a ship's doctor with the Ellerman Lines in Liverpool and the second to work at the American Hospital in Paris in order to acquire some French.

General practice in Beaufort West

Most of the general practitioners in country towns ran a one-man practice, covering the whole medical field. In my two months in a busy practice of a long established practitioner, Dr Fischer, who had also been our family doctor, I was exposed to a wide range of day-to-day medical problems, as well as a few quite exceptional ones. In view of the heat in the day in this semi-desert area, with temperatures soaring to over 100°F (40°C) it was customary to do one's routine house calls early morning, between 6 and 8 am, and then to proceed to the local hospital if there were any surgical procedures to be undertaken.

In the morning and afternoon one had walk-in clinics at the practice surgery, which was usually attached to the house of the practitioner. There was a standard charge of half-a-crown (two shillings and sixpence, corresponding to 12.5 pence in our modern decimal currency). There was also a small dispensary attached to the practice for dispensing common medicine for a nominal charge or free for the indigent patients. In one of my walk-in clinics I saw a young African boy who had very severely lacerated his tongue. It looked quite nasty, being almost bisected across by a deep gash. As the fairly intense bleeding had stopped, I thought it would be wise to treat the wound conservatively as any attempt to stitch it might produce further bleeding, and anaesthesia would also be a problem. So I reassured the mother and told her I would review it again the following day. The surgery nurse then asked her for the regular fee of half-a-crown, to which she reacted quite strongly, 'How could doctor charge me for doing nothing?' I then explained to her that short of doing nothing, I had actually provided the child with unusual service by protecting him from surgery, which would have needed a lot of stitching and might have caused a lot of bleeding, and my usual fees for protecting patients from surgeons was up to £10, but I was happy to only charge the nominal consultation fee as I felt sorry for the lad with all the anxiety he had gone through. She handed over her half crown with alacrity and a smile, and was obviously convinced she had a bargain at the price. The following day the tongue looked much better and within a week was practically healed with the only restraint being avoiding solid food.

One afternoon I was called out to a remote farm some 25 miles out of town where the wife of a labourer had a prolonged labour without any progress and was reaching exhaustion. I found the baby was the wrong way round, face-to-pubes, instead of the occiput facing forward, and there was already some evidence of fetal distress, so I explained to her and her husband that the only option was an emergency caesarean section and I would telephone immediately for an ambulance to come out to collect her (a volunteer system in the town) and for the senior nurse at the hospital to get the theatre ready and phone round for a fellow GP to assist me with the anaesthesia and procedure. I then headed back, reflecting with some trepidation on what would be my first experience at doing a caesarean section, realising that whatever the risks and problems, the situation was a critical one endangering the life of both the baby and the mother if she remained with an impacted labour. When I got back to town I had a message at my surgery that the farmer had just called that the patient had been so concerned at the prospect of surgery that she had given an almighty shove with her next contraction and managed to deliver the baby, and both mother and baby were doing fine and the district nurse who had been attending her was satisfied with their condition. I am sure my own sigh of relief was at least as great as that of the mother.

Country general practitioners in those days ran very busy single-handed practices and were on continuous call, apart from reciprocal arrangements they might be able to make with colleagues in the town, or the rare possibility of obtaining a willing locum when they wished to take some leave for vacation. It was certainly an all-embracing experience and demanded a basic competence across the board of general medical and surgical practice as well as obstetrics and paediatrics, not to mention dealing with pet dogs and cats, which intermittently turned up at one's clinic with a very distraught owner, in the absence of a practising vet in the town.

Off to London

On 7 March 1956 I duly set sail for England on the *Braemar Castle*, a one-class boat of the Union Castle Line, which did a six-week cruise up the east coast of Africa through the Suez Canal and the Mediterranean. For the cost of the fare, one had a remarkable cruise, with full board, in a floating hotel, with full entertainment, stopping en route for a few days at a time, at East London, Port Elizabeth, Durban, Lourenço Marques, Beira, Dar es Salaam, Mombassa, Zanzibar, Aden, Port Suez, Port Said, Alexandria, Genoa, Marseilles, Gibraltar, and finally into London Tilbury.

I had a rousing send-off by a large gathering of family and friends who were able to come on board for a few hours before departure, including my father and sister, a number of my father's friends from Beaufort West who were in town, as well as a large contingent of my friends from the shack, including Ginger

Johnson, Hyme Rabinowitz, Sheila MacGregor, and Bugs Muldal.

The boat stopped a day in Port Elizabeth and I duly met up with Charley Trey, who had meanwhile decided to do a further medical year there, and not join me. I was rather sorry as I always enjoyed his company and he had a good sense of humour and unusual taste in literature, including a complete addiction to Pogo comics, which he found entertainingly satirical. In East London I met up with Jenny Milligan who had originally introduced me to the shack. In our extended four-day stopover in Durban we had a mini holiday in itself, as there were a number of my classmates doing residencies at the King Edward Hospital, including Hackey Edelstein, Eddie Berman and George Boyes. Hackey lent me his car to get to and from the boat into town, with a few friends. The local customs officer came to recognise us as we passed the customs gate each day and waved us on with a smile. On the third day, he stopped us, gave us a full interrogation, and strip-searched the car! Guess he was fully entitled to get a bit suspicious at this daily commuter service.

Our cruise then continued up the east coast. One of the advantages of the single-class boat, in contrast to the regular Southampton to South Africa, two-class, fully segregated, liners, was that one had the full run of the boat, excellent dining and entertainment, and even the possibility of landing up at the Captain's table for dinner. There were frequent dances in the evenings, with a resident band, and regular Paul Jones dances with change of partners each time the music stopped. In one of these I landed up with a very elegantly dressed and bejewelled lady somewhere in her 40s, very upperty-upperty, who commented with a slight air of disdain, to a rather informally attired country yokel, 'I say, they do mean to mix us, don't they'. I was about to retort 'Never mind, Lady, I am really quite tolerant of the upper classes', but just gave her a condescending smile instead. In the course of the trip one established close friendships with a number of people and soon had a regular group at the dances and other entertainments. At each port there were also passengers who lived there and we met up with parents and were taken around local sights. Dar es Salaam was an interesting place with a narrow channel the boat had to negotiate into the harbour, and a very interesting coral reef. I had not yet acquired my later interest in Makonde sculpture. Zanzibar was of special interest for the smell of cloves as one approached the Island, visiting the many luxurious palaces of the Sultan, and the amazing agility of youths scaling effortlessly up and down the tall coconut trees. I still have a strong visual memory of the beautiful Nyali beach at Mombassa, with a sense of walking on icing sugar on the endless stretch of fine white sand. Port Sudan was a godforsaken hole, but fascinating for the flaxen hairstyles of the local men. At Port Suez a group of us went on a very interesting overland visit to the pyramids and a few days in Cairo, visiting the museum, and other sights of interest. One was struck by the amazing contrasts in this bustling metropolis of four million inhabitants with modern buildings alongside filthy hovels, and well-dressed rotund, opulent citizens, alongside wasted, almost skin and bone, undernourished tuberculotics. The traffic was overwhelming with three lanes of continuous streams of honking cars in a hurry, interspersed by an occasional seemingly static cart or donkey. The all-pervasive street vendors were like clams and just impossible to shake off, and I doubt anyone got away without a leather wallet or large leather holdall bag. The vendors were still milling around the boat with their final give-away prices as the gangplanks were being lifted.

Passing through the straits of Messina was the awesome sight of the Island of Stromboli in continuous volcanic eruption and a spectacular glow at night, and the remarkable tenacity of the fishing communities living at the base and regularly returning again after each major eruption. Shortly after landing in Genoa we had a financial experience, which was a great index lesson for the future; once bitten, twice shy. There were a number of currency exchange touts on the roadside coming off the boat. I was not interested in changing more than a single pound or two but some of our group wanted to change more. The money exchangers were prepared to offer almost twice the official rate, but only for large sums. So we were soon pooling our individual contributions, and the moneyman parted with a few crisp high denomination lire notes from a thick wad he had in his hand.

We duly accompanied our own 'banker' to a bank to exchange the money into smaller denomination for distribution, only to discover we had been completely conned. We were given totally worthless Greek drachmas, which were out-of-date, superseded currency. With a very clever slight of hand the currency crook had peeled the notes from the back of his pile, topped by a few genuine lire. Although my personal loss was relatively minor, compared to some of the group, I have managed to successfully evade any similar temptations in the future. Genoa proved an interesting place, where I spent half a day admiring the amazing sculptured tombstones in the local cemetery, had a train trip for a day to Milan, and another day trip by bus along the Italian Riviera to the idyllic little fishing villages of Portofino and Santa Margherita.

Arrival in London

After further stopovers in Marseilles and Gibraltar, we reached the English Channel, which was as calm as a millpond, and proceeded up the Thames and docked at Tilbury Docks in London on 25 April 1956 on a misty and smoky morning. I had a choking feeling, aggravated by an awaiting letter from Bugs Muldal telling of an Easter weekend in Bains Kloof and Citrusdal areas chasing Bushman paintings, in glorious sunshine. Those were the days before the clean air act of 1960, and I was soon to experience the pea-souper smogs every winter, where you could literally not see your hand in front of your face.

I checked in at London House in Guilford Street, a haven for colonial postgraduates, and set out on my first day's walkabout in the West End. A few immediate impressions on that first day were the archetypical Englishman with pin-stripe suit, bowler hat, and rolled umbrella, who seemed not only for real, but to be quite abundant; the statuesque guards at Buckingham Palace who seemed in a state of suspended animation without any visible signs of life or breathing; women selling newspapers on the street; women soliciting on the streets of Bayswater at 3 in the afternoon; and my first exposure to television in the evening.

I was pleased to meet an old friend, Rael Jaffe, from Cape Town, who was also staying at London House, as well as Teddy Sarkin and other South Africans. The following week I went with a group of them to the regular Friday evening social dinner at Hillel House nearby, where I met up with an interesting crowd of students from diverse countries, studying a range of different subjects in London, and also with a group of enthusiastic ramblers whom I joined the following Sunday for a ramble around

Dorking. The Hillel House Friday evenings became a fairly regular event and I also met up with a pleasant and sociable girl, Mavis Dewhurst, living in London, who was keen on classical music but even more on tennis. So I had the privilege of watching Wimbledon the ensuing season, including centre court for the semi-finals and the Rosewall final. I also met up soon after arrival with my classmate Simmy Bank, and his wife Sybil, who was heavily pregnant with their firstborn, and saw a lot of them in the ensuing years. Another early contact through Hillel House was Zvi Shelef, a postgraduate engineering student from Israel, who remained a lifelong close friend, together later with his English wife Joan.

I was also struck by the large number of ex-army officers who filled senior administrative posts and had still not been able to shake off their titular army status, even though it was already ten years after the end of the World War. I thus met Colonel Sprunt the day after my arrival, who was in day-to-day managerial control of London House, and then also had an audience with Brigadier Sandifer, who was in a comparable position to a warden of a university college or residence.

England in 1956

In my early days in London I used to pop in regularly to South Africa House in Trafalgar Square to read the Cape Town newspapers, the *Cape Times* and the *Cape Argus*, and also the Afrikaans paper, *Die Burger*, and the Johannesburg weekly *Sunday Times*, which had some excellent columnists openly critical of the government. They also had various country town newspapers including the monthly *Beaufort West Courier*.

England in 1956 was just emerging from the post-war period of severe constraint and there was a palpable feeling of optimism and enthusiasm. The National Health Service (NHS), still only in its first decade, seemed to have settled in well after the not inconsiderable opposition to it from the medical establishment at the time of its launch in July 1948. Its primary objective was to provide free healthcare for all citizens, based on need and not the ability to pay, and it brought together for the first time hospital services, general practitioner services and community-based services into one organisation. In 1948, Britain was just emerging from the ravages of the war, food was still rationed, building materials were in short supply and the development of new towns created new concentrations of population needing health services. On the medical front, 1948 was a time of the first attempts at heart surgery for rheumatic heart disease, and the first hip replacements. It was perhaps not surprising that within a few years there were already financial difficulties and a modest prescription charge of one shilling (5p) had to be introduced and a flat rate of one pound for dental treatment, but no one could have foreseen the tremendous expansion and escalation of costs in later years, with the advent of a wide range of new and expensive drugs, tremendous advances in technology and ever more sophisticated surgery, which now threaten the whole equilibrium of the NHS.

Looking back now, one appreciates what a privilege it was working in the 1950s in a health system that had high ideals and objectives and seemed to work well, with a minimum of bureaucracy. Who would believe you could run a hospital efficiently, and seemingly effortlessly, with one medical superintendent (also a consultant on the staff), one senior nursing officer and one hospital secretary, plus a very devoted board of governors, who were dedicated volunteers, with a commitment to public service. Many of them were ex-army senior officers looking for a transition back to civilian life.

I still recall a number of apocryphal jokes doing the rounds, which seemed to encapsulate the society at that time. The public had come to appreciate the potential benefits of the welfare state, which was well reflected in the story about the man who was asked what his occupation was and responded, 'I am an outpatient at St Thomas' Hospital'.

Looking for a job

Soon after my arrival in London, I set about looking for a job. I thought it might be helpful to test the water by popping in to various neighbourhood teaching hospitals, including the Royal Free in Gray's Inn Road, round the corner from London House, to speak to the casualty officers and get some idea if any casualty posts might be available or becoming vacant in the coming months. There proved to be little on the open market in these teaching hospitals, but the very obliging casualty officer phoned the superintendent at Orpington Hospital in Kent, who invited me out the following day. A very pleasant hospital and friendly staff and a post available, but I was concerned about the distance and isolation from central London.

My next port of call was Sir Francis Fraser, at the Postgraduate Medical Federation just off Guildford Street, to register, as was customary for visitors from the commonwealth, to get advice on possible jobs, and to lodge my testimonials and the names of the heads of department at Groote Schuur Hospital I had worked with and from whom he would obtain confidential references to hold in file for any job applications I might make. I also told him of my interest in getting some general experience across the board and was thinking of some casualty (emergency room) posts. He advised me it would be very difficult to get any posts in London and gave me some suggestions of currently available openings in Wales and in Scotland. I told him that quite honestly I was more interested in all the cultural opportunities in London than the medical ones in the backwoods.

He then scoured the advertisements in the weekly medical journals, and came across a casualty post at Lewisham Hospital in South London, which he thought worthy of applying for, rather than the more rustic Orpington option.

He also discussed with me what postgraduate work I was keen on and what higher exams I was considering. When I responded, 'none', as I was keener on general practice, he advised I needed to make a choice of medicine or surgery, so that I could at least be officially registered as a postgraduate student in his books. So to satisfy him, I said surgery.

First post in London

The following week I had a phonecall and letter from Lewisham Hospital to attend for interview, and was duly offered the post, starting on Monday 14 May. Thus began my medical experience in London as casualty officer at Lewisham.

I soon discovered there were probably two factors playing in my favour in getting the post. Firstly a recent incumbent in the post had been Ken Frater, a graduate from Cape Town a few years ahead of me, who had been top graduate of the year, and later became a cardiac surgeon. There also seemed to be some difficulty in attracting British medical graduates to casualty posts due to an incipient fear of litigation, and those in post, such as my fellow casualty officer, were reluctant to take responsibility for any procedures and simply acted as sorting officers, passing all patients on to the relevant specialist units of the hospital for management. My own attitude, undoubtedly influenced by my background training in South Africa, was completely different. I was keen to get hands-on experience and as I had already had some experience in orthopaedics during my surgical residency post in Cape Town, I was happy to take on reducing all fractures coming into the emergency room, and also to deal with any superficial trauma. I soon realised that the senior nurse in the department, Juliet Bristow, was an absolute expert at fine stitching, so anything approaching plastic surgery, such as suturing a laceration of the face, I happily left to her skilled hands.

Many of the residents at Lewisham Hospital were Guy's Hospital graduates and there were also a regular contingent of students from Guy's attached at Lewisham for training. I also made contact with John Goodliffe at Guy's, who ran an office for placing Guy's graduates in various short-term locum posts and also substantive posts. I told him of my interests in any posts of general training value across the specialties, and also of my special interest in working in Paris and also doing a ship's cruise to the Amazon. This contact was soon to prove immensely helpful.

After my appointment, I had also indicated to the superintendent at Lewisham, Dr Simmons, that I was keen to get general experience across the board, and soon found myself covering short locums in various departments, without extra pay, when residents were on leave. This included a residency with a very dynamic obstetrician, Mrs Karnichi, which provided some hands-on experience in obstetrics and also exposure to the newly-introduced exchange transfusions for rhesus disease in the newborn, under the combined aegis of the obstetrics and haematology departments. The paediatricians at that time did not have a show-in at all. The local paediatrician Hugo Gans was a somewhat eccentric individual, who was a chain smoker and held his cigarette in a figure of eight wire loop attached to his little finger. We somehow were poles apart temperamentally and just did not hit it off, so it was not surprising to me that he did not even consider me for a residency post in paediatrics available at Lewisham hospital at the time. Just as well or I might have ended up in a similar *cul de sac* as him. My next locum was in dermatology with Dr Vickers, and subsequently a surgical one, which proved to be very beneficial and also played a key part in my subsequent career. The superintendent called me in one morning and asked if I could help out, as the ophthalmic surgeon, Mr Marcelli Shaw, had indicated that he would rather manage with no resident at all than the present incumbent, who covered ophthalmology and urology. I happily obliged. This provided a number of interesting medical experiences. One weekend he asked if I could help with assisting him at a cataract operation on a private patient at a central London hospital. A week later I received a handsome remuneration in the mail, which I was reluctant to accept, but he told me the patient had already paid it, so I had no option!

On the 5th of November each year, the whole country indulges in a lavish display of bonfires and fireworks, to commemorate the foiling of the original gunpowder plot in 1605 of Guy Fawkes and his conspirators to blow up the Houses of Parliament, including the King, because of the intolerance towards the Catholics. Each year the fire brigade has a busy night extinguishing out-of-control fires and the emergency rooms of hospitals are kept busy with treating cases of minor burns plus a few serious cases. I had first-hand experience of one such serious case of a ten-year-old boy, who all but lost the sight of both his eyes. He had lit a cracker and thrown it down but when it did not go off he lifted it up to check and it exploded in his face scorching his face and both eyes. His corneas looked like burnt toast and the prospect of recovery looked pretty remote. However, the instillation of antibiotic drops and normal saline ten minutely round the clock, with a designated nurse supervising him constantly, had a slow but quite dramatic outcome and he eventually walked out with totally restored corneas and perfectly clear vision.

I found this exposure to various fields of medicine very rewarding and enough to give one basic confidence to deal with problems in these areas if one were going into general practice.

Towards the end of the tenure of my post at Lewisham, Mr Shaw asked me what I was contemplating as my next post and I told him I was quite keen to get back to general medicine. He said he would check if anything was coming up at New End Hospital in north London, with which he was also associated, and indeed a week later he told me to apply for a residency post that was to be advertised in the medical journals within the next few weeks and to give his name as a referee.

At about the same time, I received an unexpected package from the Royal College of Surgeons in Lincoln Inns Fields in London, with the good news that I had been accepted for their residential, full-time course for training for the primary examination for the Fellowship of the Royal College of Surgeons. To extricate myself gracefully from this coveted offer, and not offend anyone, I wrote a letter back expressing my appreciation, but that in the course of the casualty officer post I was pursuing at Lewisham Hospital, I had realised that my academic interests and any latent talents were more inclined towards medicine than surgery and I had accordingly decided to change course.

Laying the foundation stone

There was a very good mess spirit at Lewisham and most of the residents were of a similar vintage and had a good sense of fun. As in most hospitals there were always some gripes about inadequacy of facilities for the residents and also the intransigence of the administrative staff for doing anything about it. But things came to a bit of a head when the resident doctors were particularly riled by the lavish arrangements for the laying of the foundation stone of the new outpatients and emergency department to be built on the hospital grounds. The final straw was the omission or oversight in not inviting any of the resident staff to the official stone laying, whereas most of the other hospital staff were represented. It also seemed somewhat incestuous that the Chairman of the Group Hospital Committee would be laying the stone, and having his name embellished on it, rather than some more important dignitary. So the residents hatched a plan to have an unofficial stone laying themselves, two nights before the official one. At about midnight seven of us gathered for an 'emergency meeting' to plan the strategy, including Derek Goldman, Spens Galbraith, Johnny Meyers, Frank Mansfield, David Hayley, Johnny Walker and myself. The plan had been to

6 The Kentish Mercury, October 5, 1956.

LEWISHAM JOKERS DID JOLLY GOOD STONE-LAYING JOB

But it would have blocked main doorway!

MYSTERY group of jokers who unceremoniously and unofficially laid the foundation stone of Lewisham Hospital's new out-patients' block just 36 hours before the official ceremony, are still undiscovered after a week's probing by embarrassed officials.

What a commotion they caused when workmen discovered the stone on Friday morning cemented in the middle of what will be the main portal of the building!

The accompanying Mercury photograph shows the stone before builders were hastily ordered to chisel away the cement base and flanking brick supports.

Four young men are believed to be the culprits. And, despite their grave expressions, hospital staff admit they did a thorough, well-planned job.

Obviously it was done in daylight—probably in the short time between workmen leaving on Thursday evening and dusk falling.

To get the stone, which weighs 3a cwt., they broke into the carpenter's store and carried it 50 yards near to the spot where Group Chairman, Walter Owen, was due to lay it on Saturday. But instead of putting it in its rightful position the jokers moved into the main doorway.

Then they knocked up cement in the builders' tea bucket, cemented the stone down and constructed a column of bricks each side.

Came Friday morning—and the chaos.

Fortunately the cement-mixers weren't experts and the stone was undamaged as it was chipped from its base. Then it was locked up to wait for its proper, more sedate, laying on Saturday.

There was a grin on the face of Walter Owen as he laid the stone to mark the beginning of the £250,000 new building. Maybe he was proud of his Group's achievement. Maybe he remembered the prank of the high-spirited young men at the hospital.

Footnote: There are no medical students at the hospital but there are several trainee doctors.

The rebuilding of St. Silas' Church Hall, **Nunhead**, is to start on November 12, and members of the church have been told that although some funds have already been raised to pay for the work the church must find another £800.

Saturday morning and the stone is laid in its rightful place by Group Chairman Mr. Walter Owen (left). With him are representatives of the administrative and nursing staffs.

Friday morning and the stone already laid! This is how hospital staff saw the foundation stone. An exclusive Mercury photo.

Newspaper reports of premature stone-laying for the new outpatients department at Lewisham Hospital, October 1956

transfer the four-hundredweight stone from the shed in which it was stored at the periphery of the hospital grounds onto a hospital trolley and wheel it across the grounds to the entrance of the new building, whose foundations had already been laid. Unfortunately the trolley would not go through the shed door, so an alternative method of transfer had to be worked out, as the stone was too heavy to be carried. Following a detailed discussion in the mess, a solution was found and several curtain rails were removed and used as rollers to slide the stone along a series of large planks across the elevated doorway of the shed, and then manoeuvred onto the trolley.

After this exercise, which took the best part of an hour, we retired to the mess again for about half-an-hour to give the night nurses a chance to return across the grounds to the wards from the dining room. We then transported the stone across the grounds and placed it in the centre of the main entrance of the new outpatient block. With a few bricks piled up on either side and the addition of some rapidly mixed mortar with a traditional trowel, Derek Goldman officiated at a brief ceremony, an official photograph was taken and we headed back to the doctors' mess. At that moment the nursing orderly to the casualty department walked across the grounds and, seeing some figures moving in the darkness, let off a shrill shriek and rushed back into the casualty department. Seconds later a whole batch of hospital porters came rushing around the side of the hospital building as we headed into the doctors' quarters. Soon afterwards the whole Lewisham police force seemed to descend on the hospital, with at least three patrol cars with sirens blaring and blue lights flashing. Most of our party were rapidly into pyjamas and into bed. I made the error of joining a group on the upper floor to await things to settle down and after quite a while headed to my room on the lower floor, only to bump into a police sergeant in the corridor. He told me that about five intruders had been spotted by staff in the hospital grounds and were seen going in the direction of the doctors' mess. Had we noticed anything untoward? Nothing to speak of officer. I then helped him with a search of the resident quarters. He then noted some fresh footmarks of sand on the carpet and called the inspector. After a further appraisal of the situation, the inspector remarked, 'Sergeant, I am quite happy to call off the search. I am convinced there is no-one in these quarters beside the doctors themselves'. I nodded in agreement and was bursting to tell him ' How right you are'. He then asked to speak to the senior doctor, and the RMO (resident medical officer) was duly woken, the situation was explained to him, and he agreed that no further action was necessary. When I got to my room and noted in the mirror, as I was brushing my teeth, a large chunk of dried mud on the side of my glasses, I fully understood the confidence of the inspector's decisions.

In the morning Derek got a report to a contact he had in one of the local press offices and by the evening it was in the two London evening papers and also got wide coverage the next day in the morning papers. A general chuckle soon passed through the hospital. The perpetrators were still *incognito* and it was difficult to keep a straight face when the staff in casualty related to me the whole story. The most priceless remark came from the hospital secretary, who when telephoned by the press in the morning and asked about the stone laying, was quoted as saying 'Nothing has happened. I have heard nothing about this. If it were true I would know about it'.

It required a special crane to manoeuvre into position to lift the stone from its temporary resting place and to prepare the venue for the official stone-laying the following afternoon. This went ahead with no outward sign of anything out of the ordinary. Almost 50 years on I doubt anyone reading the inscription on the cornerstone 'This stone was laid on 29 September 1956 by Walter R Owen, DL, JP, LCC, Chairman of the Lewisham Group Hospital Management Committee' will give it more than a fleeting glance. But for the doctors involved it was a very satisfying experience to read in one of the newspapers quoting Mr Owen 'The incident won't ruffle my dignity. But it looks as though the doctors have won this round'. The photograph of the unofficial stone laying, duly framed, stood on the mantle piece of the doctors' quarters after the event. I wonder what happened to it.

Residency at New End Hospital, Hampstead, London

I was duly short-listed for the post of house physician with Raymond Greene in endocrinology and general medicine at New End Hospital, and when I came for interview, I seriously thought it was a complete waste of my time, as most of the other applicants short-listed seemed to be much senior to me in years and experience. I was thus extremely surprised when I was called back after all the interviewing was complete and offered the post. I subsequently realised that in addition possibly to the personal recommendation of Mr Shaw, there was another important factor that may have weighed things in my favour. The first registrar in unit, who had recently completed his term, was Raymond (Bill) Hoffenberg, who had been a registrar (senior resident) on the medical unit in Cape Town during my residency and had been put under house arrest by the South African Nationalist government for his political activities and debarred from any public meeting of more than three people under the prevention of terrorism act, and thus effectively debarred from pursuing his medical profession. He was allowed to leave the country on a one-way ticket and had a very successful career in the UK, becoming Professor of Medicine at the Medical School in Birmingham and subsequently President of the Royal College of Physicians. A glowing example of Apartheid's gift to British medicine.

Bill Hoffenberg, President of the Royal College of Physicians, with Elizabeth Frink, sculptress, at the unveiling of his presidential bust at the college

Meeting Robert Platt, president of the Royal College of Physicians (centre), at my lecture to the annual congress of the Chartered Society of Physiotherapists, 1960

Although this was a very specialised medical post oriented to endocrinology, it was also a very educational one for me both on the medical side and also the surgical. Mr Piercy was the successor to the famous surgeon, Geoffrey Keynes, who had pioneered thyroid surgery in thyrotoxicosis, and removal of the thymus gland for myasthenia gravis, so I had considerable exposure to these particular conditions.

Short locum at Queen Mary's Hospital for Children, Carshalton, Surrey

Following on the residency at New End Hospital, I started applying for residencies in paediatrics and also contacted John Goodliffe at Guy's Hospital again to get back onto his list. Shortly afterwards I had a call from him whether I could help out with a three-week locum at Queen Mary's Hospital for Children in Carshalton, Surrey, just south of Greater London. I went out to see the place and met up with the jovial Australian resident, Michael Harris, whose locum I would be doing whilst he was off to some youth festival in Moscow. He briefed me on my responsibilities. It was a very large and spread-out hospital with single-storey units, which had originally started off as an army barracks in the First World War. In addition to the emergency room service and the acute intake wards for medical and surgical cases, it also had long-stay facilities for many chronic conditions of childhood needing long-term care. These included individual wards for poliomyelitis, which was still very full following on the major (and final) epidemic in 1956, prior to the advent of the polio vaccine, spinal tuberculosis, rheumatic heart disease, and other conditions requiring in those days prolonged bedrest for their management. There were also two muscular dystrophy wards, which Mike told me I did not need to worry about, as the nursing staff would call me if any child had pneumonia or other acute problem needing medical attention.

Muscular dystrophy?

I had never heard of muscular dystrophy, let alone seen a case, so my curiosity was roused and the following day I made a special visit to the dystrophy wards. Each had about 20 children, mainly

Open-air concert in grounds of Queen Mary's Hospital for Children, Carshalton, Surrey, 1958. Most boys in foreground in wheelchairs have muscular dystrophy

boys, and I was immediately struck by a certain uniformity in the appearance and problems of these boys. They were in their teens and having long-stay management in the hospital as they had lost ambulation and were thus wheelchair bound. There was a school facility on site at the hospital, with fulltime teachers provided by the education authority for covering the teaching requirements of these children. Whilst fully resident during term time, many were able to go home for the school vacations if this was practical for the family.

I soon found myself completely intrigued by this unusual disease and keen to learn more about it. So I was delighted to hear from my chief, Dr David Lawson, that a residency post would be coming up in a month's time and I should put in an application for it. As fate would have it, I had a phonecall out of the blue later that same week from John Goodliffe that a post had come up in the American Hospital in Paris and would I be interested in it. In a split second my dilemma was resolved and I told him that I had now opted for pursuing some further experience in paediatrics and was not available at this time. I was duly appointed a few weeks later to a one-year senior house officer post, whilst Mike Harris still continued his registrar post. We had a great time working together, with a common sense of hard work as well as fun. Interestingly in those days, most Australians headed straight back home as soon as they passed the membership exam of the Royal College of Physicians, whereas most South Africans, for obvious political reasons, just stayed put.

A few weeks into the post, I did a lumbar puncture (spinal tap) on a child with viral meningitis, which turned out to be mumps meningitis. Despite the fact that I had had mumps as a child, I found myself soon afterwards developing a severe acute illness and confined to the nurses' sickbay. It proved to be mumps encephalitis and I was in a semi-comatose state for the best part of a week. I then made a fairly rapid recovery and was keen to get back to work but Dr Lawson insisted I take three weeks sick leave to recuperate.

So I decided to head for the Lake District in my Ford Anglia car, taking a bivvy tent. I found a camping ground near Keswick, fairly deserted in November, alongside a hotel with a very pleasant lounge and was able to spend my evenings there drinking with the residents. One delightful, very aristocratic looking, elderly lady asked me 'Well young man, what brings you to this part of the world in the midst of winter?' 'I am recuperating from mumps.' 'That's a rather indiscreet disease for a young man to have.' I was never quite sure whether she just meant I was a bit too old for the childhood disease or whether she was actually aware of the common concomitant of mumps orchitis.

When I got back to Carshalton I still had a couple of weeks of obligatory leave. I noted in the local newspaper a report on the local archaeological society and their interest in a Roman camp in the Carshalton area during the Roman occupation, which seemed to transect the periphery of the hospital grounds. After consulting the Society for their maps and some advice on digging an exploratory trench on the southern perimeter of the hospital, I thought it would be good exercise as well as relaxation and education to try my hand at it.

A couple of weeks later, I filled in the trench again and arranged a display of my finds in the hospital mess, comprising some large iron nails and a few bronze army buttons and bits of glass and ceramics, dating more to the 19th century than anything remotely more historical.

My year at Carshalton enabled me to consolidate my interest in muscular dystrophy and to pursue possible avenues of further study and research. This led me to Professor Peter Daniel, neuropathologist at the Maudsley Hospital in Denmark Hill, who was one of the few people who had a particular expertise in muscle pathology. So I started doing muscle biopsies on the boys with muscular dystrophy and taking them to him for processing and diagnosis. Before long I was enthused to try and do some research on the subject and on Peter Daniel's advice consulted Professor John Cuming, a neurochemist at the Hospital for Nervous Diseases at Queen Square (as it was then still called), who was also chairman of the research committee of the Muscular Dystrophy Group of Great Britain. He in turn advised me to consult Professor Everson Pearse, a pathologist at the Royal Postgraduate Medical School at Hammersmith Hospital in West London, who was one of the pioneers and founding fathers of histochemistry, a relatively new science of applying biochemical reactions to sections of frozen tissue, rather than in a test tube, and had recently written a standard textbook on the subject. I telephoned Professor Pearse and asked if it might be possible to arrange an appointment to come and discuss with him some interest I had in muscular dystrophy. I was somewhat bowled over, whilst expecting a possible rebuff from the famous man, to be invited to come and join him for lunch later that week.

Lunch at Hammersmith

The lunch with Pearse in itself left an indelible mark on my memory. Those were still the days when hospitals had board rooms or equivalent facilities where senior medical staff would regularly gather for lunch and discuss not only their ongoing research and interests but also the medical and hospital politics of the day and I expect resolved most of the ongoing hospital problems in this environment, without the need for lengthy committee meetings. Those were the days before democracy prevailed and provided communal dining facilities for all staff and resulted in most professors grabbing a sandwich in their office instead.

For me it was like a dream sitting at table with several of the greats and household names in the medical field at the time, such as John McMichael in Medicine and Ian Aird in Surgery.

Histochemistry at Hammersmith

Professor Pearse showed me around his laboratory, which, contrary to my expectation of something grandiose, was a single small room about 15 feet square with a single cryostat for cutting frozen sections, which was a prototype Pearse had constructed, putting an old-fashioned Cambridge rocker microtome into a refrigerated cabinet and fitting some remote controls to operate the microtome from outside. The machine was affectionately called 'Wheezy' because of its somewhat asthmatic sounding motor. I was also introduced to a remarkable group of research fellows from all corners of the world, each with a uniquely different special interest, such as Jozef Niwelinski, a zoological biologist from Krakow studying limb regeneration in the newt, Norberto Schor from the Argentine interested in kidney pathology, George Tremblay from Canada interested in thyroid function, Robert Hess from Switzerland, and Mikko Niemi an anatomist from Finland.

I explained to Everson Pearse that I had no experience in pathology and was totally ignorant of histochemistry, but was keen to do some research on muscle disease. 'When can you start?' 'Tomorrow' came my almost reflex reply. And so began my venture into histochemistry of muscle. He showed me an area of bench space in one corner about three feet square, and said that it was not occupied and I was welcome to park there.

And so I was thrown in at the deep end and had to rapidly learn a totally new language in order to converse with people who were discussing diaphorases, and dehydrogenases and DPN and TPN, as if this was their colloquial mother tongue. I soon also realised that it was uneconomical of the limited time I had available, getting the odd afternoon off from a busy residency post, to spend my time waiting in line for the use of the cryostat to cut my muscle sections.

So I very soon established a working schedule of taking the muscle biopsies at the hospital in the afternoon and then driving the half hour free of traffic to the Hammersmith Hospital and spending the evening and often a major part of the night cutting and processing the sections. This worked out very well and the only hiccup I experienced in the whole arrangement was when I came in one evening to find that some of my earlier muscle

In Pearse's histochemistry laboratory, Hammersmith, 1958. Barton Hollands, technician, and cryostat ('Wheezy') in background

My two key papers on histochemistry of muscle in 1960. Fibre types in human muscle (*Nature*) Histochemistry of central core disease (*The Lancet*)

(Reprinted from Nature, Vol. 185, No. 4714, pp. 701–702, March 5, 1960)

Reciprocal Relationship of Phosphorylase and Oxidative Enzymes in Skeletal Muscle

WHILE investigating various enzyme systems in a series of dystrophic and normal human muscles we observed that individual fibres showed a reciprocal relationship between phosphorylase and oxidative enzyme content. Although other workers have investigated the oxidative enzyme systems of normal[1-3] and dystrophic[4] muscle, no observations have been made on the relationship between the two enzymes.

Biopsies were obtained from the lateral head of the gastrocnemius in fourteen cases of progressive muscular dystrophy of the Duchenne type ('pseudo-hypertrophic' muscular dystrophy) and six normal children. All specimens were immediately quenched in liquid air, stored at – 70° C., and cut within a few hours on a cold microtome at – 20° C. and at 10–15μ.

In an attempt to explain the findings in human muscle a number of different muscles from the rat, pigeon, toad (*Xenopus*) and goldfish were also examined.

The methods employed were those for diphosphopyridine nucleotide and triphosphopyridine nucleo-

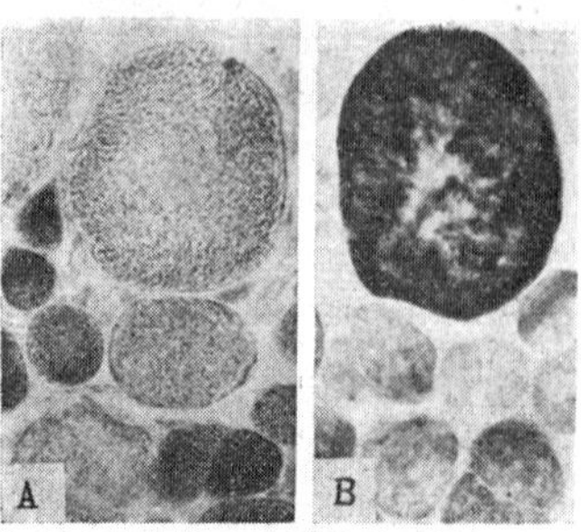

Fig. 1. *A*, Dystrophic muscle. Diphosphopyridine nucleotide-diaphorase (× 234). *B*, Dystrophic muscle. Phosphorylase (× 190)

Preliminary Communication
reprinted from THE LANCET, *July* 2, 1960, *pp.* 23–24

OXIDATIVE ENZYMES AND PHOSPHORYLASE IN CENTRAL-CORE DISEASE OF MUSCLE

MUSCLE was obtained at biopsy under local anæsthesia from the vastus lateralis of a 20-year-old man with central-core disease,[1] and from the biceps brachii of his clinically unaffected parents.

METHODS

Specimens of muscle, about 0·5 cm. cube, were mounted in a transverse or longitudinal plane on the end of a strip of card folded at a right angle, and rapidly frozen by submersion in liquid air (–180°C) for 10 seconds. The blocks were stored in a Dewar flask containing solid carbon dioxide (–70°C) before being remounted on to microtome chucks. Sections were cut 10 μ on a cold microtome (' Cryostat ') at –30°C, and mounted directly on coverslips.

The following enzymes were investigated by histochemical methods: diphosphopyridine nucleotide diaphorase (D.P.N.D.)[2]; succinate dehydrogenase [3]; diphosphopyridine nucleotide-linked *iso*citrate, malate, glutamate, α-glycerophosphate, and lactate dehydrogenases [4]; triphosphopyridine nucleotide-linked glucose-6-phosphate dehydrogenase [4]; and glucosan phosphorylase.[5]

1. Shy, G. M., Magee, K. R. *Brain*, 1956, **79**, 610.
2. Scarpelli, D. G., Hess R., Pearse, A. G. E. *J. biophys. biochem. Cytol.* 1958, **4**, 747.
3. Pearse, A. G. E. *J. Histochem. Cytochem.* 1957, **5**, 515.
4. Hess, R., Scarpelli, D. G., Pearse, A. G. E. *J. biophys. biochem. Cytol.* 1958, **4**, 753.
5. Takeuchi, T. *J. Histochem. Cytochem.* 1956, **4**, 84.

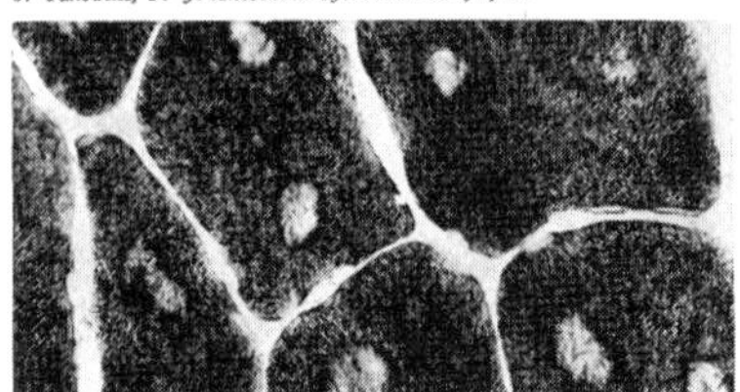

Fig. 1—Central-core disease. Phosphorylase. (×360.)

Note uniformity of reaction in fibres, and absence of activity in cores.

samples, which I had mounted on slices of wine bottle corks and stored in the cryostat unit, had thawed out and refrozen in a contorted fashion separated from their corks, and essentially beyond any sectioning and further study. Jozef Niwelinski instantly realised what had happened and confessed to me that he had made a phone call to his family in Poland the previous evening and as he could not hear on the phone against the competition of Wheezy, had switched the cryostat off and had forgotten to switch it on again. He was rather amazed that I did not assault him bodily in retaliation but showed a remarkable equanimity and for months afterwards kept apologising about the loss of my 'precious meats', as he called them. We have remained good friends over the years and have met up from time to time, including recently in 2003 when I was an invited speaker at a paediatric congress in Warsaw and went on an excursion to Krakow.

Early days in muscular dystrophy

The time I became interested in muscular dystrophy was a very opportune one, both generally in the field and also in relation to the emergence of the Muscular Dystrophy Group of Great Britain. Muscular dystrophy and muscle diseases in general were very much the Cinderella at that time of both the paediatrician and the neurologist, and very much a remote and peripheral appendage attracting very little attention. Fred Nattrass was Professor of Medicine in Newcastle and had developed a special interest in the field and in the early 1950s had attracted a bright medical graduate of Newcastle, John Walton, into the field. This evolved into a landmark review they wrote on the classification of the muscular dystrophies, published in the journal *Brain* in 1954. A parents' support group was formed to promote research in the field and this led to the birth of the Muscular Dystrophy Group, which initially was part of the very active National Fund for Research into Crippling Diseases (formerly the Polio Research Fund) but in the late 1950s eventually cut the cord and became a separate charitable foundation, the Muscular Dystrophy Group of Great Britain. John Walton confided in me that he had always been keen to become a paediatrician, mainly inspired by the legendary James Spence in Newcastle, but things didn't quite pan out that way and he had to be content with becoming a neurologist instead. He had an early interest in infantile hypotonia and coined the term 'benign congenital hypotonia' for some of the cases with a good outcome. The original secretary of the Group was Joan Vincent, who unfortunately died unexpectedly of asthma. Some years later I was honoured to give the Joan Vincent memorial lecture at a meeting in Newcastle, and spoke on the contribution of enzyme histochemistry to our understanding of muscle pathology. In his introduction Walton said he had also originally been interested in research in this area, and although I did not make any comment in response, I felt very grateful he had not made it or I might have missed all the fun.

Muscle research

At the end of my year's residency at Queen Mary's, I was keen to continue with my research and was successful in getting a research fellowship of around £500 per year from the Muscular Dystrophy Group, strongly supported I later heard, by Peter Daniel, who referred to me as 'the answer to the maiden's prayer'. David Lawson very generously offered me carte blanche access to any clinical work I wished to do in relation to the neuromuscular patients. Among the key people I learned a lot from at Queen Mary's Hospital, apart from the patients and their families, were the head of the physiotherapy department Bob Reynolds, who had built up an intimate knowledge of the muscle patients and their problems; the nursing sister in charge of the orthopaedic wards who used to make moulded jackets for the boys, dissolving scrap celluloid, which she obtained from a nearby factory, in acetone, and painting it onto muslin bandages to provide a very firm and well moulded spinal support; the school teachers, who had a tremendous insight into some of the learning difficulties of these boys, and Mary Pugh, the photographer, who was an enormous help in documenting some of the special features of these boys. Some of these early black and white pictures are still retained in the current edition of my muscle disorders textbook, and have also been used by colleagues such as Alan Emery in their publications.

One usually is grateful to one's mentors for paving one's way; occasionally one owes an appreciation to those who inspire in one a rebellious or perverse reaction. I often felt I owed a particular debt in this respect to the head of the pathology department at Queen Mary's, Dr GT Stewart, who very early on expressed his disapproval of my taking muscle biopsies out of the hospital when he could provide a perfectly adequate service for me in-house. He also took umbrage at my writing a short clinical report for *The Lancet* on two cases of influenzal encephalitis coming onto my ward during the Asian flu epidemic that year, without consulting him. We had a very good doctors' mess at Queen Mary's and the doctors were well looked after and provided excellent dining from the patients' kitchen. Small wonder that the consultants regularly ate lunch as well in our mess rather than in the hospital's general restaurant facility.

On a subsequent occasion Dr Stewart confronted me after lunch at the doctors' mess, and said he wanted to give me some sound friendly advice. I really had to make up my mind as to whether I wanted to be a clinician or a pathologist, as it would be disastrous for me to continue dabbling in both. I took up the challenge and responded that my main philosophy was to do things I really enjoyed doing and as I got tremendous satisfaction from both the clinical work with children with muscle disease as well as the study of the muscle pathology and pathogenesis, I was quite prepared to take a chance, even if it might prove disastrous for my future career. After all I was still single, had no family responsibilities and thus felt no guilt at pursuing this double track. In fact I think my reaction to his views that day reinforced my desire and intention of having a foot in both the clinical and the pathology or research camps, which remained with me throughout my future career.

Visit to Dartford Hospital; Irish coffee; clouded mentation

Having reviewed all the muscle patients at Queen Mary's Hospital, I was keen to broaden my experience and contacted other hospitals with long-stay facilities to check if they had any patients with neuromuscular diseases. There were several patients resident at a hospital in Dartford, Kent, so I arranged with the medical superintendent, Dr Budd, to visit one Sunday and see the patients together with their visiting families. The very friendly Irish paediatrician kindly also invited me for Sunday lunch, which was an extended full course meal, with a Sunday roast, at the end of which he offered me an Irish coffee. I had never had this before and assumed that as an Irishman he was perhaps particularly partial to some particular Irish blend of coffee beans. The drink was superb and a new experience for me. I had not realised it comprised equal portions of Irish whiskey and black coffee with a layer of cream floated on the top to prevent evaporation of the whisky. Small wonder I was in a state of semi-stupor for the rest of the afternoon and kept nodding off during my interviews with the parents.

Lecturer in clinical pathology at Queen Square

When my year's fellowship drew to an end, I started considering future plans and thought I might perhaps pursue a career in pathology and muscle research. I discussed this again with Professor Cuming at Queen Square, who was still chairman of the research committee of the Muscular Dystrophy Group at the time. He suggested I consider a lecturer post coming up in his department of clinical pathology, which involved routine laboratory activities in relation to analysis of spinal fluid and other routine tests, and would also provide me some latitude of time to pursue my interests in muscle pathology and histochemistry. This proved a profitable year for me in several ways. It gave me some exposure to a completely new area of neurology in relation to lipid chemistry, which was the special interest of the department, and also to routine laboratory biochemistry. I was also able to continue processing muscle biopsies coming from mainly adult patients in Queen Square Hospital. But the major spin-off of the post was that it finally convinced me that my home base had to be in clinical medicine, with some direct involvement with the patients, in order to have control of and insight into the diseases that I was studying and researching. I just found it too frustrating having to cope with the totally inadequate clinical information in relation to muscle biopsies sent to the laboratory, which made it well nigh impossible to do any meaningful research on them. In addition I also missed the personal contact with the patients and particularly the children.

Lil enters my life

Most things in my life seemed to have happened by chance, or fate, or providence, or accident, call it what you will. My long-standing friend from medical school days, Jack Abrahamson, with whom I had shared digs in my clinical years in Cape Town, who was doing surgical residency posts at Great Ormond Street Hospital for Children, had an acute crisis over the Easter weekend in 1960. He had promised to take a girl he had met out for a picnic on the Sunday and had just noted that the radiator of his vintage car had sprung a leak and was immobilised. Would I be available to provide a chauffeur service? I promptly obliged and decided to call our friend Jules Smith to make up a foursome. Well, I'm not quite sure if it was some invisible chemistry or those phenomenal Hungarian salami sandwiches Lil brought along for our picnic at Virginia Water that Sunday, but I was smitten. I invited her to join me in a week's time for a play, *A Man for all Seasons* with Paul Scofield, at the Haymarket, I had previously booked seats for. The following week we announced our engagement. When my flatmate, Leo Lange, another ex-patriate South African medical contemporary, specialising in neurology at Queen Square, went off on a holiday to Cyprus I had not yet met Lil; when he got back three weeks later, we were planning our engagement party.

We got married on 10 July at the West London synagogue, and went off on a week's honeymoon in St Ives, Cornwall. We still have some of the magnificent Bernard Leach pottery we bought at the time. Although my father had flown out from South Africa for the wedding it was not practical for my mother to come out or for Lil's mother from Australia. So we discussed the possibility of visiting South Africa at the end of the year.

MD Cape Town

An idea crystallised in my mind that a visit to Cape Town might also provide an opportunity and incentive for presenting a doctorate thesis on Muscular Dystrophy in Childhood for the University of Cape Town. So I began a correspondence with the dean of the Faculty of Medicine re the possibilities and was informed that in order to make it in time for the graduation in

First meeting with Lilly Sebok. Picnic at Virginia Water, Easter weekend, April 1960, with Jack Abrahamson (left) and Jules Smith

At our engagement party four weeks later

Our wedding in July 1960

December, I needed to send a resumé of the content to the faculty office for approval as soon as possible, and would need to have my thesis in the faculty office by the end of August, and to present myself for an oral examination around the end of November.

That was the third week in July and I had not yet written a single page of the thesis! So I immediately sent the resumé and a letter of intent to the faculty office, and got a letter of approval by the end of the month. I also had to arrange for the typing of the manuscript and in those days, before the wonders of word-processing and personal computers, each page had to be typed to perfection and any corrections meant retyping that page. I discussed this with Anne Faulds, one of the clinical secretaries at Queen Mary's Hospital, who agreed to tackle it in spite of no previous experience with such a task. One good fortune was that there was still an efficient postal service in those days, with only one class of mail, and without fail every draft or tape recording I posted from North London with the 5 o'clock evening mail collection was duly delivered at Queen Mary's in Surrey first post the following morning and conversely any typed draft posted back by 3 pm was delivered in North London the following morning. And thus we managed to slot together the various cogs in the production cycle and to get the whole project completed from beginning to end in four weeks. Lil and I had a bendy rubber Pluto dog at that time, which we kept on my desk as a monitor each day of our mood and spirits, with head and tail either up or down.

This had not allowed for the time of transit from London to Cape Town needing at least five to seven days. So I kept up the correspondence and sent a letter a few days ahead saying all was ready and was being prepared for despatch and eventually I was able to send by special airfreight delivery a package of four bound copies of the foolscap sized, 250-page thesis.

But not without one final crisis. On the Friday of the final week, Lil had to go out to Carshalton to collect the unbound copies of the thesis from the secretary at Queen Mary's and bring it back by train to Victoria and onward by tube, for my final check before taking to the bookbinder that afternoon. I was at work at Queen Square and had a frantic call from Lil that she had had a most terrible accident. All sorts of dreadful things crossed

Writing MD thesis for University of Cape Town, August 1960

Pluto, our bendy rubber dog, provides daily barometer of progress; thesis packaged for personal delivery to British Airways cargo at Heathrow airport

Graduation at Cape Town University with my parents and Natalie, December, 1960

my mind. She then explained she had lost the thesis and was in an obvious state of shock and panic. She had fallen asleep on the tube train, woken as the train doors opened at her station, and jumped out leaving the thesis behind. 'Only the thesis?' I responded. 'Thank God. For a moment I thought you had lost a leg or something drastic!' 'Should be no problem. Just go back onto the tube and get off at the next station and each station in turn till you reach the end of the line and check if someone has handed it in. I shall meanwhile phone the terminal station to alert them in case the package is still on the train'. At the very next station someone had handed the parcel in. The copies had been printed with an old-fashioned Ozalid system in the hospital, used for doing case summaries, where the top copy is typed on a transparent sheet and multiple copies can then be run off from it.

By the time Lil got back it was too late for the binders and we had already planned to celebrate with a trip to Stratford for the weekend, taking in a play on the Friday night and also the Saturday. With the availability of the extra weekend I was able to also scan through the final draft and picked up a few glaring errors we had missed in the early stages. So I felt reluctant to send it in uncorrected and accordingly phoned the secretary on the Monday morning with the corrections and a request to redo those pages and to put them into the afternoon's mail. On the Tuesday morning I was finally able to take the opus in for binding and on the Thursday to collect the finished product and to drive it out direct to the cargo department of BOAC at Heathrow airport and to send it off personally to South Africa. I was also able to phone through to Cape Town to inform them the thesis was in flight.

When I arrived in Cape Town in late November, I immediately gathered myself and my thoughts to be at the office of the professor of medicine the following day for my viva, which had already been scheduled. I was waiting in the secretary's office when Professor Brock rushed in and I stood up to greet him. 'Sorry I cannot stop to speak to you now, I am in a bit of a hurry to get to an examination of a candidate for an MD thesis.' His secretary then slipped into his office to clarify the situation, and that I indeed was the candidate.

Histochemical symposium in Krakow

In May 1960 I had the excitement of participating in an international histochemical symposium in Krakow, attended by some of the leading histochemists from both sides of the Atlantic, and had an opportunity to give a short presentation on my histochemical studies in normal and diseased muscle. I was never quite sure why I got included in this auspicious meeting, but perhaps Jozef Niwelinski had a hand in it and finally assuaged his guilt for the loss of my 'meats'.

I had great difficulty getting a visa for my visit to Krakow in 1960 and in spite of applying some six months ahead and repeated enquiries to the Polish embassy in London, it still did not materialise. It was at the height of the cold war and not least of the problem was the delay at the South African end, where they had to finecomb my records to ensure there was no ulterior motive for going to an Eastern Block country, as I was still on a South African passport at the time.

It finally came through the day before I was due to travel and I had to collect it in person. There obviously was some jinx on my travel as we had a further crisis on departure. Having arrived at the airport more than an hour early, Lil and I had a little drive around the surrounding countryside before heading back to the airport. Having reached the check-in desk an hour ahead of the flight, I was met with a regret that they could not accept me as the flight had just closed! No amount of pleading was of any avail and as the direct flights to Warsaw of British Airways were not daily I had no alternative but to get a flight via Amsterdam the following morning.

The week in Krakow was an interesting as well as harrowing one, in this old city with its impressive castle and Jagiellonian university, which had escaped any war damage, alongside the old Jewish quarter which had once been a hive of Jewish learning and orthodoxy, and the notorious Auschwitz extermination camp nearby.

Crisis in Krakow

On my final afternoon I thought it would be worth checking the flight times of my connecting flight from Krakow to Warsaw the following day. My friend Jozef Niwelinski took me to the local LOT airline office, where we had the shocking news that all bookings on that flight had been cancelled as the minister of health had needed the plane for a party of visiting health delegates. The only alternative way to make my flight the following day was by train and checking the rail timetable the only appropriate train was due to leave in about 45 minutes. After a frantic rush back to my hotel to collect my belongings we barely made it and had to cross several rail tracks to get to the appropriate platform. Jozef had been put in charge of a railway station during the war and was obviously aware of the intricacies of the system. He had also been traumatised by the sight of the cattle trucks filled with desperate humans en route to Auschwitz, which came out in conversation from time to time. He boarded the train with me, was apologising profusely on behalf of the Polish bureaucrats all the way till we reached the first stop about an hour later at a small junction called Tunel, where he got off to await a train back at some time. I had a further anxiety when the train came to an abrupt halt at about 2 am and seemed to make no effort to go on again. It transpired that the clocks were going back that night and they had discovered it was easier, and presumably a lot more economical, to just stop all scheduled transport for an hour than to rewrite the timetables!

In the compartment with me was a very pleasant lady who got into conversation with me in English and was obviously very sympathetic to my ordeal. It turned out she was a professor of dermatology in Warsaw and had a sister who was a neurologist. I later met up with the sister, Professor Irena Hausmanowa-Petrusewicz, a very formidable lady with a very formidable intellect, who had built up a very prestigious neurology department in Warsaw and also a special unit for the study and management of neuromuscular disorders. Irena later told me of the story her sister had related to her of the interesting young boy from South Africa, who was doing some unusual histochemical work on muscle diseases. We have met on many occasions over the years at meetings as well as visits to Warsaw and during a visit in 2003 as a guest of the Polish Paediatric Neurology Society, Lil and I had the pleasure of dining with both sisters, and also the rare experience of being driven back to our hotel by the dermatologist, who had a unique sense of direction, which

Dinner with Irena Hausmanowa-Petrusewicz, neurologist (left), and her sister. Warsaw 2003

radiated out from her hospital. So we headed in the completely opposite direction, back to her hospital first, before heading out again to the hotel.

When we eventually reached the hotel, Irena had already phoned three times to check we had arrived back safely and was very relieved when we called back. She had tried very hard to dissuade her sister from taking us back rather than a taxi but there was obviously no way one of these determined ladies was going to concede to the other.

Their age remains a well-guarded secret, as well as the question as to who is the older; I understand they are within two years of each other and somewhere in their mid 80s.

Annus mirabilis

1960 proved to be a momentous year for me, not only socially but also academically. In addition to meeting and marrying Lil, and completing and successfully defending my doctorate thesis, and joining the graduation in December, it also saw the publication of two of my key papers on muscle histochemistry, which proved to be of fundamental importance in the later application of histochemistry in the routine laboratory analysis of muscle biopsies. The first was the publication in the science journal *Nature* of my recognition of distinct fibre types in human muscle, based on the reciprocal relation of oxidative and glycolytic enzymes in the individual fibres. The second was in the medical journal *The Lancet*, on an application of histochemistry to the muscle biopsy of a patient with central core disease, which showed that the cores were devoid of enzymatic activity and thus a non-functioning part of the muscle, in spite of their structural appearance of being more compact. In addition the muscle fibres themselves were of uniform fibre type and enzymatic activity, in contrast to the normal checkerboard pattern, thus establishing a role for histochemistry in the study of diseased muscle. I still regard these two papers as amongst the best papers I have written.

4

Sheffield

When my year's activity in clinical pathology at Queen Square started drawing to a close, I consulted my previous paediatric chief David Lawson for advice on how to break back into a paediatric environment. He advised me to contact Professor Alan Moncrieff, head of the Academic Unit at the Hospital for Sick Children at Great Ormond Street, usually referred to as GOS. He also warned me not to be put off by his somewhat brash and detached approach to any discussions and not to feel badly done by if our conversations only lasted five or at most ten minutes, as he was always a man in a hurry and rarely allowed more than ten minutes for any interview. He also promised to phone him, as he had worked with him at GOS during his own training period in paediatrics in earlier years.

I made the appointment with Moncrieff through his secretary and met up with him at the appointed time with a feeling of perhaps wasting his time and was it really worth my effort coming at all. To my surprise he was unexpectedly chatty and personable and listened at length to all the research work I had been doing on muscle disease and my unequivocal decision that I needed to get back into clinical practice after the few years I had spent predominantly in the laboratory. A half hour passed and we were still chatting. He asked me if I had seen a notice in the journals of a lecturer post in paediatrics in Sheffield and I told him that indeed I had, but as a MRCP diploma (Membership of the Royal College of Physicians) was a stipulated prerequisite, I had considered myself ineligible. He felt very strongly I should definitely put in an application and thought that my MD degree on my thesis work would compensate for not having the membership. Even though the closing date for applications had passed earlier that week, he would contact Professor Illingworth in Sheffield on my behalf to accept a late entry.

So I duly rushed off an application, with my relatively short curriculum vitae, to Sheffield in the Saturday morning mail. On Tuesday morning I had a letter from Professor Illingworth asking whether I might be able to attend for interview on the following Monday. The interview was a somewhat relaxed affair, as I recall, in the boardroom of the children's hospital, attended in addition to Illingworth by Bob Zachary, the head of paediatric surgery at the Children's Hospital, and John Emery, head of pathology, plus some statutory representative from the university. I well recall one of the questions from Illingworth, which was an essentially rhetorical one: 'You will be getting the Membership, won't you?' This was presumably to get past the stipulated requirements for the post.

After my interview, I thought I would surprise with a phonecall a close friend of mine from medical school, Issy Pilowsky, who had a lectureship in the well-known psychiatry department of Professor Erwin Stengel. He seemed not at all surprised and somehow was expecting a call from me. What had transpired was that before I went for my interview, I thought I would have a haircut at a nearby barbershop. I popped my head into the shop, saw it was full, and said I'd call back later. Sitting in the barber's chair was an expatriate South African, Les Blumgart, who had qualified in dentistry at Wits University in Johannesburg and was now a medical student in Sheffield. As soon as he finished his haircut he phoned up Pilowsky. 'Issy, a South African farmer has just arrived in town,' to which Pilowsky replied, 'That must be Dubowitz!' My Beaufort West accent always seems to pick me out in any crowd.

Move to Sheffield

A few days later I received a letter from Illingworth that the committee had decided to offer me the post and could I get in touch with him to finalise a starting date and other formalities. I was ecstatic as well as amazed. Considering that I had essentially only done a single year of residency in paediatrics, it was quite incredible being offered a lecturer post with clinical equivalence to a senior registrar position. I felt very humbled that Illingworth had taken me on trust and at the same time felt committed not to let him down. It also inspired me to take a similar approach when making appointments in the ensuing years.

Ronald and Cynthia Illingworth

Illingworth had been appointed in 1947 as the first professor in Child Health in a newly established academic department of paediatrics at the Children's Hospital and had also been instrumental in bringing together the expertise of Bob Zachary, the superb paediatric surgeon, and John Emery the paediatric pathologist, in addition to the gradual expansion of his own clinical unit. He was always a clinician at heart, an astute observer, and had a special interest in normal development. His textbook *The Normal Child* was a masterpiece of clear writing in superb basic English and remained a best seller through its many editions. His wife, Cynthia, also a fully trained paediatrician, co-authored some of his later books on child development, and also a fascinating book on the childhood of famous (and notorious) people. He also conceived one weekend of putting together a practical book for practising paediatricians on common symptoms in paediatrics, which were badly dealt with in the usual textbooks, much more interested in the rarities of disease than the commonplace. He gradually built up a dossier of common causes of common symptoms such as headache, bedwetting, temper tantrums and so forth and produced a book which again was an instant success and opened the way for comparable books in many other specialties.

The background to the vacant post was an interesting one. In the late 1950s and early 60s there was a great shortage of consultant posts in the clinical specialties and a great bottleneck of time-expired senior registrars chasing the small number of consultant opportunities. The same applied to senior lectureships with consultant status in clinical academic departments, where new posts or promotions from lecturer to senior lecturer were in competition with all other university departments for the very limited funds available each year. When the paediatric department was successful in achieving a promotion from lecturer to senior lecturer, it had two long-standing lecturers in post, Kenneth Holt and John Rendle-Short, both of whom had been lecturers for over ten years. Kenneth Holt got the promotion.

So John Rendle-Short opted for seeking other pastures and headed for a chair of paediatrics in Brisbane, Australia, thus vacating the post. Of interest to me was that he had a special interest in cardiology and had established a close association with Dr David Verel, an adult cardiologist who was just in the process of setting up a regional cardiac centre at the Northern General Hospital, with Rendle-Short having a commitment for the paediatric patients. As I still considered myself a general paediatrician and keen to gain clinical experience across the board, I thought it would be a great pity if this new facility were lost to the paediatric department. So I agreed to continue where Rendle-Short had left off and each Tuesday morning for the next five years, until I went to the USA for a year, I did the cardiac catheterisations on all paediatric patients, thus consolidating some knowledge in clinical cardiology and building up a file of personal records of some 450 patients.

Illingworth had a wonderful ability to give people responsibility and let them get on with their efforts, with little interference beyond keeping a watchful eye and always being available for consultation. He thus gave me the full running of a paediatric ward, under his nominal consultancy, as I did not have consultant status with my lecturer post. And all I, in turn, had between the patient and me was one house officer, whom I had to supervise and also train whenever a new appointee took up post. If a resident had difficulty with an intravenous infusion or a spinal tap, I was always on call to provide the necessary backup. So I essentially filled the role of consultant as well as registrar to the unit. The two senior lecturers, John Lorber and Kenneth Holt supervised separate units, with John Lorber having a special interest in hydrocephalus and spina bifida and setting up a world renowned centre in Sheffield for management and research in this field, together with the expertise of Bob Zachary, the surgeon who did all the operative work, John Sharrard, the orthopaedic surgeon, and John Emery the pathologist. Kenneth Holt had a special interest in cerebral palsy and developmental problems.

I still recall some of the expressions of condolence and sympathy at my Sheffield appointment from some of my close London colleagues, along the lines of 'Hard luck old, chap, there just are not enough posts in London for everybody'. There was one notable exception and that was Bob Cohen, a close friend who had been a fellow resident in medicine with Lil at the Hammersmith, and now held a senior medical post at the London Hospital, later to become chairman of the department. 'Hold on a moment; I just want to close the door so no one overhears. Heartiest congratulations. That really is great news and a wonderful opportunity. Don't let anyone kid you. Some of the best training posts these days are in the provincial centres and you'll see a much wider range of medical cases than in the more rarefied and limited environment of the London teaching hospitals.' He was palpably enthusiastic and genuinely pleased at the other end of the phone line. And he proved to be absolutely right.

Back to the muscles

One of the great advantages of an academic centre such as Sheffield was that it drained a very large region and attracted a large number of referrals over the whole spectrum of paediatrics. It was thus possible to set up any type of specialised clinic and referrals steadily started gravitating to it. I started a special muscle clinic for referral of muscle patients in addition to the two general outpatient clinics I ran each week. I then also applied to the Muscular Dystrophy Group of Great Britain for funds to support a technician to assist me with processing the muscle biopsies and a cryostat for preparing the frozen sections for histochemical study. I initially arranged to house the cryostat and the technician

Old Department of Child Health building, a converted house.
My office was on the upper floor, Illingworth's lower left

in John Emery's pathology department, but this did not work out as neither he nor I seemed to have any authority or control over our first appointee. Fortunately he left, after a short period of singularly poor performance.

I then moved the cryostat to my office and personally appointed a bright young enthusiast, Joan Wingfield, straight from finishing her schooling. She turned out to be an absolute gem and in addition to her meticulous care with preparation of the sections, she rapidly also developed a diagnostic eye. I well recall that when I decided in 1963 to do a muscle biopsy on the enlarged calf muscle of the genetically carrier mother of a boy with Duchenne dystrophy, to see if there was any pathology, hitherto never reported, she excitedly came to tell me that the biopsy was definitely abnormal. She completed a comprehensive training in laboratory work by attending part time courses, and eventually moved up the ladder and achieved a senior position in charge of a haematology laboratory.

My next choice of technician was also an unusual one, as I was impressed by one of the applicants, Julie Franks, who had no experience at all in biology but had attained a senior technician status in the glass technology department of the university, but was keen to switch to a more biologically oriented field. She caught up with muscle pathology in a matter of weeks and remained with me for several years.

Sheffield: a new language

One could be forgiven when coming to Sheffield for the first time for thinking that one was in a foreign country, given the almost unintelligible language they speak. This is because of the regional dialect in Yorkshire, which needs a total re-attuning to recognise the language. This is partly the pronunciation, one of the most characteristic of which is the pronunciation of 'u' as 'oo', as well as the use of particular words. The word 'love' pronounced 'loov' is a commonly used term of address, and one rapidly becomes used to its regular use in everyday conversation, but still a bit surprised by the unexpected, when greeted with 'thanks luv' when offering your bus fare to the turbaned Sikh bus conductor. I also had trouble initially when I did our week's shopping at the large market down town. On one occasion I was sent from one fish stand to another when I was trying to buy butter, which they interpreted as 'batter' until I demonstrated to one stall holder the act of spreading butter on bread, 'ah, you mean "boooter"'.

I had similar problems with my initial children's outpatient clinics. A common presenting symptom from the mother was 'He's mardy, doctor'. I rapidly realised 'mardy' is a generic term for being generally unwell. Fortunately I had a superb nursing assistant at my outpatient clinics, Marge Middleton, Yorkshire to the core, who became my constant translator and guide. She was also bemused to hear these local children with their keen attunement to language, repeating numbers after me, in Yorkshire dialect with a South African inflection. It was a steep learning curve for me, but I rapidly learned on the job. One special experience, when I was already feeling quite confident with the local dialect, was the presentation of a young toddler with 'a pain on his tail, doctor'. I immediately suspected an anal fissure, a common and painful condition in young infants with a crack in the skin around the anal orifice, often associated with constipation. I carefully examined the nether region but could find no evidence of any local abnormality and instructed the mother to dress the infant again. I then reassured her that I could find no abnormality. She looked at me with an expression of incredulity, 'But doctor, the tail is in the front, and not the back!' I wonder how many other countries have the tail as an appendage in front?

Another anecdotal dialect experience was the occasion when both Allie Moosa, of South African Cape Malay origin, who had been working with me in Sheffield for some years, initially as a resident and then as a research fellow, presented a paper immediately after me at a meeting in Scotland of the British Paediatric Neurology Association. During the coffee break after the session, my long-standing colleague and friend from Edinburgh, Keith Brown, came up to me and exclaimed, 'Christ man, Victor, what are you doing to these chaps? They are even beginning to speak like you!' He had been unaware of Allie Moosa's South African roots, and thought he was Indian.

Illingworth's prayer meeting

Every Monday afternoon at 2 pm Ronald Illingworth met with his senior members of staff in his office to discuss any matters of special interest on the unit and also to relate any particular errors of commission or omission of doctors coming before the Medical Defence Union, on whose advisory board he served for years and was unique in achieving a 100% attendance at the Board meetings each year. After the meeting, which had always been called the 'prayer meeting', we did a full ward-round of all the patients on the unit in both the Children's Hospital wards and those at Thornbury annexe. This provided a wonderful opportunity for all the medical staff to see and discuss all the patients on the various wards and units of the department.

It was particularly ironic, with all his admonishing on prevention of medical negligence, that Illingworth was to fall victim himself some years later. He placed a hot Pyrex dish from the oven onto a cool surface in his kitchen and it exploded and resulted in a severe gash across his wrist and hand. He took himself to the emergency room of the teaching hospital without revealing his identity and the casualty officer duly sutured the wound. A few days later he realised the cut must have been deeper than he thought and had severed some of the tendons. An orthopaedic consultant advised to re-explore the wound and to resuture any tendons or nerves that were severed.

When he was admitted for the procedure he noted a whole string of errors on the part of the nursing and medical staff, ranging from being offered a welcoming cup of tea by the reception nurse, in spite of having an anaesthetic soon after, to not being asked to sign a consent form or having the affected limb appropriately marked.

When he woke from anaesthesia after the operation he was surprised to find himself surrounded by a group of masked people with caps and gowns. For a moment he thought he might have arrived on the Elysian plains! But he then noted that both his hands were bandaged. Yes, they had operated on the wrong side and did not realise it until they were right down to the intact and undisturbed tendons. And to happen to him, of all people. One can just imagine the reaction of incredulity when he attended the next board meeting of the Medical Defence Union.

Nurturing medical students

In Sheffield, Ronald Illingworth had established a very good programme of clinical teaching in paediatrics for the medical students, which was for three months, the longest in the country. There were usually a total cohort of about 25 at a time and in addition to three regular lectures per week, shared between the four senior staff, they were also divided into small groups for attachment to one of the senior staff. During this time my group of five or six students shadowed me on all my rounds and outpatient activities. They thus had direct contact with the patients we were seeing. I always introduced them as well to the parents and asked if they agreed to having these trainee doctors attending to help them gain clinical experience before being let loose on the public, and they invariably agreed.

There was another system in Sheffield which I thought excellent, which was an optional system that academic staff could volunteer for called a 'tutorial group', comprising one medical student from each year of study. They remained a close-knit group throughout their training and each year the senior member would qualify and a new first-year student would join. This worked very well for the students themselves as there was always someone in the year above to give them first-hand advice, and often to also pass on books and class notes.

From a tutor's point of view, Lil and I tried to arrange regular social functions for the group at least once per term and would either bring them to our home for an evening for a meal and informal discussion, or take them to a theatre such as the Sheffield Repertory Theatre or the Nottingham Playhouse, an hour's drive in my VW Kombi minibus, which could accommodate the whole group. In many ways one's responsibilities and contribution were more peripheral than the purely academic and we often were in a *loco parentis* type of situation providing advice on some personal problem, or helping out such as the occasion that one of my tutorial group, a very bright student and one of the top of her year, who was also a dog lover, was presented with a large litter by her Labrador bitch. So we happily accepted one of the pups.

I think it a great pity that many academics look upon their teaching commitments as a chore rather than a privilege, and as a diversion from their more important research or other activities, and this attitude can easily rub off from one generation to the next.

Another remarkable attribute of Illingworth was his punctuality and meticulous attention to timing. He regularly came into the department at 8.30 each morning, including Saturday, and left promptly at 5. If he came to dinner at one's home, he would politely stand up for departure at 10 pm. Soon after I started in Sheffield, he invited me to the annual meeting of the British Paediatric Association in Scarborough and asked me to meet him in the department's car park at 2 pm on the day. I got there about 2 minutes after 2 to see him driving out of the car park, and made a dash for his car. 'I thought you weren't coming,' he commented. Every Christmas he used to invite members of the department for dinner at his home, and if he suggested coming at 7.30, there would be a queue outside his door a few minutes ahead and someone would knock on the door, punctually on the minute.

He also had a photographic memory of road routes, and continental train connections between cities. In 1961 Lil and I had already planned to attend a genetics conference in Rome, motoring down accompanied by my friend, Hymie Nossel. I asked Illingworth advice on a good route, and he suggested going over the Splugen Pass in the Alps. He then took out a sheet of paper and wrote out all the towns from Dover across the channel via Abbeville, all the way to the pass, and then beyond into Italy. He then pencilled in an approximate travel time from place to place, suggested stopover points en route, and also highlighted a few places where there had been some roadwork and delay when he had last travelled on that section, possibly a few years earlier. He had always been a keen photographer, and was a Fellow of the Royal Photographic Society, and in his student years had cycled all the Swiss alpine passes, and had sold photographs to the national daily newspapers, to earn money to cover his student fees.

Lil becomes a paediatrician

When I first met Lil, she was specialising in endocrinology and had been sent out by her professor of obstetrics, Lance Townsend, after completing a residency in obstetrics, to specialise in endocrinology, in order to start a unit of endocrinology within the obstetrics department in Melbourne. She had completed a house officer post at the Hammersmith with Professor Russell Fraser, head of the prestigious endocrine unit, and subsequently undertaken a research project, funded by the Medical Research Council, cannulating the bile ducts of rats, in order to study the metabolism of various endocrine hormones.

When we moved to Sheffield she had to get the authority of the Home Office to move her animal licence for experimental work with animals to her new post in Sheffield, and also awaited the official transfer of her personal MRC grant to continue her work in Sheffield in the endocrine department of Professor Donald Munro. She found herself in a catch 22 situation, where the MRC refused to transfer her grant until she had confirmation of her animal licence and the Home Office refusing to transfer her licence until she had confirmation of her MRC post and research programme.

At that time Lil was approached by Illingworth whether she might be able to help out with a locum vacancy at senior registrar level on the parallel paediatric unit of Dr Tom Colver, which had unexpectedly fallen vacant, while they were advertising to fill the post. On the strength that she had done a junior residency post in paediatrics as part of her residency rotation in Melbourne, she

At our first house in Sheffield, 25 Slayleigh Avenue, Fulwood, with Lil's mother "Mutti" (rear), and Marlene and Issy Pilowsky, their son Paul and twin daughters, Lynn and Cathy, and Lil (right)

was appointed to the locum position. Although the two units functioned completely independently of each other, with separate junior staff, there was already some precedent for cross-fertilisation, as the two heads had married each other's registrars. So Lil entered through the back door, so to speak, into a career in paediatrics. It was not long before she found herself enjoying it and perhaps even preferring clinical work with children to cannulating bile ducts in rats. So she continued in the locum post while the authorities were sorting out the advertisements for the definitive post (*sine die*).

Home paediatrics

Our firstborn did not arrive for some three years, not for want of trying, and in many ways our dog, Zuk, filled the role of our surrogate first child. We had acquired him by chance soon after we moved to Sheffield. We had been down in London, and called in at the Koadlows, an Australian family living in Ealing and longstanding friends of Lil from her Melbourne days. Lil noted this very active pup running around in their back yard. She was surprised when the Koadlows asked if she would like him. The story was that their Polish neighbour's bitch had had a litter of pups and as they were having difficulty finding homes for them that had contacted the RSPCA about putting them down. So this very lively mongrel pup, a true image of the classical shaggy dog, joined us on our way home. We rapidly had second thoughts on the wisdom of our decision when he started retching and vomiting at frequent intervals all the way back.

But he rapidly settled down in our home in Sheffield, and proved to be a remarkably intelligent and responsive dog. He also became quite well known in the Fulwood area. He particularly befriended a young physicist who lived across the road from us, and used to regularly walk with him down to the bus stop in the morning. On one occasion our friend was somewhat bemused to overhear a conversation between two elderly ladies at the bus stop with him and Zuk. "That poor dog. He has no home life at all. I believe the owners are both at work all day. They're foreign you know.' Considering that Zuk had the run of the whole Fulwood village, and had probably served several of the bitches in the area, judging by all the young dogs appearing locally resembling him, I don't think any dog could have wished for a better life. We also started getting poison letters in our letterbox 'Could you please control your dog?' We were rather puzzled by this, so asked our neighbours, who found out it was the lady at the bottom of the road, who had a very well groomed and manicured pedigree white poodle, who was rather friendly with Zuk and used to regularly visit our house and the two dogs would then frolic in the somewhat muddy stream that flowed through the bottom of our garden. So we dropped a friendly note through her letterbox, could she please control her poodle that was regularly trespassing on our property and we couldn't take responsibility if he came to grief in the stream at the bottom of our garden.

No. 1 David

When David was born in February 1963, it was in the midst of one of the most severe and protracted winters in Sheffield for many years, with persistent snow on the ground and subzero temperatures for weeks on end. This made transport very difficult as Sheffield is built on seven hills and any heavy snowfall inevitably lead to a snarl up in all transport. We also had problems

Zuk, mongrel extraordinary, our first 'child'

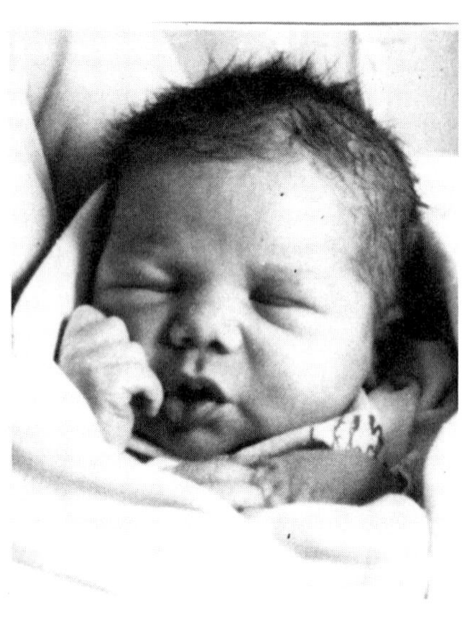

Our firstborn, David, on day one, 3 February 1963

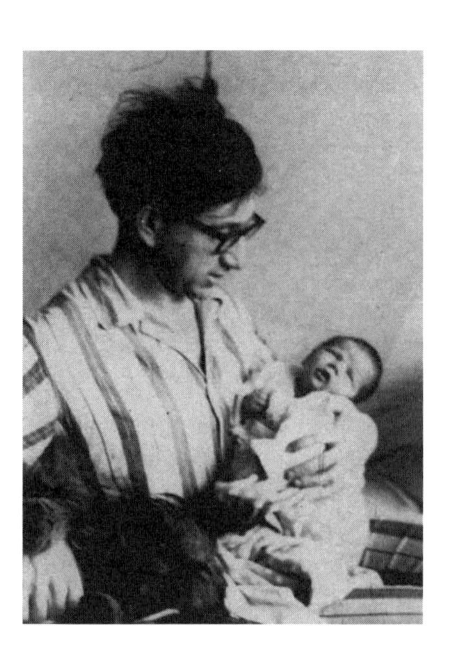

Early morning vigil, a new experience

with Zuk disappearing for prolonged periods, including overnight, until we discovered through a phone call from some residents on the other side of Fulwood village, across the main road, that their bitch was on heat and that Zuk had parked himself on their doormat, awaiting entry, and on occasion was literally frozen stiff in the morning. Such dedication and devotion to duty.

There is something special about one's firstborn. For a start one takes a lot more photographs than you ever do for the later arrivals. One also worries a lot more about feeding and other problems all new parents face, which usually do not present a problem with subsequent infants. I guess one largely learns by experience and develops confidence and reassurance. Never a truer word than the comments of Professor Illingworth when he popped in after David's birth. 'Now you shall learn your paediatrics.' One can certainly obtain the book knowledge from the books, but you cannot speak to parents as a parent as well, with the same amount of reassurance and authority, until you have experienced it yourself. And even looking back now, some 40 years on, to the newborn period, I can still relive our anxiety when David needed a forceps extraction for delay in the second stage, sustained some bruising on the side of his scalp, which then became infected, which made him irritable and not feeding well, which caused maternal anxiety, which suppressed the milk supply, and within days we were into a vicious circle. Some good advice came from two directions. Firstly, from one of those traditional midwives, who could almost will the milk to flow, by initially manually helping to express the milk from the engorged breasts, and that amazing comment she made to Lil which somehow encapsulated it all 'for successful breastfeeding, you have to be a bit bovine, dear'. And then some advice, I now forget the source, to promote flow of milk by adequate fluid intake plus some special agent, to wit daily Guinness stout, and a mineral mixture available at Boots, the chemists, which seemed to be a mixture of phosphates and nitrates, more reminiscent of a plant fertiliser than a human medication! But it worked and within days the whole vicious cycle was broken and everything moved onto an even keel. The important thing was the reassurance to persist, and not go for the simpler option of just accepting the problem and switching to bottle-feeding.

Holiday with David at 6 weeks at Lake Lugano

כלי רכב חדיש - הורים

With David around two years and Mike four months at Eilat, Israel, after a bus ride through the Negev Desert from Beersheba. Newspaper report in national newspaper, *Maariv*, of doctors travelling with young children, anathema in Israel at the time

When David was around six weeks old, we felt sorely in need of a short break and a bit of sunshine after one of the most severe and prolonged winters in Sheffield. We had planned to go to somewhere like Majorca or Ibiza and consulted Illingworth who had no reservations about taking a 6-weeker travelling with us, but was concerned not to risk going to a place with anything short of the highest standard of hygiene. He accordingly recommended Switzerland, with which he was well acquainted, and named a few ski resorts such as Zermatt and the like. That proved to be a bit beyond our budget but we came across a good package at Lugano, with an all inclusive train travel and hotel. We thought it would be wise to splash out a bit for a first class sleeper compartment for ourselves at a supplement. Everything was fine, apart from the fact that the heating system failed in our first class carriage, the only one on the train to be singled out, which did not make for a comfortable ride. The venue was ideal as we could spend a lot of time hiking up the nearby hills, with David in a backpack type seat, a relative novelty at that time, or do day trips on the cheap ferry service between picturesque small villages along the lake's coastline. One imprinted memory was an occasion when we were waiting for the ferry and Lil realised she had left a bag behind with some essentials for the baby, so she left me holding the baby while she nipped over the road to the hotel to collect the package. Almost instantly a cluster of Italian speaking women, who had been ogling David and cooing at him, grabbed him bodily from me and rewrapped him and proceeded to give me some basic instructions on how to handle an infant. It obviously came as a shock to them that any caring mother should abandon a small helpless infant to the care of a husband. The choice of Lugano proved to be a wise one; had we gone for Zermatt, there might have been a sting in the tail as there was a severe outbreak of typhoid at the resort at about the same time. So much for trying to anticipate the hygiene of a resort.

During his first year David also had a visit to Cape Town which was his first introduction to the Dubowitz family and an occasion for the meeting of four generations, together with my father and grandmother. We also took him to the shack at Llandudno and at the age of about eight months he particularly relished the barbecued *boerwors* sausage.

Lil continued breastfeeding David for well over a year. The nipple also proved to be the best pacifier with air and other travel

Four generations Dubowitz, with Esther, Charley, myself and David, Cape Town 1963

and the only investment needed was one of those Mexican ponchos to throw over your shoulders for privacy. I often feel tempted to suggest this to distraught mothers with yelling infants during flights. Of course, fathers have a role to play as well, and I soon realised that there was a very closely knit interrelationship between the breastfeeding mother needing to get a few hours of undisturbed sleep, the infant being at its brightest and most active on waking in the early hours of the morning, and the father having a particular responsibility for placating and entertaining their infants at that time. And no paternal leave for nursing fathers in those days. In point of fact, Lil decided not to take the eight or twelve weeks of maternity leave she was entitled to, but chose to continue with her clinical work as long as she felt fit enough. So she literally ended up doing an outpatient clinic in the morning, going down the road to the Jessop Hospital for Women for her regular check, being told by the obstetrician that he wanted to admit her right away for bed rest and early induction as her blood pressure was too high, and after a considerable discussion allowed Lil to go back first to finish off her clinic.

David also had competition for attention. Zuk, who had got used to having all the attention of an only child, was now reluctant to take second place, and developed a habit of jumping on Lil's lap every time David cried for a feed, as if to say 'my turn first'. But he soon took on for himself a role of self-appointed protector of David. Lil went back to work soon after David arrived, thanks to the help of the matron (senior nurse) in charge of the Thornbury annexe of the Children's hospital where Lil was working at the time, who provided hospitality in her apartment on site for David and his portable lobster-trap playing pen. When asleep David was in a traditional pram in the grounds and Zuk parked himself under the pram and would not budge or let anyone near the pram, including close friends he knew. This went on till David was about six months or so and sat himself up in the pram, when Zuk just resigned his role, as if to say 'that's a big boy, you are own your own now'.

My first parental experience of a common paediatric problem was when David at the age of about a year had a fever and a generalised convulsion lasting about a minute, but seemed at the time to be going on forever. The books, and experience, tell you it is perfectly benign and nothing to worry about. But it is extremely worrying! So from that time on whenever I spoke to parents of a child having a febrile convulsion, instead of going straight on to reassure them, I first said, 'Terrifying isn't it? You think the child is going to stop breathing or possibly even to die' And then I would proceed to fully reassure them as to the benign nature of the fit and the absence of any sequelae, except in the very rare situations where there may already have been some underlying problem.

In the early Sheffield days, David was very content when waking during the night to amuse himself with whatever toys he had in his cot or subsequently look at books once it became light enough. He managed to climb out of his cot long before he was two and also had no problem scaling up the staircase. We became concerned that he might roll down the stairs, so we installed a suitable protective gate at the top end of the stairs. This seemed to deter him for a while, until one morning I heard an almighty thump and rushed out of my bedroom to discover that he had managed to climb over the gate and promptly rolled down the stairs. Fortunately he was uninjured. We realised the sensible solution was to remove the gate and had no further problems.

One of David's greatest fans was Szusza Denes from Budapest who had arrived in Sheffield the week that Lil was in the

Zuk guards David at Thornbury Annexe of Sheffield Children's Hospital

David contented in his lobster playpen at matron's flat at Thornbury, whilst Lil was busy on the ward

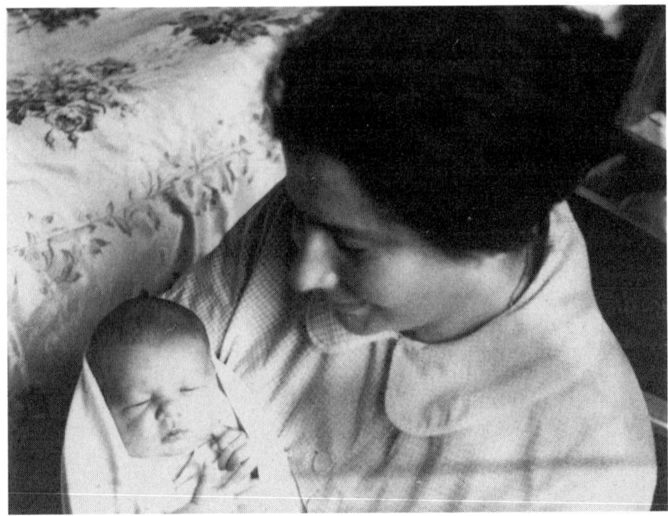

Michael arrives. Day 1, 11 July 1964

Szusza Denes with David in our garden. 1963

maternity unit having David. She was doing a training in nursery nursing and staying for a protracted period with the Zacharys who personally knew her father who was a leading paediatric surgeon in Hungary. As Szusza had no English and Lil was the only Hungarian that Bob Zachary knew in Sheffield, he arranged for them to meet and we have remained lifelong friends. Szusza had a wonderful way of communicating with young infants and would spend hours playing with David in our garden.

No. 2 Michael

Michael was nearly born in our car en route to the Jessop Hospital. We had spent the day, together with my father, at Rhyl on the Welsh coast, and following a fairly bumpy ride back on country roads, Lil announced she was having labour pains. As we passed through Fulwood, Lil had the urge to push and by the time we got to the labour ward the head was right down and she delivered shortly after.

Following the birth of Michael in July, 1964, we had an extended summer with no respite or holiday, so decided to search for some winter sunshine and ended up combining it with a visit to Jack Abrahamson, now a surgeon at the Rambam Hospital in Haifa. After considering various options we decided on the Red Sea resort of Eilat, which was still a relatively small resort, with only one major hotel at which we were recommend to stay. We thought a bus ride through the Negev desert via Beersheba should be of interest. Everything went smoothly despite the forebodings of many friends on taking small infants on a prolonged bus ride. Eilat was also a very enjoyable relatively quiet resort, apart from several groups of scuba divers it seemed to attract from Scandinavia and other countries.

One morning we were standing at the local bus stop waiting to go to the beach when a young Israeli girl behind us got quite friendly and chatty. After the usual detailed questioning of our home base and family background and the origin and occupation of our family on both sides, she came to her main interest. I had David aged just under two in his carrier backpack on my back, and Lil had Michael, who was about four months, suspended in a papoose type carrier in front of her. 'Do you think it is possible to travel with small children?' 'Sure, that's why we are here.' When she heard we had actually come on the bumpy ride through the Negev with the regular bus, she was in a state of disbelief. We finally told her we were actually paediatricians and could see no harm in infants coming along anywhere under the protective custody of their parents. She told us in Israel there was a strong resistance to children being taken on such trips with parents and the medical profession certainly advised against it. She then revealed that she was actually a reporter for a Jerusalem newspaper and would like to do a feature article on travel with children and asked if she could send a photographer to our hotel the following morning to take a picture of our children suspended in their carriers. We duly obliged with a request to send us a copy of the picture. Meanwhile we more or less forgot about the whole episode until Jack or his wife spotted the article with our picture in the supplement section of the Jerusalem *Maariv* newspaper some months later and sent us the cutting.

Parents are much more confident managing their second child. I think one may also underestimate the important role of an older child. This was brought home to me very vividly early one Sunday morning when I heard some activity in the corridor and quietly peeped out of my bedroom door, to find Michael, aged about two, sitting on the potty, with David kneeling alongside and very gently pleading with him 'Michael, if you sit on your potty and you make a nice poo, Mummy and Daddy will be vvvvveeery happy . . . .' And so it came to pass that Michael became potty-trained from that day on, thanks to the good services of David. From an early age, Michael seemed very relaxed and laid back and always happy to do things in his own good time and at his own pace. When we went hiking in the Derbyshire hills, he always seemed to be lagging some yards behind and whenever we called him, we always got the familiar response, 'I'm cooooming!'

After David's arrival in February 1963, Lil continued working full time and taking David to work with her. When Michael arrived some 18 months later, she continued clinical work in a part-time capacity. We had many discussions with Illingworth about working mothers. His own views, expressed in his books on normal development, were based on his own family experiences, and essentially recommended mothers of school-age children not to go back to work. Lil took a converse view, that if mothers were more content with working than with staying at home, they were better off going to work but ensuring they were always at home and available whenever the children were home from school. This ensured a contented mother as well as a contented child. I think Illingworth gradually changed his views, based on the apparent success of Lil's approach.

We also decided at an early stage that it was not inevitable, or indeed necessary, for parents to curb their leisure activities with the arrival of their children. Whilst the children were in infancy it was no great problem to take them along on holiday trips, and as they got older we adapted our holidays to their needs and soon favoured camping, which gave us the required flexibility and freedom.

When we planned a year's visit to the United States in 1965, David was two-and-a-half, Michael a year, and Lil was pregnant with Gerald.

During my year's absence my post was filled by another expatriate South African from Cape Town University, Frank Harris, who was later to become Professor of Paediatrics at Liverpool and later Dean of Medicine at Liverpool and subsequently Leicester. He and Brenda also stayed in our home, with their two sons, one of whom, Evan, qualified in medicine and then entered politics and won a seat in the House of Commons for Oxford on a Liberal Democrat ticket. Our dog Zuk moved in with our friends Cissie and David Goldberg on the other side of town and settled in well with them.

At Illingworth retirement with Frank Harris, who filled my post whilst in the USA, later Professor of Paediatrics in Liverpool, and Dean of Medicine, Liverpool and Leicester

5

New York

In 1965 I got itchy feet and decided it was a good time for the customary BTA (been to America) qualification, which was almost a *sine qua non* of an academic career. As my orientation in paediatrics had been largely towards a neurological bent, I thought that a good general grounding in paediatric neurology, a subspecialty which was extremely thin on the ground in the UK, might be a good target. Having sought advice from many colleagues, I wrote to David Clarke, the well know paediatric neurologist at the Johns Hopkins Medical School in Baltimore, and was accepted for a one-year fellowship. I had also been in correspondence with the Institute of Muscle Disease in New York about the possibility of a year's research, sponsored by the Muscular Dystrophy Association of America, with a specific research proposal I had in mind, and this also drew a positive response. I opted for the general training in paediatric neurology. However, a couple of months before I was due to take it up, I had a letter from David Clarke that he was leaving Baltimore for Lexington, Kentucky, and I would be welcome to join him there. Alternatively, his successor John Menkes, who was particularly interested in degenerative diseases of the nervous system and an international expert on lipid disorders, would be happy for me to join him in Baltimore. Neither of these two options seemed as attractive now as the possibility of a year in New York doing basic muscle research at the Muscle Institute and linked with a clinical appointment in the nearby Cornell University Medical School, which I was able to arrange with William (Bill) McCrory, the head of paediatrics.

We travelled to the USA via Australia, in order to meet up with Lil's mother, and several members of her mother's family, who had survived the holocaust by getting tickets for the last available ship out of Europe, when already committed to transportation from Vienna to an extermination camp. They ended up in Shanghai for the duration of the war and, after having to leave China at the end of hostilities, emigrated to Melbourne, to be followed by Lil and her mother, who had survived the holocaust in Hungary. Lil flew out direct to Australia with the two children, whilst I deviated to Switzerland to present a paper at the International Neuropathology Congress in Zurich and also to visit the famous paediatric centre under Professor Ettore Rossi in Berne, and a biochemist Richterich doing muscle enzymology work and a paediatric neurologist Ullrich Aebi, whom I had met at various paediatric meetings.

I had a somewhat unusual experience in Berne, attending the weekly grand round in the large lecture theatre, sitting alongside Professor Rossi in the front row. The resident doctor presented a classical case of muscular dystrophy with all the classical features, and in the usual Germanic tradition the Herr Professor had the final word, and Professor Rossi summed up that this was a typical case of Duchenne muscular dystrophy. He then turned to me, introduced me to the audience, and asked if I had any comments to add. 'Nothing really,' I responded, 'except I do not think it is a muscular dystrophy.' There was a stunned silence! No one ever disagrees with the professor! I then explained that the child got up from the floor in an unusual manner and, unlike the classical Gowers manoeuvre of 'climbing up one's legs', as seen in Duchenne dystrophy, he had actually managed to get into a squatting position first and from that posture had managed to rise into a standing posture. I had never seen this in any patient with muscular dystrophy but recalled having seen something similar in a child with another type of neuromuscular disorder, spinal muscular atrophy.

In the course of the afternoon, whilst we were having some informal discussions, a jubilant Richterich popped in with the news that he had just done the serum creatine kinase enzyme level on the boy we had discussed in the morning, and in contrast to the grossly elevated level of several thousand units one would expect in muscular dystrophy, it was completely normal and thus in keeping with a spinal muscular atrophy. The lesson I learnt that day, which I have always pursued, is not to be afraid to stick your neck out if you have a firm idea or opinion, even though you risk having it chopped off.

Meanwhile, Lil had quite an eventful trip to Australia for different reasons. With two infants under three and almost eight months pregnant, she was allocated a bulkhead seat with an adjacent bassinet. As she seemed to be coping quite well, the stewardess asked if she could manage an additional infant who was crying incessantly and seemed to be inconsolable! To add insult to injury, the plane hit a tropical storm en route and had to deviate to Rangoon for an unscheduled stop of several hours till the weather abated.

Whilst we were in Melbourne, Lil sought advice from her erstwhile professor of obstetrics, Lance Townsend, about her delivery in New York and was personally referred by him to the new head of obstetrics at Cornell Medical College, a Professor Fuchs from Denmark. Soon after our arrival in New York, Lil duly contacted Professor Fuchs, armed with the personal letter from Lance Townsend. He was very charming and keen to help but found himself in a cleft stick with the local bureaucracy. In spite of being head of the obstetrics department, he was unable to practise obstetrics without resitting the state board's exams in obstetrics, which he quite rightly refused to do, in view of his longstanding experience in the specialty and senior academic position. So the various authorities were trying to sort things out. I think an additional humorous note was added by Lil's consistent misspelling of his surname, due to her dyslexia and inability to spell in three languages. He referred her to Dr Ryan, a very competent and outgoing Irish expatriate in his department, with whom we got on extremely well.

Whilst in Australia we also took advantage of seeing some of the country and were able to route our round-the-world ticket to take in Brisbane and the barrier reef, going up as far as Cairns, and taking trips to the offshore coral islands.

In addition to Lil's family, we also caught up again with Les and Elsie Koadlow and their children, whom we had seen a lot of during their time in London. We were able to arrange with them some visits to nearby areas of interest, including the Snowy Mountains, where David had his first experience on skis.

I also had a special experience in the 'it's a small world' category. I had arranged whilst in Melbourne to visit the laboratory in Canberra of Professor John Eccles, the renowned physiologist and Nobel Laureate, who had initiated the cross-innervation studies of fast and slow muscle which I intended researching in New York. As we were about to board the flight

Stopover in Australia. David and Michael meet Lil's mother 'Mutti' in Melbourne

David's first ski lesson. Snowy Mountain

Green Island, Great Barrier Reef. David and Michael with Lil and Gerald (*in utero*)

from Melbourne there was an announcement for me to come to the service desk. Very apologetically I was told that unfortunately they had double-booked my seat, owing to an apparent confusion of the names, Dr Dubowitz and Dr Danziger, and would I mind taking the adjoining seat. Fred Danziger was a fellow medical student from Cape Town, whom I had not see for some ten years since graduation. We had also been co-actors in the production of Tennessee Williams' *The Long Goodbye*, as the two furniture removers, who almost brought the whole set down. It turned out that Fred had become an anaesthetist, was in practice in New York, and was earning so well that as a bachelor still, he needed to spend some money on far flung educational vacations, to avoid giving it all back to the tax man. We were subsequently to see a lot of him in New York.

David has his finger on the button

Soon after arrival in New York we had to spend the best part of a day getting my bank account sorted out, as I had arranged for the transfer of funds from my English bank direct to a sister branch they had in New York. Unfortunately it was located in the lower east side so we had quite a trek. There were also no end of forms to complete to arrange transfer to a more conveniently located branch. The bank had an open plan layout and the manager's desk we were at was located fairly centrally in the reception area. David, aged two-and-a-half, was a bit bored with the whole proceedings and entertained himself by an exploratory tour under the manager's desk. Suddenly in the midst of our discussions a series of alarms went off and all hell broke loose, with a posse of armed guards with revolvers appearing from nowhere and surrounding the central reception area, with automatic closure of the main front door of the bank. After a tense standoff for a few minutes, there was a sudden relief and a burst of laughter when the armed guards spotted David under the manager's desk. He has always had a fascination with plugs and switches and apparently spotted some interesting buttons under the manager's desk. He was also fairly selective and did not choose the regular button but a larger prominent red one. The regular button was an ordinary alarm, but the red one signified a real emergency, such as an armed hold-up, and immediately alerted the armed guards as well as the local police station. It is often difficult for Americans to appreciate the British sense of humour, but on this occasion we certainly shared a hearty chuckle with the bank manager.

Blackout in New York

The day proved to be an even more eventful one for us, as we suddenly noted whilst on our way home in the bus that all the streetlights and also the building lights went out. That was the great power failure affecting not only New York City, but also the whole eastern seaboard from Canada down to New York, which lasted right through that night. Fortunately we were in a bus, which at least got us home to our apartment in 74th street at York Avenue, rather than in the train subway system where large numbers of commuters were stuck in total darkness for hours. When we told friends about the bank episode with David, they had suspicions that perhaps he had a role in the blackout as well.

The next experiment David undertook in New York might have had more disastrous personal consequences. He undid a paper clip and then explored the intricacies of the electric sockets at floor level in our apartment. He was somewhat surprised as well as shocked by the brilliant flash this produced as well as the rather painful burn he sustained on his finger tips. Just as well the Americans have 110 voltage. I don't see any connection between this episode and his later interest in electronic engineering, but perhaps the general fascination for the subject was already there.

David settled in very well at the United Nations Infants School in New York, which was within reasonable walking distance of our apartment and truly international and multi-ethnic. On one occasion some months later when Lil was walking him home, he stopped in the middle of a pedestrian crossing and promptly emptied his bladder. Lil was completely puzzled as he had already achieved perfect bladder control and had not had any 'accidents'. 'Why have you done that?' she asked him. 'I don't like my new teacher!' came the instant response. I guess the moral of the story is not to consult a psychologist but to just ask the child when there is a behaviour problem. With a bit of luck a straight question may occasionally produce a straight answer.

David also had an interesting exposure to art whilst in New York. Lil and I decided we should take out an annual friends-type subscription to one of the main art galleries and as we had absolutely no knowledge of modern art, thought the Museum of Modern Art the best choice. Apart from the free access to all the magnificent major exhibitions and the substantial discount on its catalogues and publications, they also had a special course for preschool children, which we took up. In no time David was bringing home the most colourful and incredible works with his own interpretations on the shapes and colours. There was also a special treat for the parents and the children got a free pass to the museum and could bring their parents along. So we had a tour of the museum with our three-year-old. The first picture that absolutely transfixed and mesmerised him was a large Miro near the entrance, with a central bright red orb, and other coloured structures around. That continued to be his favourite, perhaps relating to the way they were taught to appreciate form and colour. The other picture that held his fascination was the famous Picasso *Les Demoiselles D'Avignon*. After gazing at it in absolute silence for a protracted time, he came out with a classic 'Look at the ladies under the shower.' I still see that image every time I look at the painting.

One further experience with David almost convinced us of the power of genetics. Both Lil and I have always enjoyed listening to music and in our early years in London and subsequently in Sheffield, regularly attended symphony concerts. On the other hand, we both seem to suffer from an irremediable phonetic disorder of being totally unable to produce a single note in tune. It was thus not altogether surprising to us in New York when our three-year-old David started singing with equal discordance, which we sympathetically looked upon as a double genetic impact from us. Some months later, on one of those special public holidays, possibly Lincoln's Day, when most of America seems to indulge in a shopping spree, the music outlet shop, Sam Goody, had a special offer of a total hi-fi package for about $100. In addition, they offered six records for free. Amongst these were some children's records, which we duly selected. Shortly after that we noted that David started singing perfectly in tune and has continued to do so ever since. We concluded that he had such a good ear for music that he had been able to mimic us perfectly prior to exposure to the records. In later years at university, to drive the point even further, he joined a madrigal group.

Gerald arrives

Within a couple of months of arrival in New York our no. 3 son, Gerald, was born. With three under three, Lil was unable to get any part-time employment, so resigned herself to being a full-time mum. For the peace and equilibrium of the whole family, we soon perfected a very workable arrangement for assuring some sleep at night. As we had a rather small apartment, with only two bedrooms, one for us and one for the children, we took to wheeling him out in his pram into the corridor at night from the age of about six weeks. He was fully breastfed, but if he woke at night, I would instantly wake up and try to placate him, or pass him on to Lil if he was too persistent.

I often spent my out-of-hours time in evenings or over weekends doing photographic work in the Muscle Institute, either in relation to the photomicrography of my tissue sections or black and white photography of the children, which had always been a passion of mine. One Sunday afternoon, whilst in the midst of it, I got an emergency telephone call from Lil. She was frantic. 'Come home immediately. They are all three yelling incessantly and in unison. I am at the end of my tether. Come quick before I strangle one of them!' So I charged home, to be confronted by a totally exhausted and dejected Lil and three red-eyed boys, who had got themselves into a perpetual and seemingly irreconcilable crying mode. Once one could calm at least one of them down, peace soon returned.

It occurred to me that human behaviour follows the same pattern and formula as statistics, where the number of degrees of freedom is one less than the sample. Whatever number of children you have, you can convert chaos and pandemonium into perfect calm and bliss by removing one of the sample.

Later that week I was contemplating what to buy Lil as a birthday present, when I passed an art gallery in Madison Avenue of contemporary artists and a notice, 'nothing over 75 dollars'. I instinctively walked in and there facing me was the obvious answer to my choice; a portrait study of a rather dejected mother, with her large arm around three equally dejected infants. It could

Gerald arrives, New York, November 1965

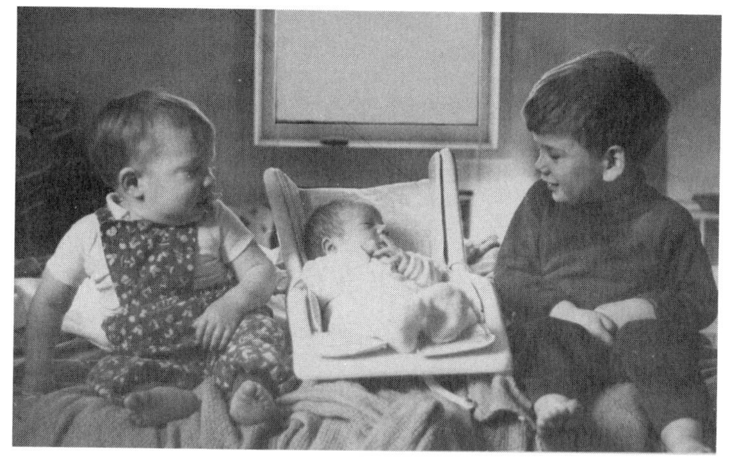

David and Michael with Gerald

Lil with the troop

just as easily have been a commissioned portrait of the scene that confronted me on that Sunday afternoon (see p. 135). It has hung in our lounge ever since. One close friend of ours in New York, who visited us soon after the purchase, was so upset by the pathos of the picture when I told her it was a family portrait that she burst into tears.

Institute for Muscle Disease

My year at the Institute for Muscle Disease proved an interesting and educational one from many points of view. It had been built and staffed by funding from the Muscular Dystrophy Association of America (MDAA) as their showpiece institution for state of the art research in the muscle field, and creamed off a large part of the annual income of the MDAA from the annual telethon held over the Labour Day weekend at the beginning of September, and hosted by the comedian Jerry Lewis. The director was Dr Ade Milhorat, one of the pioneers of encouraging an interest in muscular dystrophies in the present generation of clinicians. The Institute had succeeded in attracting a number of outstanding scientists in various disciplines which had potential impact on the muscle field, such as Michael Barany and his wife in biochemistry, Alexander Sandow in physiology.

The only clinician in the institute was Dr Milhorat, who also had a faculty position in the nearby Cornell Medical College. I

Institute for Muscle Disease, New York, 1965

had been in correspondence with Dr Milhorat in order to arrange my year's fellowship, which was funded by the Institute. Soon after arrival I went up to the tenth floor, to introduce myself to Dr Milhorat and pay my respects, to be confronted by a very protective and stone-walling secretary, who kept promising to arrange an appointment for me and kept deferring it with the standard response, 'Dr Milhorat is very busy'. After a week I was becoming increasingly frustrated, as I wished to get my laboratory research under way and was having difficulty getting anything set up by the bureaucratic administrative department, who occupied the whole lower floor of the building. I accordingly confronted Dr Milhorat's secretary with an ultimatum to pass on to Dr Milhorat. Whilst I fully appreciated how busy he might be, I had come a long way to do a year's research programme and if I could not have an audience with Dr Milhorat within one week and get my programme established, I intended packing up and heading off for Johns Hopkins in Baltimore to take up my alternative option. This strategy worked and within a few days we had managed to meet Dr Milhorat and to wade through all the bureaucracy.

I had planned a very clear-cut research programme I was keen to do. A group of physiologists in association with the Nobel laureate, John Eccles, in Australia, had shown that if you switched the nerves between fast and slow muscles in animals, you could change the twitch characteristics of the muscle to those of the corresponding fast or slow nerve. I was keen to see if this experimental switch also changed the very distinctive histochemical pattern of the slow and fast muscle I had been studying.

Whilst I was able to establish my laboratory facility on the second floor of the Institute devoted to tissue sections and histochemistry, and had a very enthusiastic fellow traveller, Ethel Cosmos, working on chick muscular dystrophy, I soon realised there was practically no cohesion within the Institute as a whole, and each unit or discipline, confined to a separate floor, was working in complete isolation. I established a relationship with Dr Sandow, director of the physiology laboratories, and he provided me with useful advice on measuring the twitch characteristics of the muscles in parallel with my histochemical studies. I also tried to get some collaborative work going with

Barany on the biochemical characterisation of the fast and slow myosins but he was not to be deviated from his own narrowly focussed path of basic research, comparing slow muscles of the sloth with fast muscles of the hare. Eventually within a month or so of my departure, he was impressed with the striking histochemical changes I was able to demonstrate from the cross-innervation, and agreed to do some biochemical assessment of the muscle specimens.

During a six-week period in the summer, I had a medical student from Chicago, Donald Newman, working with me, and we looked particularly at the effects of cross-innervation in neonatal animals in comparison with self-innervation following section of nerves. We worked well together and were able to complete the study in the short timespan, and he was rewarded with first authorship on a paper published in *Nature*.

During my year in the States, I also had the opportunity of visiting many of the active neuromuscular units in Boston, Bethesda (NIH), Los Angeles and others and presenting my experimental work. One rather problematical schedule was at Harvard, where I was billed to talk immediately after a lecture by the psychiatrist, Dr Sargent, from London, who was an authority on hysteria and various tribal customs, with trances and other phenomena induced by religious ceremonies. He was also a great showman and had a spectacular series of film recordings he played to a capacity audience. I was fearful that I would have no audience at all for my succeeding talk on histochemistry of muscle, but did have a good attendance of enthusiasts from a somewhat different orientation.

I was also fortunate to have a parallel position as a member of the paediatric department at Cornell Medical College, which gave me clinical access to patients in collaboration with Dr Hart Petersen, the neurologist, and subsequently also to some of the orthopaedic faculty at the separate Hospital for Special Surgery, an orthopaedic hospital formerly named the Hospital for the Ruptured and Crippled, where Dr Levine had a special interest in the deformities associated with muscle disorders and Dr Wan Ngo Lim was the consultant paediatrician. This gave me the opportunity of attending the weekly grand rounds in both institutions and keeping in touch with clinical medicine. More importantly, it consolidated a close friendship with Dr Wan Ngo Lim.

Wan Ngo Lim

Wan Ngo Lim

Wan Ngo Lim was one of the most remarkable people we have met. She had a tremendous compassion for people and before long adopted us as one of her large family of friends. It was almost as if we had refugee status in a foreign land and needed caring for. Perhaps she had a particular empathy for people like ourselves coming into a totally new environment from abroad, as her family had been refugees from mainland China and she had had an uphill struggle to get recognition as a paediatric specialist and obtain American citizenship, which needed an individual bill through congress for individuals like her. She was born in 1920 in Burma, where her father was a very successful general practitioner. During the Second World War they had to move from Burma to China and she trained in medicine in Shanghai. She came to the United States in 1950, and decided to stay and eventually was joined by her four younger siblings, to whom she seemed to act *in loco parentis* and took a personal interest in their welfare.

She had a tremendous capacity for relating to people in all walks and at all levels. Thus she might readily arrange one of her remarkable dinner parties at one of her favourite Chinese restaurants, where everyone seemed to know her personally, bringing together some of her residents with some senior consultants and perhaps the dean of the faculty. She was also on first name terms with people like U Thant, then Secretary General of the United Nations. She had an equal compassion for her young patients. She also seemed to care for the children or grandchildren of many of her colleagues. When residents wanted advice on their careers, she was usually the first person they would consult.

We got to know her extremely well and she remained one of our closest friends. In the 1970s she visited us in Sheffield, and more or less took over looking after Lil's mother, a very fit and active lady in her late 70s. It was obviously a very deep-rooted Chinese tradition and honour to care for the senior citizens in their family, and it certainly was a remarkable challenge for us to emulate, in a society where the elderly are often sidelined and discarded by their family, and the concept of an extended family living under one roof, as in China, is somewhat alien.

Wan Ngo was always immaculate in her dress and appearance and also had a taste for simplicity and quality in most things. From time to time she would give Lil and myself some particular gift that instantly became a special treasure for us, such as beautiful gold brooch of simple but extraordinary craftsmanship she gave Lil many years ago, which she still wears on most special occasions, and a pure leather attaché case she took me to select personally at a quality leather goods store. But the most moving was a few years ago, when she was diagnosed as having a malignancy, for which she was operated, but the prognosis did not seem very good. She decided to retire from active practice and moved to stay with her sister in Portland, Virginia. When we next met up she gave Lil a most exquisite string of natural pearls, which she frequently used to wear herself, with the wish that Lil would enjoy it as she did not feel she would have much opportunity left to enjoy it herself. It was over 15 years on when we last met up in June 2003, and she was still her old self, although frail compared to her heyday and restricted by her doctors in her travel. She died in July 2004.

Outdoor activities

During the winter months after the arrival of Gerald, Lil managed to get out to the local parks within walking distance of our apartment, which had a sandpit and other activities to amuse the two older boys and allow them to get rid of excess energy, and to provide a break for Lil as well to get out from the confines of the apartment.

In the spring we bought for 50 dollars an old Chevrolet car, surplus to the needs of a family we met, and by American standards well past its use-by date. After fitting it out with new brakes and tyres, it served us extremely well through our stay in New York, and enabled us to escape from the city over weekends. I was rather sad to see it being taken away to the sanitation department car disposal pound, after I could not find any takers (for free) after posting notices at the hospital and medical school. One of our favourite weekend retreats was the Taconic State Park, some 120 miles north of New York, an idyllic campground for families with small children, with well placed and equipped campsites within the woods, and with an excellent shallow bathing pool and other playground facilities. We visited it some ten weekends, spanning from Friday afternoon till Sunday evening or Monday morning. We purchased a large family size tent, which served us well. One weekend we noted a young couple at a nearby campsite with a small bivvy 'two man' tent and enquired where they had purchased it. Turned out he worked for a sporting company and this was the first tent he had ever bought and it proved far too small for the two of them. If we were interested they would be happy to part with it at the same discounted price they had paid. So when they left we duly acquired it and on our next weekend David and Michael were extremely enthusiastic to have their own tent. During the night there was a thunderstorm and Lil and I kept going out to check if they were all right, only to find them sound asleep. When we got up in the morning they were still asleep, notwithstanding the fact that their feet, adequately covered by their one-piece pyjamas, were submersed in a puddle of water at the open end of their tent.

Lil takes the boys to the local parks in New York

The boys playing in the park

David (3rd from R) at United Nations nursery school Christmas party, 1965

Taconic State Park campground, about 120 miles north of New York

Taconic Park. David and Michael acquire their own tent

Gerald's first camping at Taconic at 6 months

Our faithful old Chevvy

David supervising Michael

Michael supervising Gerald

Celebrating Passover in New York with Phil and Rhona Lanzkowsky and their children, Hymie and Renee Nossel (right) and David on her lap, 1966

Diaspora of South African doctors

During our year in New York there were three close friends and contemporaries of mine from medical school, Hymie Nossel, specialising in haematology at Columbia University Presbyterian Hospital, Phillip Lanzkowsky, specialising in paediatric haematology, who had also spent time at Cornell Medical College, and Jules Smith, specialising in radiology at the Sloan-Kettering. We were soon to establish close family interrelations, much as we had done with a few of our close friends in Sheffield. There were also a number of other South African doctors in New York we got to know, including Fred Danziger, the anaesthetist I had bumped into in Australia, and Syd Louis, doing neurology.

In addition to maintaining fairly regular contact with each other, we also tried to arrange get-togethers on special occasions, such as the Passover celebration. We also became very friendly with the Dopheides from Holland in the same apartment building as us. He was working at the Rockefeller Institute and their children were of similar age to ours.

At the crossroads

As my fellowship in New York was drawing to a close, I found myself in a quandary about my future career, and having to decide whether I wanted to pursue some opportunities in the States. I soon learned that when the dean of a medical faculty writes to you that they are seeking a candidate for their paediatric neurology unit and do you know of someone suitable, it is inappropriate for you to send them a list of the people you consider most eligible for the job. It is the American way of asking you whether you are personally interested in the position and the appropriate response is to express some interest and at least go and have a look at it (at their expense). I also learnt that American academics are doing this all the time, as there are always negotiating points such as a higher salary for the particular position, in contrast to the fixed salary for the same academic grade throughout the university system in the UK. In addition, it is often a good bargaining chip with one's own faculty if one is being head-hunted by another institution. It is all part of the academic market place, and akin to the Reaganomics which Margaret Thatcher introduced into our health care system a few years ago.

Although there were several tempting opportunities on offer at various academic institutions, Lil and I finally decided that we would rather bring up our children in the English environment in contrast to the totally different sense of values in the American. Of course there were many South African expatriate contemporaries of ours in the USA who were trying to create a microcosm for themselves of upholding their own principles and ways of life within the broader context of the society around them, but at the end of the day it is difficult not to be swallowed into the consumerism cult. Some words of wisdom I had at the time when discussing my career prospects with my close friend Hymie Nossel, 'It may be difficult to find good posts, but remember it is much more difficult to find good people.'

So in November 1966 we headed back to Sheffield.

6

Back in Sheffield

Not long after our return to Sheffield, I was promoted to Senior Lecturer in the University Department of Child Health, and Consultant Paediatrician to the Children's Hospital. I decided not to reinstate my previous cardiology commitment but to concentrate on the muscle work and also the neurology of the newborn, in addition to my general paediatric clinical and teaching responsibilities.

Muscle research

After my return from the States, I was particularly keen, in addition to my well-established muscle clinic, and the processing of muscle biopsies by my personal technician, to also pursue some channels of original research. After numerous previous unsuccessful attempts, I was finally also able to convince the research committee of the Muscular Dystrophy Group, that it was quite unreasonable to expect me to run a comprehensive clinical and investigative service for muscle patients single-handed without any clinical support. On the face of it, it seemed that a large part of the annual budget of the Group was automatically creamed off for supporting the multiple activities of the Newcastle group, and anyone else had to be content with individual research projects. The establishment of a post for a clinical research fellow was a quantum leap forward, and enabled me to appoint Allie Moosa, an honours graduate in medicine from Cape Town, who was already acquainted with my muscle clinics whilst a paediatric resident in Sheffield. I arranged for him a training in electrodiagnostic techniques for neuromuscular disorders with Professor John Simpson in Glasgow. He was also able to relieve me of doing all the muscle biopsies.

The paediatric academic department was also on the threshold of moving from the old Victorian house in which it had been

Demolition of the old department building

housed for many years, into a new custom built department building with not only accommodation for its staff, but also the possibility of research laboratories, which I fought hard for in the environment of a completely clinically oriented department, which was of course the main forte of Illingworth. Meanwhile my technician continued to process the muscle biopsies in the cryostat in my office, and was still active in the old building after all the academic staff had moved to temporary quarters, and the heavy equipment moved on site and started demolishing the building with a swinging heavyweight cannon-ball.

Illingworth, reflecting his very cautious and parsimonious Yorkshire upbringing, had always prided himself that his departmental budget had never been overspent and that each year he was top of the league for saving the university money. To his surprise I started being a bit critical of this and pointing out that a friend of mine in Fuel Technology, was getting a lot of support from the university for his research, and that the budget of their department was always overspent, but the university picked up the tabs each year, thanks presumably to the generosity of the paediatric department. I also discovered that all departments of the university, as of right, were entitled to a senior technician to help with the nuts and bolts of running a department. Child Health had never taken this up. So I confirmed with the registrar of the university that this was indeed available for Child Health and I duly advertised for a research assistant, with a view to starting a programme of tissue culture of normal and diseased muscle, and hoping to attract a graduate at a salary that was in fact more generous than a research fellowship. My luck was in and I soon struck oil. One of the applicants impressed me. Audrey Bishop had been working with Eric Blank, in the clinical genetics department, for some time, and was now looking for part-time employment for family reasons. She was experienced in the culture of skin cells (fibroblasts), which could provide a good basis for our research endeavours. So I duly appointed her at half-time, and saved the university half the available funds. Our tissue culture programme was under way.

It was not many weeks later that I had an unexpected call from Professor Alan Roper, head of the department of genetics of the university, and an authority on fungal genetics. They had just offered a research post to a very bright science graduate, who responded that she was very impressed with them but not in particular with their work! She was more interested in doing some genetic work with a human orientation. Any chance I might be able to oblige? 'Send her over.' Needless to say I was completely bowled over by this very attractive, very dynamic, sparkling, Manchester BSc honours graduate, Yvonne Skeate, and she was equally enthusiastic about our tissue culture programme in muscle disease. 'Hold on. I'll see if I can work something!' I was convinced there was no way I could miss such a heavenly opportunity. I telephoned directly to the registrar of the university. In those days you could actually speak to people in authority, without all the protective tiers of secretaries and other subsidiaries you now need to wade through. 'You remember the recent half-time appointment I made into the senior technician post in Child Health. Will it be OK to use the remaining half to appoint a full time junior research assistant. I have an ideal candidate sitting in my office.' 'No problem. As long as you don't exceed the available budget.' 'Done.'

And that was the start of a very productive partnership between Audrey Bishop and Yvonne Skeate, which rapidly set up an active tissue culture programme, adapting existing techniques on the standard chick embryo cultures to newborn mammalian cells and finally muscle, which needed some permutations in the nutritional media for the cultures. They subsequently achieved a world first, of successfully culturing mature, adult human muscle, which had not been achieved at that time and many experts were predicting might not be possible. It was then a small step forward to culturing diseased human muscle and starting to do comparative studies between dystrophic and normal muscle. I found it fascinating to see these cultured muscle cells maturing from a stage of single cells to clusters of fused cells, as in normal muscle, and to develop the characteristic striations and to actually start contracting rhythmically in the isolated environment.

Yvonne later moved on to matrimony and to research on pancreatic cells in the hope of permanent treatment of diabetes. It is always very disappointing to lose a productive research associate but with a bit of luck one is often able to attract an equally dynamic successor. So Yvonne was succeeded by Belinda Gallup, another bright science graduate, who continued the fruitful partnership with Audrey Bishop. Audrey Bishop subsequently left to accompany her husband, who was a science teacher of science teachers, working for UNESCO and being seconded for extended periods to third world countries, such as New Guinea. This in turn gave me the opportunity of a stopover in New Guinea en route from Australia a few years later.

Belinda Gallup completed her three-year research programme, which included a visit to Edith Petersen's unit at the Albert Einstein Medical College in New York to learn the techniques of co-culture of nerve and muscle, which greatly enhanced the maturation of the muscle in culture, with sustained, spontaneous rhythmic contractions. She successfully defended a PhD thesis on her research. She then sought broader pastures and was also contemplating matrimony. She was appointed to a senior position in the blood transfusion service in the Bristol region and has continued a research programme in relation to immunological aspects of blood up to the present time.

Once our tissue culture programme was generating interesting results and publications in peer review journals, I was able to apply for more substantive research fellowships for three-year projects to the Muscular Dystrophy Group or the Medical

Research Council. In this way I was able to attract to Sheffield Jan Witkowski, as a more senior post-doctoral fellow, who had previously worked in the Medical Research Council unit in Hampstead in London, and already had experience in tissue culture techniques.

I also embarked on a new research programme of trying to transplant muscle between normal and dystrophic animals, such as the mouse or hamster, which had a genetic muscular dystrophy, to try and unravel the pathogenesis of muscular dystrophy and the possible influence of the nervous system on the dystrophic process. I obtained funding for this programme from the Medical Research Council and appointed into it Joe Neerunjen, who had followed a somewhat unconventional route into science. He was originally from Mauritius but had completed his schooling through to A levels at a public school in England. He then decided to opt out and not pursue an academic career, and ended up doing technical laboratory jobs. He then relented and started with evening courses in science at the Open University, and finally graduated through the West Ham College of Technology with a BSc in the University of London, and proceeding to an MPhil. He currently held a post as assistant experimental officer at the Meat Research Institute in Bristol, but was now keen to change tack and to join a research project. I was struck by his enthusiasm for pursuing a career in scientific research, rather than a more secure but less demanding technical post, and his work with meat seemed a good stepping stone into muscle research.

The new Department of Child Health building provided excellent laboratory facilities for the researchers and in addition brought the clinicans and scientists under one roof, so that we were able to establish a close-knit, friendly and well-integrated team of muscle enthusiasts. In addition to the scientists, technicians and clinicians, our two secretaries, Dorothy Ackroyd, my academic secretary, and Chris Webster, our research secretary, were also very much part of the team.

Another very special facility I was able to develop in Sheffield was clinical photography. Illingworth himself was an enthusiastic photographer, and had also utilised the facilities in the medical art department of the hospital for recording clinical cases of special interest. I saw this as an important component of my muscle

With my academic secretary Dorothy Ackroyd in my office in the new department building

The Sheffield Muscle team, 1972
Back row from left: Brian Brown, Dorothy Ackroyd, myself, Jan Witkowski, Joe Neerunjen
Middle: Chris Webster, Allie Moosa, Belinda Gallup
Front: Christine Heinzmann, Elaine Woodcock, Bridget Lunn

With John Walton and Ingrid Gamstorp at the International Congress of Neurogenetics and Neuro-ophthalmology in Montreal in 1968

work as well and had already utilised a similar facility in my days at Queen Mary's Hospital for Children. I was able to establish an excellent collaboration with Alan Tunstill, the head of the photographic department at the Children's Hospital, and would regularly accompany the children from my clinic to the photography unit to discuss the best views for showing certain features. We were thus able to standardise a series of views for both older children as well as infants with specific muscle problems.

In addition to active membership in a number of national and European paediatric and paediatric research societies, such as the British Paediatric Research Society and the European Society for Paediatric Research, as well as the Physiology and Neuropathology Societies, I also participated in all the consecutive international muscle congresses, starting with the first one convened in Milan in 1968 and sequentially in Newcastle, Perth, Montreal, Los Angeles, Munich, Kyoto, Adelaide and Vancouver. I also contributed to more general international congresses of interest, such as the International Congress of Neuropathology in Zurich in 1965 and the International Congress of Neurogenetics and Neuro-ophthalmology in Montreal in 1968.

Neonatal neurology

After our return from the United States in November 1966, and the interim arrival of no. 3 son, Gerald, Lil now opted for doing some community infant-welfare clinics, to keep her hand in. She subsequently felt the urge to get back to some research again and thought the best bet might be working with newborn infants on the neonatal unit, who would be less fussed at what time of the day or night she came to see them. She was then able to plan her 24-hour schedule, by being home through most of the day, when the children were awake and needing her attention, and to then give the infant a top up in the evening before his bedtime, which then left her more or less in freedom to go in to the newborn unit and assess the infants at night.

My research fellow Allie Moosa and I had started a systematic study of various neurological signs in the newborn infant in relation to maturity. Various authors had tried to relate the presence of a particular sign to a particular gestational age and we were able to show that this was not reliable, as individual signs might range over several weeks of gestation. We also studied additional neurological signs that might show a maturational process in relation to gestation. Instead of relating the presence of an individual sign to a particular gestation we scored each sign on a numerical scale in relation to its change with gestation on a zero to three or four point scale.

Allie also embarked on a systematic research study of the change in conduction velocity of the motor nerves in the arms and legs, with maturation of the infant. This project had arisen in response to a request out of the blue one day from Ronnie McKeith, founding editor of the journal *Developmental Medicine and Child Neurology*, if I could do an editorial review for his journal of an interesting publication he had just come across of nerve maturation in the newborn kitten. I wrote back 'Thanks Ronnie. I shall be delighted to do your editorial. I know absolutely nothing about the subject.' I then did a bit of a literature search (via Index Medicus in those pre-Medline days) and found a single publication by Ingrid Gamstorp, the well-known Swedish paediatric neurologist in Uppsala, on the change of nerve conduction velocity with increasing age in human infants. This looked like an interesting technique for studying nerve maturation, and seemed simple and non-invasive. I accordingly approached the university medical physics unit up the road from the children's hospital and found an enthusiastic collaborator, a young physicist Brian Brown, who was interested in the application of his specialty to monitoring of human biological functions. The subject was right up his street and although he had no experience of measuring nerve conduction, we were able to set up the system fairly rapidly with the use of surface electrodes for application of an electric impulse along the course of a long nerve in the arm or leg, and to calculate the conduction velocity from the difference in time taken between two stimuli at different points on the nerve to reach the muscle and produce a twitch. Not a very far cry from the physiological experiments beloved by all medical students of stimulating the frog sciatic nerve and recording the twitch of the gastrocnemius muscle mechanically on a smoked drum.

The Dubowitz score

Lil was now firmly oriented to working with newborn babies and set up a systematic study to assess the gestational maturity of newborn infants. The plan was to compare a series of superficial or 'skin' criteria which had already been defined and scored in relation to maturation by Valerie Farr in Aberdeen, with a series of neurological criteria which would initially be defined and selected on the basis of their change with maturation and the ability to define and score stages in the maturational process. It was also important to clearly define each stage in the development so that one could get consistency of interpretation between different observers.

Lil then set about doing a systematic assessment of all infants born at the Jessop Hospital for Women, whose newborn nursery was also under my care. After documenting all the individual signs on specially prepared forms, she would then interview the mother and get full obstetrical details such as the last menstrual period, the regularity of the cycle and the certainty of the date of the last period. This would eventually form the basis for comparing the score on the clinical assessment, with the gestation according to the dates of the mother. After meticulous documentation of some 400 newborn infants, Lil found that in 167 of these the data from the mother were reliable and clear-cut and suitable for further analysis. This cohort of 167 babies out of the original 400 assessed then formed the basis of the correlation of the documented clinical signs in relation to the recorded gestation.

Our main interest was the comparison of the neurological score, which was the summation of the score of the ten selected neurological criteria, against the superficial score of Valerie Farr, based on a summation of 11 individual items. I had anticipated that the neurological criteria would be a more sensitive index than the superficial. This proved wrong and to my slight disappointment the superficial score proved to be a bit more reliable. However, what Lil did find was that when she added the two scores together and compared this with the documented gestational age, there was a much closer correlation with gestation than either alone. Thus was born a totally new scoring index for gestation of the newborn baby, based on a combination of criteria and giving a result that could be plotted as a linear graph against the gestational age and gave an accuracy that was probably as close as one would be able to get biologically, given that the actual date of conception itself might vary in relation to the menstrual cycle and might not necessarily be in midcycle. The standard deviation of the score was just under one week. The range of gestation of the babies assessed was from 32 weeks through to full term at 40 weeks and a few going a week or two beyond.

In the 1960s the survival of infants below 32 weeks was very low and it was only some years later that the survival improved, following the more effective and aggressive treatment of respiratory distress syndrome in the newborn infant, and subsequent measures to prevent the syndrome. Gradually survival became routine down to 28 weeks' gestation and lower, till the very borderline of viability at around 24 weeks' gestation. But the main contribution of our scoring system was the clear distinction in a baby of say 2500 grams, the original official definition of 'prematurity', as to whether this was indeed a premature baby of 36 weeks' gestation, and appropriate weight for gestation, or a more mature infant of say 38 weeks' gestation, who was in fact undernourished, and small-for-dates in relation to gestational age. This was an important distinction as it entailed a totally different management and support in the newborn period, with the truly premature infant being more prone to the respiratory problems of the immature lungs and the small-for-dates more mature infant to the effects of the undernutrition, such as, low blood sugar in relation to a more mature state of the lungs and also the nervous and other systems.

Lil was just in the process of collating her data and preparing the various tables and graphs together with our stick figure charts of the neurological criteria for publication when we had a chance visit from William McCrory, head of paediatrics at Cornell Medical College in New York, in whose department I had worked in the mid 1960s. He was very interested in the whole study and suggested that instead of publishing it in the *Archives of Diseases of Childhood*, the main paediatric journal in Britain (which Americans never seemed to read or refer to!) that it would have a much broader exposure in one of the major American paediatric journals, such as the *Journal of Pediatrics* (of which he happened to be editor). So we duly sent the manuscript to his office and in due course we had two very glowing reviews, together with an acceptance letter and only a few small suggestions for amendments. The one reviewer, William Battaglia, head of paediatrics in Denver Colorado, had actually signed his review (an option that reviewers rarely take up) and had only one suggestion for the authors, 'Would it be possible for the authors to get a proper artist to draw those stick figures, as the freehand present series were rather irregular and inconsistent?' I must confess that I really felt a bit hurt at this, as I thought my drawings were really quite cute, and somewhat humanised, as I had taken the liberty of varying the expression of the face in some of them (artistic licence). But we accepted the advice in good spirit and engaged a graphic artist to prepare a more stylised series of stick figures, after briefing him very carefully on what each figure was meant to show.

The article appeared as the lead paper in the July 1970 issue of the *Journal of Pediatrics*, and we had a remarkable flood of some 200 requests for reprints within a month. The system was very rapidly introduced as a routine in newborn units in the USA and soon became the routine of the nurses charting the infants rather than the resident doctors. It also soon got the eponymous title of the Dubowitz Score and became simply the Dubowitz. When I was giving the annual Bilderback lecture in Portland Oregon some years later, my host, Bob Neerhout, in introducing me said it was not unusual for an eponymous name to be an adjective, such as Dubowitz Score, or even a noun, 'What is this baby's Dubowitz', but he had just overheard his residents on the neonatal unit that week saying 'have you Dubowitzed this baby?' An eponymous verb! Only in America.

Clinical assessment of gestational age in the newborn infant

A scoring system for gestational age, based on 10 neurologic and 11 "external" criteria, has been applied to 167 newborn infants. The "external" score gave a better correlation with gestation than did the neurologic score, but the combined total score was better than either alone. The correlation coefficient for the total score against gestation was 0.93. The error of prediction of a single score was 1.02 weeks and of the average of two independent assessments was 0.7 weeks. The method gives consistent results within the first 5 days and is equally reliable in the first 24 hours of life. This scoring system is more objective and reproducible than trying to guess gestational age on the presence or absence of individual signs.

Lilly M. S. Dubowitz, M.B., B.S., D.C.H.,* Victor Dubowitz, B.Sc., M.D., Ph.D., M.R.C.P., D.C.H., and Cissie Goldberg, B.A.**

SHEFFIELD, ENGLAND

IN RECENT years there has been increasing interest in the assessment of gestational age in the newborn infant and in differentiating the short-gestation from the small-for-date infant. A number of clinical parameters have been used. These have fallen into two broad groups—a series of neurologic signs, dependent mainly on postures and primitive reflexes, and a series of superficial or external characteristics.

THE NEUROLOGIC ASSESSMENT

The original impetus for the neurologic assessment came from the classical work of the French school under André Thomas and subsequently Madame Saint-Anne Dargassies.[1] Various criteria, based mainly on tone and primitive reflexes, were assessed and a

From the Departments of Child Health and Sociology, University of Sheffield.

Presented in part at the Twelfth International Congress of Pediatrics, Mexico City, December, 1968, and at the Fifteenth Meeting of the Paediatric Research Society, Sheffield, March, 1969.

**Recipient of a research grant from the Endowment Fund of the United Sheffield Hospitals.*

***Address: Dr. V. Dubowitz, Department of Child Health, University of Sheffield, Sheffield 10, England.*

Vol. 77, No. 1, pp. 1-10

Publication of *Clinical assessment of gestational age* paper in *Journal of Pediatrics*, 1970
It became known worldwide as the 'Dubowitz Score'

We were also very pleased that the system found rapid application in underdeveloped countries, where malnutrition was an ongoing problem and low-birthweight babies almost the norm. The score provided a simple and practical tool for a rapid assessment in the newborn of whether an underweight baby was indeed premature or more likely a mature baby but undernourished. This was particularly useful in communities where the mothers very rarely had any idea of the date of their last menstrual period and were more likely to relate it to the phase of the moon rather than a calendar date. We also had the opportunity of travelling to some remote corners of the globe such as the Sepik area of New Guinea or the Karen refugee camps on the Burmese border in northern Thailand to assess newborn infants, who were often very small and born in a community where malnutrition was one potential factor but where malaria was also endemic.

During a visit to Cape Town we were also able to make some interesting comparative studies between the local White, Cape Coloured and Black newborn infants with very different nutritional and cultural backgrounds. We were also able to do further studies with another clinical instrument we developed for assessing not only the maturity but the state of normality of the nervous system in the newborn infant in relation to its maturational status.

Meanwhile Lil had gathered together her data into a doctorate thesis in Medicine (MD) for the University of Sheffield and thus became an alumnus of that University.

Readership in Sheffield University

After my return from the States in 1966 I also prepared a thesis on my histochemical studies in developing and diseased muscle for a PhD in the University of Sheffield. In 1968 I was promoted from Senior Lecturer to Reader in Child Health and Developmental Neurology, in recognition of my academic contributions. This is a title dating back to mediaeval times when academics had a role of reader and although the title has persisted, responsibilities have changed. It is now a purely academic title, on an individual basis rather than a substantive university post, based entirely on academic achievement, and occupying a niche between senior lecturer and professor. Indeed the criteria for promotion to Readership within one's university post were extremely stringent, certainly in the University of Sheffield, and involved consultation with senior academics within one's specialty, both within the United Kingdom and abroad. The nearest comparable equivalent in the American academic system would perhaps be a full professorship, without being a chairman of a department.

Paediatric Research Society and OSP

The paediatric research society had been established in the early 1960s by a group of young paediatricians in training, mainly in academic lectureships and similar positions, in order to provide a forum where they could actively present and discuss ongoing research activities, after they had become somewhat disillusioned and bored with the cut and dried (and often very dry) presentations at the annual meeting of the senior echelon British Paediatric Association. New members were only accepted after giving a paper to the society and being proposed by an existing member. It was a very active society, meeting yearly, and was always stimulating and educational. As I recall new members had to be under 40 and the voting rights were lost at 45 and membership expired at 50 to keep the society young and vigorous.

In the late 1960s I was secretary of the society for three years and hosted the meeting in 1968 in Sheffield. I thought it might be an occasion for introducing some extramural education for our society, so I added a contribution at the end of the day's programme, with a speaker introduced by me. The title was simply OSP, and got various people guessing as to what protein it might represent. When we reached the last talk of the session, which I was chairing, I apologised to the audience that we would have to vacate the lecture theatre, as another meeting had been scheduled for it some time back, but we had secured a lecture theatre at the Weston Park Museum across the road.

We duly assembled there and I introduced the very attractive and vivacious young curator of the museum, who held the audience spellbound for an hour with a detailed talk on the origin of Old Sheffield Plate and a presentation of many of the unique pieces from the museum's collection. Old Sheffield Plate was introduced by Thomas Boulsover in Sheffield in 1743, when he discovered one could fuse a thin sheet of sterling silver to a very much thicker sheet of copper by heat fusion, and then roll it out into a very thin single sheet. It could then be used for the manufacture of candlesticks and other household articles, comɫh(hparable in style and workmanship to solid sterling silver, but a fraction of the cost. The production ceased in the 1840s when electroplating of articles with silver took over, needing much less skill and time. Many of our members started looking out for and collecting pieces of Old Sheffield Plate in small antique shops around the country, and always reflected on the talk when we met; in others the lasting memory was the immaculate knee-length leather boots of the speaker.

Chasing chairs

Although I was very content in my environment in Sheffield, both academically and clinically, and also geographically, with the wonderful open country at one's doorstep, as well as socially, Illingworth encouraged me to start applying for Chairs of Paediatrics being created at various medical schools. This was quite an interesting experience, although one soon became aware one was often just there to make up the numbers and to ensure that the statutory requirements were met. The post was duly advertised, an appointments committee set up and a shortlist of applicants interviewed, although it was obvious to all that the outcome was already a *fait accompli*. This certainly applied at Kings College Hospital in London, where the incumbent senior lecturer and head of the unit had been instrumental in collecting the funds for establishing the chair and was the obvious choice. I remember noting at the interview that one of the panel was obviously bored with the whole procedure and kept looking at her watch, as if to say 'why do we have to waste so much time on this candidate, just prolonging the agony'.

A similar situation arose with the establishment of a new Chair of Paediatrics in Oxford, where everyone knew via the grapevine that the favoured candidate was Professor Peter Tizard at Hammersmith. However, the post was duly advertised in the medical journals and circulated to heads of paediatric departments, and I was again advised by my local mentor to apply. I did so, on the assumption that the most certain way not to get a post is not to apply, and in any event the same external advisors often popped up again at the appointments committee and it was probably no bad thing to throw one's hat in the ring. A couple of weeks later I got a letter from the Medical Faculty in Oxford

At the retirement party for John Emery

At the retirement meeting for Ronald Illingworth

thanking me for my application and that the advisory committee had met and decided on the appointment of Professor Tizard. Well, at least justice was seen to be done and perhaps it was a bit more gentlemanly not to put the candidates through the ritual of a mock interview.

The Family

After our return to Sheffield from the States, Lil became concerned that David might be dyslexic, even though he was still only around four years old and had not yet started infant school. This was because he was able to write down from memory not only the different petrol station brands, such as Esso or Shell, but also more complex names such as our street, Chorley Road. At the same time he was unable to read even the simplest word such as cat or bat. Lil discussed this with Illingworth, who was somewhat dismissive of an over-anxious, over-perceptive mother!

After starting infant school at the excellent Church of England school down the road with an excellent all-round teacher, Mrs Drakeford, David was soon to prove Lil wrong when he rapidly acquired reading ability and sailed through the first three books of 'Janet and John' and could read at random any page, with staccato intonation of the words, characteristic of children learning to read. But Lil proved to be right after all when she tried to get him to read unknown passages. Mrs Drakeford was amazed and had neither suspected it nor had a similar experience before in all her years of teaching. What David had done was to memorise all the books in the context of the illustrations by listening to the other children reading the same passages to the teacher and was then able to recite them from memory.

We had a somewhat unusual and unexpected musical experience with Michael at the age of about five in Sheffield. David was having piano lessons from a very nice American music teacher, whose husband was on a post-graduate engineering attachment at Sheffield University. Michael started nagging us that he also wanted to have lessons and we approached the teacher, who told us that he was still too young. She preferred them to be at least seven years. We accepted this and told her to tell him the reasons. However, he was not going to accept this lying down and insisted that he was still keen to have lessons. She then asked him why, to which he replied that he 'enjoyed playing music' and asked if she would like to hear him play something. He then produced 'Peas pudding hot' on the piano, which impressed her. 'Who taught you?' she asked. 'I taught myself.' At school they were taught to play 'Peas pudding hot'

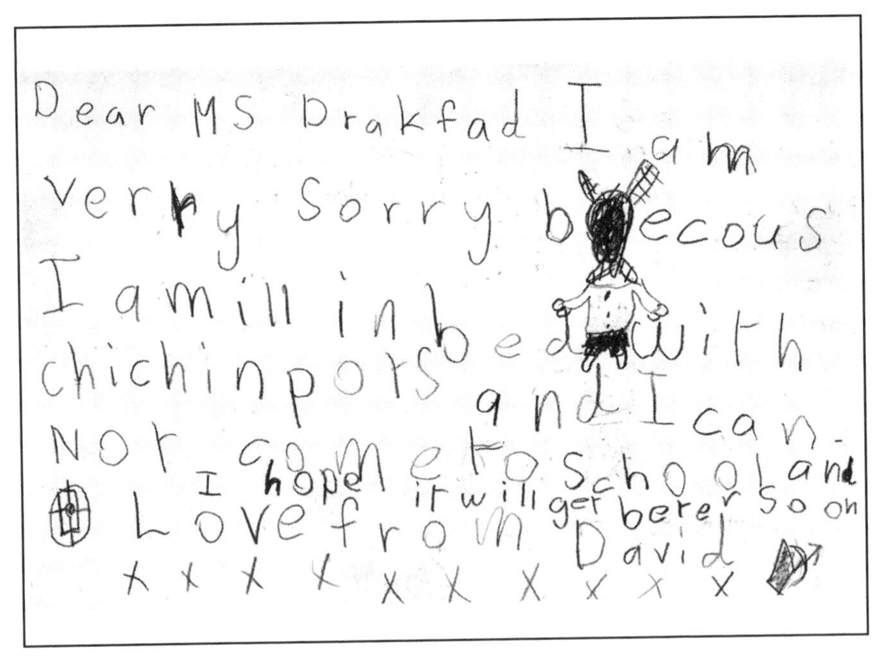

Dear MS Drakfad I am
verry Sorry becous
I am ill in bed with
chichinpots and I can
Not come to school and
I hope it will get beter soon
Love from David
x x x x x x x x x x

Letter from David (aged 6) to his teacher Mrs Drakeford apologising for his absence from school with chicken pox

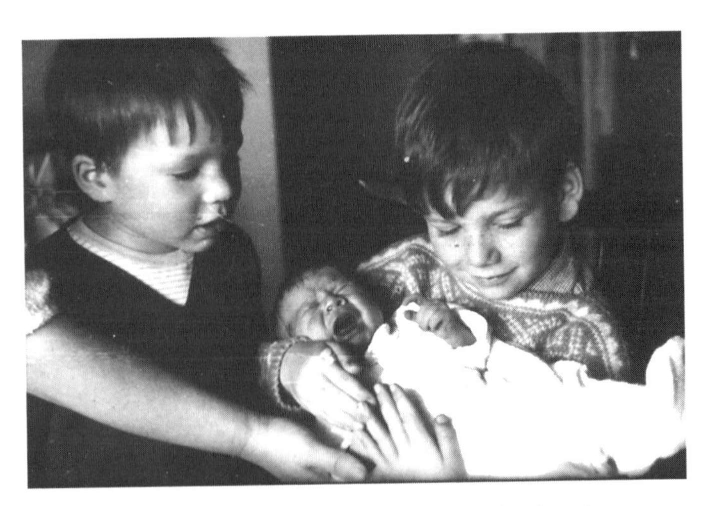

David and Michael meet their new brother Daniel for the first time after recovering from their chicken pox

on a recorder and he had apparently just transposed it to the piano. He then offered to play it differently and proceeded to do so, in several different keys. Such enthusiasm, she said, cannot be ignored. And she accordingly took him on. He subsequently went right up to grade 8 and was encouraged by his definitive teacher, Anthea Cohen, to consider a career in music but he fortunately realised that there was a quantum leap between an ability to play music and becoming a professional pianist. Michael was also keen on clarinet lessons at an early age but was advised it was not possible until his front teeth were fully grown. No sooner had he started his lessons some time later, than he slipped at the side of the swimming pool, and chipped off a permanent front tooth, further delaying his clarinet playing until the tooth was capped.

From an early age, Michael seemed to have a flair for figures, and whilst still at school, was accurately predicting the sale value of houses, including our own. In school examinations he also seemed able to calculate the chances of particular topics coming up. He also seemed to have good argumentative skills and we felt convinced he would probably head for a career in business or law, as he seemed to have the gift of the gab. However, from the age of about five or six years, he already started expressing a determination to become a doctor. We tried to gently dissuade him and to tell him there was plenty of time to think about it in the future.

He also inherited our collector's instinct and from an early age had a passion for old furniture and to this day he is constantly looking at sales and picking up interesting items at auctions and then either keeping them or trading them with dealers for other items that he more enthusiastically wants to acquire. He later also developed a serious interest in wine and when at college in Oxford was the Keeper of the Cellar. He somehow always had an insight, or whatever it requires, on what wines and vintage ports to lay down for later consumption or bartering.

No. 3 Gerald

Gerald has the unique distinction in our family of being an American citizen by virtue of his birth in New York in December 1965. During our year in the States we went camping

In the garden of our second house, 50 Chorley Rd, Fulwood
Spring

Summer

Winter

The boys hiking in Padley Gorge. Gerald at rear has the oversized rucksack

for ten consecutive weekends through the ensuing summer months in Taconic State Park, some 120 miles north of New York. We had bought a large family tent, which proved very effective. There were also excellent facilities for small children paddling and bathing in a shallow pool. American society may appear to be pretty emancipated, if one were to judge by television programmes, but there are still areas of tremendous prudery. So we almost found ourselves under arrest for indecent exposure in public when Lil was one day changing Gerald's nappy (diaper) alongside the pool, and we were pounced upon by a very officious ranger, fully armed and with full policing responsibilities.

When we came back to Sheffield we were keen to pursue these weekend camping trips. We chanced our luck on two successive summer weekends, one at Fountains Abbey in North Yorkshire, and the other in the Lake District. On both occasions we were completely rained out and spent most of our time in our minivan.

In 1967 we had a very enjoyable family holiday at a small fishing village on the west coast of Sweden near Stromstad. We had been keen to tour the west coast of Ireland in our Volkswagen camper. The Irish tourist board advised us to contact the individual town tourist offices. At the same time an advertisement appeared in the local Sheffield newspapers with a special offer, to mark the opening of the new Tor Line ferryboat service from Hull to Göteborg, of two adults plus two children plus a car and two weeks in a fishing cottage on the west coast at Strömstad for the princely sum of 100 pounds sterling.

I still have a vivid memory during the boat crossing from Hull to Göteborg, of Lil and myself sitting in the lounge entertaining David and Michael, after having put Gerald to sleep in our cabin on the lower bunk and duly closed the door which we thought had a handle out of the reach of an 18-monther, who had only recently achieved independent ambulation. A sudden announcement came over the tannoy system, which we instantly realised was for us. 'Will the parents of an infant who has crawled across the main reception area of the boat please collect him at the Purser's desk!' He had not only extricated himself from the cabin but had managed to negotiate a number of corridors to find his way to the main reception deck of the boat. Doesn't bear thinking of all the other possibilities had he decided to be a bit more venturesome in his explorations.

We duly arrived in Strömstad after motoring up from Göteborg. The cottage was delightful and well equipped and in a spectacular position on a rocky promontory by the ocean. However, it did not seem conducive to the long-term survival of three small children, with a somewhat precipitous edge to the rocks from which adults could readily dive or slide into the ocean. So the following morning we were at the tourist office pleading for something a bit more appropriate and secure for small children. We were offered a cottage at a small fishing village of Rässo, south of Strömstad. This proved ideal, near a sandy beach and a very helpful fisherman's wife, who had actually built the cottage herself and was in the process of constructing another one. She had obviously found a productive way of filling her time whilst her husband was at sea. We were subsequently to go on two further occasions to the same place.

One-armed bandit

One visual memory of a later Tor line trip in 1971 was the fascination of the three older boys for the one-armed-bandit machines that swallowed up people's money and occasionally encouraged them on with a small return. We constantly had to retrieve them from watching some of the habituated adult devotees glued to the machines. Some years later David revealed a closely guarded secret. On the trip, the three of them had sneaked out of the children's play area where we had left them, and had been watching one of the Scandinavian addicts playing away continuously at the machine until he finally had a reward back. He then wisely decided to call it a day, and presumably feeling quite relieved to find himself still in credit, handed David one of his kronors as he left. David then enthusiastically inserted the kronor into the machine, and pulled the lever, holding it for some time, watching the images rotating by, enviously watched by his two brothers. Suddenly all hell broke loose. The machine became quite apoplectic and starting disgorging its contents in a continuous stream, with a deafening metallic noise. When the process finally settled they counted their loot; 200 Swedish kronor. They had hit the jackpot. But what to do now? A serious dilemma. Perhaps they should just share it between them and say nothing. But we would be bound to find such a large treasure trove and to ask awkward questions. They dismissed this option. Next option was to just tell us exactly what had happened and hopefully we might be quite pleased with the windfall and just wish them luck and let them spend it or spend it for them. But we had specifically asked them to confine their entertainment to the children's play area, which was well endowed with all sorts of interesting activities, and not to go to the adult lounge and gambling corner. On balance they decided this was not a wise option either. Only one option left; to just continue the orgy and play the machine. They opted for that one and between them continued to play for some while until they eventually ended up empty handed and the machine got it all back. A very wise decision, we thought, and a very good experience for them. None of them have developed any sort of gambling instinct or urge.

No. 4 Daniel

Daniel arrived in June 1969, some three years after Gerald, and in many ways was distant enough from the closely-knit three

Dan with his grandfather in Cape Town 1969

Dan is transported African style by May, the Hansen's housemaid older boys, who had less than three years between them, as to almost be an only child.

When we went off to the International Paediatric Conference in Mexico in 1968, Lil was not quite sure whether she was pregnant or not. However, it became more obvious en route with severe morning sickness. In Mexico we visited Merida and Chichen Itsa and were very careful with our eating habits, always selecting small clean cafes and sticking to cooked food. We had no problems at all until the final banquet at the official luxury hotel of the Paediatric Congress in Mexico City, when Lil had a tremendous dose of Montezuma's Revenge as they call it, with severe diarrhoea and vomiting.

Daniel gave us quite a bit of anxiety in the neonatal period. Although born at full term and with no apparent problems in the pregnancy, he was pretty flat and unresponsive at birth, thanks to the midwife not believing Lil that she felt ready to push, and giving her 150 mg pethidine. Dan arrived 20 minutes later and needed resuscitation. As I was present at the birth, the nursing staff had not alerted the resident paediatric staff so I was left to cope with the immediate resuscitation procedures. Fortunately he responded rapidly. However, he soon after developed a severe respiratory distress syndrome, with a full-blown clinical picture of laboured, grunting breathing and the classical ground glass appearance on the X-ray. This is a condition almost entirely confined to premature infants and very rare in mature fullterm babies. But then doctors and allied professions always seem more prone to get the unusual problems. This respiratory distress took a full week to recover, and he had to stay in the intensive care unit.

He meanwhile developed a large inguinal hernia, a common and fairly benign occurrence in infants, and probably aggravated by the respiratory problem. It continued to enlarge after he came home but could be easily reduced. However we were facing a new dilemma as we had preplanned a visit to South Africa about four weeks later, and in particular to the Kruger game park, which was optimal in the South African winter season in July. I was reassured by one of my close paediatric colleagues that large inguinal hernias in infants never strangulate, so we let the arrangements stand.

The weekend before we were due to fly out, I went off after lunch on the Saturday to do some extended shopping. When I

David and Michael waiting for the bus to Rondebosch Boys Primary School whilst in Cape Town in 1969

got home at about five there was a note from Lil that she had taken Dan to the Children's Hospital for operation on his hernia. Apparently it had bulged out soon after I left, and would not go back, and the child was crying persistently with obvious discomfort. This is referred to as an incarcerated hernia. She phoned the paediatric surgeon at the Children's, Bob Zachary, a superb clinician and surgeon, who told her to take the infant in for admission right away and he would be on his way as well and also alert the theatre to the need for emergency surgery.

By the time I got to the hospital Daniel was back in the ward. And not a moment too soon, as the bowel was already showing signs of deficient blood supply from the strangulation and we were lucky that it still seemed viable and did not require any resection.

He made an uneventful recovery, was home the next day, and we duly headed off for the game park in South Africa. I shudder at the thought of what we would have done if the strangulation had happened in the park! And the moral of the story is one never says never in medicine!

After our visit to the game park we spent three months in Cape Town on an exchange with Professor John Hansen who had worked in Sheffield children's hospital in the 1950s and was keen to spend a short sabbatical there. We very conveniently exchanged our jobs, our houses, our cars, our dogs, indeed everything short of our wives. David and Michael were also able to obtain a place at the local Rondebosch Boys School, where they integrated well, given their head start with the earlier age of starting schooling in England.

Dan takes aspirins for Lil's headache

After our very successful family holiday at the small fishing village of Rässo, south of Stromstad in 1967, we returned again to the same cottage the following summer and a third time in 1971.

One afternoon whilst the three older children were playing on the beach we left our Volkswagen minibus parked within sight nearby in some shade, with Daniel, who was something this side of two years at the time, asleep in the rear compartment by the rear window.

When we came back to check him later, we found he had not only woken up but had ventured to the front of the van and had managed to open the glove compartment and to explore the contents, which were strewn about. Of most concern was that a tin container which had four residual high dosage aspirin tablets Lil had got at a local pharmacy for a severe bout of migraine, was open and the contents gone. When we showed him the container he kept saying 'all gone!' Whilst he seemed perfectly all right, I was extremely anxious as infants are very sensitive to aspirin and four tablets of strength about three times the usual adult aspirin tablet could be fatal. I telephoned my paediatric neurology colleague and friend, Ingrid Gamstorp, who was in Jonkoping at that time, halfway across Sweden. She advised us to get urgent attention and to take him to the local district hospital in Stromstad, rather than trying to get to a larger centre such as Goteborg.

We duly drove to the small local hospital and after providing the preliminary details to the reception nurse in the emergency room, a very friendly young doctor duly arrived and I provided a detailed history of events. He examined the child and pronounced that everything seemed fine and he did not think we needed do anything further but wait and see. I had not mentioned I was medical but expressed the view that I felt there was a high likelihood the child had taken the tablets and I would be much happier if a tube could be passed into the stomach to at least get rid of it.

He then asked the nurse for a stomach tube and they duly produced an adult Ryle tube, a real hosepipe in relation to the child. After a fairly traumatic battle it seemed obvious he was not going to get it down, so I suggested perhaps it was a bit big for the child and possibly they had something of more appropriate size. This was produced and he managed to get that down. He attached a syringe and sucked back and nothing came out and was about to remove the tube. At this stage I thought it in everybody's interest to reveal my medical background. I then advised that as the child had nothing to eat or drink for about two hours, perhaps his stomach was empty and it might be helpful to inject some fluid down the tube to wash the stomach out. He agreed and then asked the nurse for some sterile saline. After a prolonged absence she came back that they did not seem to have any at hand. He was extremely concerned and rather critical of the nurse and the hospital. So I came to the immediate rescue with the remark that as the mouth, oesophagus and stomach are not really sterile, there was no need for sterile saline and why not just try some tap water. He was visibly relieved. After injecting 20ml of water, he sucked back an appreciable amount of aspirin grains from the dispersed tablets. This was repeated through three or four further washouts before the fluid became clear. I agreed it now seemed reasonable to withdraw the tube, to the great relief of everybody, not least Daniel, who by this time looked completely exhausted and was dripping with perspiration, not to mention his father. The nurse offered him a glass of milk, which he dismissed with such vehemence that he almost knocked it out of her hand. It seemed obvious he was not going to have anything to do with the 'enemy'. The casualty officer then suggested we take him home and if we were at all concerned to bring him back. 'You know the toxic effects of aspirin?' he politely added. He seemed relieved when I nodded. We thanked him and the nurse and headed off.

When we got back to the van, Dan immediately devoured almost a whole litre of milk, and for the first time all evening gave a slight smile. He was obviously relieved to get away from the torture chamber.

That night none of us had much sleep. Dan started overbreathing; a common feature of aspirin intoxication, and became extremely hyperactive and irritable within a short time of us arriving back to Rässo. He was literally climbing up the wall and was extremely restless. It was obvious he still had a considerable amount of aspirin on board, despite the large amount that had been washed out. As he seemed fully alert and conscious I thought it would be reasonable to just ride out the night and I felt that neither he or I were up to a repeat of the stomach tube exercise. I phoned Ingrid Gamstorp and she concurred, and was also against any sedative medication. He finally passed into a sound sleep and his breathing pattern normalised and when he woke a few hours later he seemed fine.

We headed back to the hospital in the morning to settle our bill and to reassure the casualty doctor that all was well. I was already concerned I might not have enough currency, given the high cost of living in Sweden. But to my amazement and relief, the nurse on the emergency room told me there was a standard charge of seven kronor, equivalent to less than one pound sterling.

'And could I see the young doctor to thank him for his help?' I asked. 'The doctor? He left this morning to go back to medical school. He is a medical student still in training, and was only doing a locum cover for two weeks while the general practitioner in the town, who normally covers the hospital, was on vacation.' Guess we all came out pretty well, considering he had probably never seen an adult let alone a child with aspirin toxicity, or passed a stomach tube before. I guess he may have been more indelibly imprinted by the experience than Dan. Perhaps he's become a paediatrician, or alternatively a geriatrician, depending on the impact of the experience.

7

Back in London

The great thing
in this world
is not so much
where we are,
but in what direction
we are moving.
— Oliver Wendell Holmes

Quite ironically I found myself involved in a completely reverse situation to my previous somewhat abortive chair-chasing experiences, when the Chair of Paediatrics fell vacant at Hammersmith, after the move of Peter Tizard to Oxford. The post was advertised but I did not bother to apply at all as it was common knowledge that the incumbent Reader in the department and a longstanding senior colleague of Tizard's would be appointed and Peter Tizard had openly expressed his choice as well, although in the British tradition departing professors have no official involvement at all in the appointment of their successor.

Around the time of the post being advertised I took off for an International Muscle Congress in Perth, Australia, with a stop-over in India en route out and a circuit via Melbourne, Brisbane and New Guinea on the way back. Whilst stopping over in Melbourne, where I was also approached about the position of Director of the Children's Research Institute, I had an urgent message from Illingworth via Lil as to why I had not applied for the Hammersmith chair and would I immediately contact Illingworth and confirm my interest in the post and send in a formal application as soon as I got back.

On my return, Illingworth advised me to see Professor Otto Wolff, head of the premier chair of paediatrics at the Institute of Child Health at Great Ormond Street, and successor to Moncrieff. He explained to me in considerable detail how the neonatal unit had been established at the Hammersmith Hospital as a neonatal arm of the Hospital for Sick Children at Great Ormond Street in the time of Moncrieff, and Peter Tizard had been seconded to the post as Senior Lecturer. He pioneered the first unit in the country for intensive care of the newborn infant, which gained an international reputation. He was subsequently promoted to a readership and then a personal chair within the post, which remained administratively part of the Institute of Child Health, although having academic and consultant status at the Hammersmith Hospital and Royal Postgraduate Medical School.

A Chair of Paediatrics at Hammersmith

With the post now falling vacant at the Hammersmith, the Institute of Child Health, in consultation with the Royal Postgraduate Medical School, had decided to establish a Chair of Paediatrics at the Hammersmith Hospital and had been given the necessary authority by the University of London, under whose umbrella both institutes fell. They also now had a much broader vision of the Chair and wished to expand it academically into other areas of paediatrics in addition to maintaining the special interest of the specialised neonatal unit. They were thus keen to attract suitable candidates across the paediatric board, and thought that I was a potentially suitable candidate, given my longstanding interest in the neurology of the newborn and also my special interest in muscle diseases, in addition to my exposure to general paediatrics during the 10-year tenure of my post in Sheffield.

I was duly shortlisted for the post and called for interview together with Jon Scopes, the current Reader on the unit, whom I had known for many years and had seen quite a lot of during the time we were both in New York in the mid-sixties, and two others, one being Max Friedman, another expatriate South African but from the other main medical school of Witwatersrand (Wits), who was also a close friend and with whom I actually stayed over the period of the interview. On the interviewing panel were Otto Wolff representing the Institute of Child Health, and Chris Booth, head of the Department of Medicine at the Royal Postgraduate Medical School, plus the Principal of the University of London, Sir Douglas Logan, in the chair, and a number of additional people representing other statutory bodies. The interview was a prolonged and in-depth one and for the first time I felt it was really a serious and potentially meaningful one. It was oriented mainly to one's vision of the future of the department at the Hammersmith and how one would set about achieving various goals.

When I was asked at the end if there were any questions I had, I asked about the departmental budget and the availability of funds for equipment for replacing my current equipment in relation to muscle biopsy processing in Sheffield and also the possibility of bringing a lecturer and a technician with me from Sheffield. I was met with a stunned silence. It transpired there was no departmental grant or any available funding and I would have to negotiate this with the Institute of Child Health, and also the Postgraduate Medical Federation, under whose collective budget the Postgraduate Medical School and all the postgraduate institutes, including Child Health fell.

I also raised the question of removal expenses given I had to transfer my household to London, lock, stock and barrel, and there was no increase in my salary as all medical academics from senior lecturer up, were on the clinical consultants' scale, having reached parity after years of effort after being on a lower university rate before. Moreover, the cost of a barely equivalent house in London, if one could find one, was at least double the cost of a comparable house in Sheffield. I also discovered that the University of London was particularly mingy with travel expenses and only provided a second class rail fare plus a small per diem allowance for attending for the interview for the chair, whereas the University of Sheffield provided all its academic staff from lecturer up with a first class rail fare.

I met up soon after with Professor Wolff and Dr George Newnes, the Dean of the Institute of Child Health, and also with Professor George Smart, Director of the Postgraduate Federation, to try and at least get some earmarked funds to get off the ground.

Homeless in London

I really started having serious reservations about moving to London, given all the additional problems with housing at that time with an escalating market and a new phenomenon of gazzumping, a pernicious system of estate agents hiking up the price after a price had been agreed, on the grounds of additional offers coming in. Fortunately we met up with David Baum, at that time a senior registrar in the paediatric department at Hammersmith, at a meeting of the Paediatric Research Society in London, and when Lillly related our plight and asked for advice on any camping sites, where we might be able to park our

Volkswagen combi car, for temporary residence, he told us his brother Harold, a biochemist at Queen Elizabeth College in Chelsea, living in Golders Green, had bought a house in Barnes, south of the river, and was moving in the autumn, and intended putting his house on the market later in the year. Would we be interested in seeing it? We leapt at the opportunity, but were somewhat despondent when we arrived on the Sunday morning at the somewhat small-looking, semi-detached house. We could see no way of squeezing our four children plus a dog and potentially a mother-in-law into it. We were reluctant to even go in, but felt we owed it to David, who had made the arrangement. Once we were inside, we realised how deceptive the outside appearance was and that it had five bedrooms, as well as a large basement, the extent of the house, which had not been opened up. Two hours later we had agreed a deal, and we duly moved in in September, and have been there ever since.

A personal chair in Sheffield?

I had a serious discussion with Illingworth and told him that all things being equal, if I could get a personal chair in Sheffield, I would be much happier continuing in my post than starting afresh in London with all the hidden problems. I had serious intentions of withdrawing my application if this was a likely possibility. He duly arranged for me to see the Vice Chancellor of Sheffield University, the day before I was due to attend for interview for the Hammersmith chair. He was very friendly and relaxed in our discussion and told me quite frankly that the policy of Sheffield University had always been to encourage academics to move on and up, and they essentially only gave personal chairs to people who were of academic eminence but considered incapable of getting a chair on the open market! What this essentially entailed was that anyone whom they felt capable of competing for open chairs should do so and only those who in a sense were in a super-specialised cul de sac and unlikely to get an open chair, and thus unique to Sheffield University, would be considered for a personal chair. So that was the end of that road.

In striking contrast, I subsequently discovered that the Post-graduate Medical School was absolutely awash with personal chairs and of some 25 professors there were only a handful in definitive established chairs and all the rest had built up individual units and been promoted to a personal chair within it.

I duly had a formal letter a few days later from the Principal offering me the newly established Chair of Paediatrics in the Institute of Child Health, at the Hammersmith Hospital and with academic reciprocal rights in the Postgraduate Medical School as a member of their academic board and other academic committees. I was asked to sign my acceptance as soon as possible, with a suggested starting date of April 1st, and return the duly signed forms to the Principal's office.

I really felt in a cleft stick, enthusiastic on the one hand to accept this prestigious appointment at one of the key academic centres in the country and to take on the challenge of consolidating and expanding its existing standing in the paediatric field, and at the same time very concerned about the various hurdles that lay ahead, not least financially, and attempting to get to the starting post and at least into an equivalent position to my current one in Sheffield.

In addition to the whole upheaval for my family and having to find a new academic or clinical niche for Lil and schools for the four children, I also had to consider the position of my longstanding technician, Christine Heinzmann, and my various research fellows, including Jan Witkowski, who had just joined me in Sheffield from the MRC unit in Hampstead, mainly, he confided in me, to be near the hills of Derbyshire in view of his passion for mountaineering.

I was not ready to respond to the Principal till a full two weeks later, and in my detailed letter drew his attention to the very regulations referred to in the letter of appointment, and my concern that no provisions had been made at all to meet these prescribed conditions. I felt it important to spell this all out in relation to my letter of acceptance, so that if I found myself up against a brick wall and unable to make any headway in relation to adequate facilities for my muscle team, I could still pull out ahead of taking up the post and submit an appropriate letter of resignation.

By this time I had managed to negotiate some underwriting of my moving expenses by the Institute and also some funding for equipment and the possibility of some support from the Muscular Dystrophy Group for my technician if I moved to London. I rapidly came to realise that my best time for any bargaining was going to be before I signed acceptance of the post, and although I had been told of the honeymoon period for about a year after taking up a new position, when your colleagues might show some degree of sympathy for your needs, the time came all too rapidly when you were part of the free-for-all and competing with all your colleagues and having to resort to the same cut-throat and back-stabbing tactics.

On accepting the post in February 1972, I also made it quite clear I would not be able to take up the position until September at the earliest, to give me sufficient time to sort out not only the totally disruptive move of my academic activities but also finding suitable housing for my family in the difficult and financially taxing move from the provinces to the metropolis, and settling the children into a totally new social and school environment.

Academic hurdles

Although located at Hammersmith Hospital, the department of paediatrics was still administratively part of the Institute of Child Health on the other side of the city in Guilford Street, and I was a full member of the academic board at the Institute. I had a letter from Professor Wolff and Dr Newnes on behalf of the Institute that I should consider setting up a muscle clinic at Great Ormond Street, which I also thought worth pursuing. However, this was completely stonewalled by the consultant neurologist at the hospital, in charge of the neurology services, Dr John Wilson, who wrote that he could see no need at all for such a clinic, as he was perfectly capable of handling any muscle patients through his general neurology clinics.

Another major problem that soon became apparent on the Hammersmith site was space for any research activities. The Neonatal Unit had its office accommodation in very limited prefabricated huts in juxtaposition to the obstetrical department, with whom it was closely associated. In addition Tizard had obtained funds from a special fund operated by the Aldermen of the City of London from a bequest of a former Lord Mayor of London, Sir William Coxen, who had been born with a club foot and had covenanted the money to be used for research into congenital conditions in infancy. Tizard had been able to secure a large enough grant from them to build a series of lean-to laboratories, the Coxen laboratories, against the side of the neonatal unit with access directly from the unit, and had also secured a recurrent annual grant to cover various short term research projects.

Meanwhile Tizard had taken the unprecedented step of expressing his displeasure at a meeting of the academic board at the Hammersmith with the appointment of his successor and the fact that his highly commendable protégé had not been appointed to continue the work on the neonatal unit he had established. Rumours soon started going around the Unit that I had intentions of closing down the neonatal unit and establishing a muscle unit in its place and diverting all the funding in that direction. So my very first task was to reassure all the staff that I had no such intentions at all and indeed was very keen to consolidate and further expand the excellence of the neonatal unit and that any additional academic activities I started would be entirely funded by additional resources I would have to find for the purpose. As I personally had a special interest in neonatal neurology, I certainly had every intention of pursuing and promoting it.

I also have to say that whatever personal opinions Peter Tizard may have expressed to the academic board or to anyone else, he was absolutely magnanimous with me personally and treated me in an absolutely open hearted and friendly way. He invited me down for dinner at his home, Islip Manor, and opened a bottle of vintage claret for the occasion and wished me well in my new post. He then proceeded to give me a remarkable thumbnail sketch of each member of the department, from the academics to the clinical secretaries and the various part-time technical staff involved in various activities, and providing an indispensable contribution to the department. I in turn was also able to assure him that I was very keen to devote my energies not only to sustaining the neonatal unit but also contributing to it and also to ensuring the continuing support for all the established members of staff. I have recently tracked down the letter I received from him after our informal dinner meeting, which was within a couple of weeks of my being offered the post, and I think the two final paragraphs are a clear indication of his magnanimity under what had obviously been a difficult situation for himself.

> It was very nice seeing you yesterday evening, and I must say I was considerably reassured by what you told me. As you know I had felt that the neonatal work might decline with your appointment simply because you might feel – entirely reasonably – that your neuromuscular work should take precedence.
>
> I have been very happy in the seventeen years I have worked here and am sure you will find it an equally congenial and stimulating atmosphere. Moreover I have no doubt, and I mean this very sincerely, that the work and reputation of the Paediatric Department here will be enhanced by having you in charge. I will certainly do all I can to help you settle in.

Tizard was a remarkable man, with a tremendous flair and command of language, and a great after-dinner speaker. He came from a very distinguished background, with a famous father, Sir Henry Tizard, a renowned scientist, later rector of Imperial College, who had chaired a committee in the 1930s to advise the government against the imminent threat of a German invasion and had developed radar (abbreviation for radio detection and ranging) as a defence against enemy aircraft.

Peter was wonderful at public relations, and amongst his many activities (which I continued) was to have regular dinner evenings at the Hammersmith every few months for all the outside paediatric consultants who transferred their prematurely born neonates to Hammersmith for intensive care on the specialised neonatal unit. He also got his colleagues and junior associates to tell individual stories of interest in relation to the unit or would get them to demonstrate the difficulty in extracting milk from an infant feeding bottle with an inadequate teat, for the entertainment and amusement of the diners.

He also seemed to have an inordinate ability to recruit various part-time people onto the unit on fairly nebulous and short-term soft money from various charitable sources. I soon realised a similar situation existed with the appointment of junior resident staff on the unit, who frequently were appointed on recommendation of colleagues in the UK or abroad and given fairly open-ended appointments to stay until they had a further post to move on to. In due course I tried to establish a regular cycle for the various resident posts on a fixed term of appointment, so that we could advertise and fill the posts by appropriate shortlisting and interview, whilst at the same time encouraging any high-flyers from abroad to continue coming but also putting in a formal application for an appropriately timed post.

We also regularly had clinical research fellows coming with their own funds and we were able to arrange an honorary residency attachment to the unit and they in turn provided a great backup for our on-call rotation of the residents and were happy in return to keep their own clinical activity going. This continued well into the 1970s until once again the politicians intervened and would not provide any increment in residency pay without fixed contracts and introduced units of medical time and special arrangements for working additional hours beyond the basic contract. This wiped out all the voluntary workers at one fell swoop. It was somewhat reminiscent of a notice that came from our local infant school around that time that in the interests of economy the school would no longer be able to employ volunteer lunch-time helpers (mainly parents, with no salary anyway).

I also very rapidly acquired some home truths that had never crossed my mind before. I had assumed that all the senior staff were university appointments but now discovered that apart from Tizard's own post, which had now been transposed into the foundation established chair, there was only one other university supported post and that was the senior lectureship one of Jon Scopes, in which he had been promoted to a readership. The other senior academic, Pamela Davies, who had an international reputation for her pioneering work on the long-term follow-up of the premature babies, who were now surviving the vicissitudes of the newborn period, thanks to the advances in neonatal intensive care, was on grant support, as was the eminent neonatal pathologist, Jonathan Wigglesworth. Tizard had been extremely successful in attracting grant support and had obtained a large programme grant for five years from the Nuffield Foundation to support all the senior personnel involved in the neonatal research programme. And to my dismay this grant was coming to an end in a matter of weeks. I was beginning to wonder if this had not been an opportune time for Tizard to move on to the greener pastures of Oxford and to pull out the carpet with him! So one of my first priorities was to get an urgent application to the Nuffield Foundation for a further three year extension of the support for Pam Davies' salary and programme. One other substantive post which was very important to the unit was that of a biochemist, provided by the hospital service, to undertake all the essential biochemical investigations on the babies on a micro scale, with the use of pinpricks of blood rather than the usual syringe-loads. Elizabeth Hughes was the key figure in this post.

The muscle team

My next major problem was setting up at Hammersmith my ongoing muscle clinical and research unit comparable to the Sheffield one.

The key person in the whole clinical and investigative programme was my technician, Christine Heinzmann, who assisted with the running of the clinics in addition to processing the biopsies. Being born and bred in Yorkshire, and knowing how insular the Yorkshire people are, I was doubtful she would want to leave her homeland. To my surprise, she was quite enthusiastic, but with one main proviso, that I could find a post for her boyfriend, Peter Hutson, who had just completed a BSc. Fair exchange; so I discussed with the paediatric biochemist, Elizabeth Hughes, if she could find a niche for Peter in her department, till he found a more definitive position and I would try and find some short-term funding.

The next person I had to break the news to was Jan Witkowski, who had enthusiastically joined my unit in Sheffield only a few months earlier in order to escape to the Derbyshire hills to satisfy his passion for rock climbing, and had already set up a very productive research programme on cultured muscle cells from patients with muscular dystrophy, and here I was trying to banish him back to London. No problem, he was enthusiastic to join me in the new venture, even if it meant a U-turn back to London. Another recent member of the muscle group was Joe Neerunjen. He had no reservations at all on moving back to London.

My clinical muscle research fellow, Allie Moosa, supported by the Muscular Dystrophy Group, had completed an MD thesis on his Sheffield work on the maturation of motor nerve conduction velocity as an index of gestational maturity in the newborn infant, and shown this to be a very reliable index of neuronal maturation. He was now also well versed in neuromuscular

Christine Heinzmann and Peter Hutson after emigrating from Yorkshire to London

disorders and fully competent in the electrodiagnostic and muscle biopsy techniques in children. He was thus another key person in our team, given that a large part of my time was going to be tied up in administrative matters in keeping the paediatric department on the road.

One of the *quid pro quos* I negotiated with the Institute of Child Health was to establish a lecturer post with the newly established Chair of Paediatrics I was taking up at Hammersmith, at least for an initial three year period, to enable me to set up my special muscle interest, without encroaching at all on the staff or facilities in relation to the well-established neonatal unit, as I had already reassured the existing staff on the neonatal unit.

Laboratory space at Hammersmith

My next major problem was finding space for the research team I was bringing with me from Sheffield, comparable to the fully functional muscle research laboratory with tissue culture facility I had in the new department of child health building in Sheffield. Finding space at Hammersmith proved to be a much bigger headache than I had anticipated. I approached the head of Medicine, Chris Booth, who had been extremely helpful and supportive in many different ways, and he was quick to assure me that all available space in the medicine department was fully utilised and I was unlikely to find any spare space at all. This proved to be correct, even after I had physically walked all the corridors of the hospital, popping my head round the door into various labs and other spaces, and introducing myself and explaining my mission of looking for a little bit of space for the small team of enthusiasts I was bringing down from Yorkshire. Even some of the obvious areas of underused space could not possibly be made available as they were always on the verge of new expansion with new grants in the pipeline and so forth.

I did however strike some oil, of a sort. The Dean of the RPMS, Selwyn Taylor, a surgeon, was very sympathetic and helpful, but explained the dichotomy in the situation as the department of paediatrics was part of the Institute of Child Health, who were basically responsible for providing the facilities, but in practical terms this was really in the gift of the Postgraduate School, who owned the facilities on site. He advised me to discuss the problem with David Hill, the eminent physiologist, who had a long-term established post within the department of medical physics, and had been a next door neighbour when I was first attached to Pearse's lab in the 1950s. He also held the position of vice Dean, and had responsibility for the allocation of laboratory and office space on site. He noted that the rheumatology unit within the department of medicine were just vacating a couple of temporary buildings on site in the area that had been the historical labour yard, where the indigent occupants of the sick house facilities at the turn of the century also had to provide physical labour of chopping up stones. The buildings had been condemned and were due for demolition in a few months. A week may be a long time in politics, I thought, but it may be even longer in research. So I immediately set about staking a claim on the use of these limited facilities to at least set up a muscle biopsy laboratory and a tissue culture facility to get our efforts off the ground. As this was only a temporary respite, I meanwhile continued my tours around the site, cap in one hand and begging bowl in the other.

I discovered on the third floor of the Medical Research Council (MRC) cyclotron building a large laboratory that seemed to be patently underpopulated, with only a few technicians gracing the fairly generous bench space. What a contrast I thought to the closely congested laboratory of Everson Pearse where I worked in the late fifties. It belonged to the department of surgery and I immediately discussed the possibility of some landing space for my team to get us off the ground, and provide an interim solution for the period between vacating the condemned labour yard facility and finding something more permanent. Professor Dick Welbourn, the head of surgery, was extremely helpful and more or less gave me carte blanche to use whatever facilities might be available within their research laboratory, in consultation with his senior technician. And so ended, at least in theory, my initial anxieties of potential homelessness, as the new professor of paediatrics, in the world-renowned postgraduate medical school in London.

The cyclotron building had originally been built to house the first hospital-based cyclotron in the world, to provide radioactive materials for diagnostic and therapeutic efforts. In its heyday the Hammersmith Hospital and Postgraduate Medical School had always been at the very forefront of innovative research and development and attracted the most active minds in the field. Thus it was the place that pioneered the first kidney transplants in the world, and developed the first bypass machines for open heart surgery. It had a very active medical physics department, with some superb technicians, able to craft all sort of innovative equipment, and we subsequently capitalised on this in relation to some of our new research in the newborn sphere.

In post

Once I took up my post, I was keen to get things off the ground as soon as possible and one of my first tasks was to get a muscle clinic started in order to maintain some continuity with our previous clinical and research activities.

As there were essentially no facilities at all for adequate children's outpatient clinics, which were being run off the corridor of the children's ward, I set up a muscle clinic in the general outpatients department of the hospital, alongside the main hospital emergency department. I soon discovered that children were being admitted to adult wards for various surgical procedures, or to the adult neurology unit for management of convulsions or other neurological problems. So I started a walkabout of the hospital and wherever I found children under 14 years in adult units, I negotiated with the consultants for them to be admitted to the children's ward to provide an appropriate environment for them, which included specially trained children's nurses and also schooling by regular teachers, provided by the Inner London Education Authority (ILEA). They still remained under the nominal care of their respective consultants, but we agreed that our paediatric residents would take some degree of day-to-day surveillance of them.

It soon also became apparent that a similar arrangement needed to be made for children coming to the emergency room. This became an urgent matter for me, after a severely asthmatic child was sent home by an inexperienced casualty officer and was admitted moribund later in the night, and some cases of non-accidental injury (child abuse), inflicted by parents, were missed by the casualty officers and the children put at risk by being returned to an unsafe environment. So we issued an edict that no children would in future be discharged from the emergency room, without being seen by a paediatric resident, and we were in time able to justify an additional paediatric resident post to rotate through the casualty service.

Clinical rounds

I followed the tradition I had learnt from Illingworth in Sheffield of doing a complete round of all the wards once a week, which served not only as a good forum for discussion and clinical diagnosis, but also a good educational resource for the residents.

So we established a regular ward round on Thursday mornings, seeing all patients, and I would regularly surprise the residents when they fleetingly passed a patient, and said this is only a 'tonsils', and I would stop and ask 'Tell me doctor, is it a medical tonsils or a surgical tonsils?' And after a blank response, I would clarify I was interested to know if the child had a medical problem to justify the removal of the tonsils, or whether it was simply part of a surgical vogue at the time of removing children's adenoids and tonsils for all sorts of ails.

There was one particular occasion that proved very important for the patient, and hopefully also for the residents.. We were passing a bed with a child who was 'Only a day case for tooth extractions'. 'Could you please check how many teeth are to be extracted?', I asked, 'and whether it is under local or general anaesthetic?' The resident checked the notes and indeed there were several teeth to be extracted under general anaesthesia. Could he please telephone the dental surgeon (who did a weekly session at the hospital) that I was concerned about giving the child a general anaesthetic as he had myotonic dystrophy (which was obvious from his facial features) and children with this condition are very sensitive to certain anaesthetics and may not wake up again after an anaesthetic, and need special attention and monitoring.

In addition to my weekly general wardround of the paediatric wards, I also took a personal interest in the neonatal unit and did a weekly round of all the babies in the unit. I also set up a weekly round with Harry Gordon, a senior lecturer in the obstetric department, so that we could assess some of the at-risk babies *in utero* and try and collectively decide the best management for them. My incidental experience in obstetrics years earlier during my casualty post in Lewisham gave me the confidence to examine the foetus in utero by abdominal palpation, and one soon got quite adept at guessing the potential size of the infant. It also made for a closer liaison of the obstetricians with the neonatal staff, so that they were aware of babies with potential problems ahead of their birth. So we had an active involvement with the perinatal care of specific problems such as Rhesus incompatibility, babies of diabetic mothers and other maternal conditions likely to affect the newborn baby. I was later able to expand this further, in collaboration with Professor Murdo Elder, Head of Obstetrics, with a major grant from the pharmaceutical company Glaxo Wellcome, with no strings attached, for a five year period, to provide an annual salary for a perinatal research fellow so that we were able to set up an active, and somewhat novel, two-year rotation in perinatal medicine, with a six month residency in obstetrics, six months in neonatal paediatrics and one year's research. This attracted some highly motivated candidates from both an obstetrical and a paediatric background.

I also established a regular clinic with the adult neurology department, whose head Chris Pallis was a superb clinical teacher, and it was of mutual benefit for our paediatric group to see some of the adult problems, whereas we in turn could expose them to a new world of neonatal neurology. Being a traditional neurologist, Chris would routinely want to know the plantar reflex response (Babinski reflex) on our newborn infants, which does not carry the same significance as in adult life. I enjoyed teasing him by asking him 'which way would you like it?' and I could elicit either an up-going or a down-going response of the big toe depending on which direction I stroked the sole of the foot. He could never come to terms with this seeming paradox in neurological response.

I subsequently adopted a fairly strong line on the total inadequacy of the children's outpatient facilities conducted off the corridor of the children's ward, in a poky room referred to as the dungeon. I followed a similar tack to Illingworth, who fought very hard for a new children's hospital in Sheffield, arguing that the walls in the terrace of Victorian houses, which were still being used as wards for inpatients, were held together by all the tubercle bacilli lodged there from all the cases of tuberculosis and tuberculous meningitis, before the pioneering days in the 1950s of the fist successful antibiotic treatment of tuberculous meningitis in children.

The Postgraduate Medical School at Hammersmith Hospital always prided itself in demonstrating to postgraduates from the third world what could be achieved under third world conditions! I said that if conditions at Hammersmith were as bad as in the third world, this was potentially acceptable, but if they were worse than I had personally experienced in third world countries, it was an intolerable situation, and something needed doing.

And so we were able to achieve a purpose-built children's outpatient unit as an extension of the children's ward and also to provide extra inpatient accommodation on an extension to the existing ward on the upper floor above it. This extended ward later provided an international standard in the assessment of children with muscular dystrophy. I used to assess the function of these children by getting them to walk as fast as possible from one end of the ward corridor to the other, a distance of 27 feet. Our senior physiotherapist, Sylvia Hyde, subsequently used this as one of the measures in developing a scoring system for assessing function in boys with Duchenne dystrophy. When we later went metric, the walking time over ten metres became an international standard measure of function, as did the Hammersmith Motor Ability Score, developed by Sylvia Hyde and Oona Scott.

Hosting a combined meeting of the Medical Research Society and the Physiological Society

Soon after I took up my chair at Hammersmith I had an invitation from the Physiological and Medical Research Societies to organise at Hammersmith a one day symposium on muscle that would be of mutual interest to the two societies, as part of the first combined meeting of these two prestigious societies. This was an exciting challenge and also an opportunity to present some of our own work in relation to culture of normal and diseased muscle, and also my cross-innervation studies. I invited Bruce Carlson from Philadelphia to give a paper on transplantation of muscle. He had read the original papers in Russian of Studitsky, who had pioneered studies on regeneration of muscle in mice after a whole muscle in the leg was removed from its compartment, chopped up into small pieces, and then reinserted. As long as the nerve and blood supply were present in the compartment, the muscle would fully regenerate within a a few weeks and regain its function. This was a technique Neerunjen was planning to apply to the crossing of muscle between normal and dystrophic animals.

I was not a member of either society at the time but following on my contributions to the conference was elected to membership of both and regularly attended their annual conferences in ensuing years.

With Mike Brooke at the publication of our book, *Muscle Biopsy, A Modern Approach*, in 1973, aimed at introducing enzyme histochemistry in routine processing of muscle biopsies

Our whole team gradually settled into the new environment and the more spacious facilities in the cyclotron building, which provided a better environment than the labour yard for our laboratory work, but still not ideal. A long-term solution eventually evolved from a completely new initiative.

Development of the Jerry Lewis Laboratories

The initiative for the development of custom built laboratories for the muscle research programme at Hammersmith came from a visit of Bill Gibson, an early pioneer in muscle physiology and research, who had worked with the legendary Charles Sherrington in Oxford at the turn of the century and was a lifelong friend of AV Hill, who won the Nobel Prize for his pioneering work on muscle contraction, and was the father of David Hill at Hammersmith. Bill Gibson was currently the Vice-Chancellor of the University in Victoria, in Vancouver Island, Canada, and a regular visitor to England. He was friendly with David Hill and via him met up with Richard Edwards and myself. He was told of our major problem with finding space for our muscle research team and the idea hatched in his mind of putting an application to the Muscular Dystrophy Association of America for the building of a suite of laboratories on the Hammersmith site, to house our combined research efforts. Richard Edwards was a senior lecturer in the Department of Medicine and in addition to his training as a physician had special expertise in respiratory function and also in muscle energy metabolism. He had worked with the muscle physiologist Bergstrom in Sweden and had introduced into clinical practice the Bergstrom needle for taking muscle biopsy samples, which Bergstrom had developed for sampling muscle from athletes in the course of physical exertion. Although Richard had a small amount of laboratory space in the respiratory department, he was keen to move to more spacious facilities. The main problem now was to identify some space on site to build some customised laboratories for our purpose.

Once again I started a meticulous tour of the hospital grounds, where it seemed as if every square inch of free ground space had been used for temporary or permanent buildings. Gone were the days when I first came to Hammersmith in the 1950s, when one could sit outdoors on benches alongside a fountain, and there were areas of grass, as well as tennis courts. One of the physicians once described the Hammersmith Hospital as the only bomb site in London on which no bomb had actually fallen.

I eventually discovered a flat roof space on top of the B Block of the hospital, facing on the front of the hospital and containing wards. I discussed it with Chris Booth, Head of Medicine who agreed there were no claims on it, and certainly not from the Medicine Department, but he felt sure there was a constraint on building on that area due to the foundations of the building not being able to sustain any further building.

I then tracked down the original building plans of the hospital and there seemed to be no apparent limitation expressed on the addition of a further floor on top of that section. We then got an architectural opinion and there seemed to be no problem and in fact one could put cross-girders across the area so that all the weight was evenly distributed down the sides. We then started preparing plans to utilise the whole area and to provide mainly laboratory space, with a minimum of office space. Finally we put in a combined application from the three of us to the Muscular Dystrophy Association of America for a capital grant of 300,000 dollars to construct the building, and an assurance of no further commitment from the MDAA for the maintenance or the research, which we hoped to attract from the university and other sources. Although there was a precedent in the MDAA for funding laboratories and ongoing research on a centre grant basis, all these centres were within the USA and there was a very strong opposition on the committee to the funding of any such centres abroad. Bill Gibson, who was a longstanding member of the MDAA research advisory committee, made a strong case and fought very hard on our behalf, stressing the importance of good quality research on a global basis, and finally won through.

Thus we were able to build the whole unit on the roof of the hospital, fully funded by the MDAA, and officially opened by the well know American comedian, Jerry Lewis, now president of the MDAA. He was their main fundraiser, with the annual round-the-clock telethon over the Labour Day weekend in September. By coincidence he was visiting London for a short run of his stage show at a musical theatre in the Hammersmith area, and was delighted to take on the official opening as well. All went very well with the opening of the labs, on a splendid

With Jan Witkowski and Jerry Lewis at the opening of the new Jerry Lewis Muscle Research Laboratories in June 1975

A bird's eye view of the laboratories on the roof of the Hammersmith Hospital

sunny June day in 1975, with traditional English afternoon tea, with strawberries and cream, on an area of roof adjacent to our labs. Unfortunately Jerry's show did not fare as well and went down like a lead brick and his anticipated audiences of yesteryear, when he was at his height in the 1950s, did not show up, and those who did come were just not on the same wavelength with his humour. So it had to close after a night or two. I think this somewhat soured his whole memory of the London visit and the Jerry Lewis Muscle Research Centre at Hammersmith.

A new academic building for the department

In parallel with the totally inadequate facilities for children's outpatients, we were not much better off in the accommodation for the academic staff who were housed in a temporary building alongside the obstetrics department. When I arrived at Hammersmith plans were in place for a total rebuilding of the whole hospital in four phases, and the paediatric department with a new building providing facilities for both paediatrics and obstetrics, together with a state-of-the-art neonatal unit, was in phase 1, thanks to a supportive grant of £250,000 Peter Tizard had obtained from Action Research for the Crippled Child. During my first year we had regular meetings with the building committee and the architects and had practically reached the stage of deciding where the electric outlets would go. But then

The Duke of Edinburgh officially opens the Action Research Perinatal Building of the Department of Paediatrics and Neonatal Medicine, 14 March 1978. With Alastair Dudgeon, Dean of the Institute of Child Health, left, and Leolin Price, barrister, chairman of the executive committee right

there was a change of government in 1974, and the whole scheme was shelved and it was back to square one again. I later went back to Action Research with a new application of £200,000 for the construction of a new building to house the university department of paediatrics and neonatal medicine, and to be designated the Action Research Perinatal Building. They were prepared to support my appeal with one major proviso, that the building would be completed within one year, as they were extremely disappointed in the collapse of the hospital rebuilding programme. I had already earmarked a vacant plot of ground on site I was given clearance to use and by using the same architects we had retained for the muscle unit, we duly started drawing up the design plans in parallel with applying to the borough council for permission to proceed with the building. The building was duly completed within the year and officially opened by the Duke of Edinburgh in March 1978.

Further expansion of the muscle unit

The new laboratories provided superb facilities for our muscle research and also galvanised our muscle research group into a closely integrated team. It was also a great advantage working in parallel with Richard Edwards and his group, who were particularly interested in metabolic aspects of muscle function. Richard introduced to adult muscle patients the needle biopsy sampling of muscle he had acquired from muscle biochemical and metabolic studies on Swedish athletes whilst working in Sweden with Bergstrom, and we were later to also introduce needle biopsy as a routine technique in our paediatric practice.

We were also able to provide continuity between the clinical investigations and research in relation to our patients on the one hand, and our basic research in relation to the tissue culture and transplant work on the other. Much of the culture work related to normal and diseased human muscle obtained at biopsy and part of the muscle transplant project involved the introduction of human muscle into the compartment of an immunodeficient strain of mice, which did not reject foreign muscle.

Jan Witkowski continued the tissue culture programme and set up a research programme of studying the motility of cultured muscle as well as skin cells from patients with muscular

Chatting with Elizabeth Hughes, paediatric biochemist

Farewell to Stan Rom, senior registrar, on his appointment to a senior lectureship in the medical school of the university of Medunsa for African students, in Pretoria

Steve Appleyard, Jan Witkowski and Helen Statham from muscle unit

dystrophy, female carriers of muscular dystrophy and control muscle, with some remarkable documentation of the motility of these cells with time lapse cinematography. Jan subsequently spent a year as a postdoctoral fellow in the laboratories of Andrew Engel at the Mayo clinic in Rochester, Minnesota. During his absence we were able to appoint Helen Statham to the post. She had a special interest in the importance of calcium in cells in relation to the pathogenesis of diseased muscle.

Following his return from the States, the research committee of the Muscular Dystrophy Group who were funding his work, suggested Jan undertook a programme of retraining in molecular genetics, in order to pursue research in this growing field. After a period working in the Cancer Research Institute and then in the MRC laboratories at Mill Hill, he visited the United States again and found a permanent niche there, initially in the molecular genetic laboratory of Tom Caskey in Houston, Texas, and subsequently, as executive director at the renowned Banbury Centre at Cold Spring Harbour, New York, which organises scientific symposia and postgraduate courses in the molecular genetic field, and counts amongst its course faculty many Nobel laureates.

Joe Neerunjen also proved a very productive researcher and produced a number of seminal papers on his work and also completed an excellent thesis for a PhD in the University of London. I have a vivid recollection of the highly unusual and somewhat unconventional viva he had in defence of his thesis. Professor Lewis Wolpert of the Department of Cell Biology at the Middlesex Hospital Medical College within the university had been designated by London University as internal examiner and convenor, and two additional external examiners were appointed and I was present as observer, as his supervisor. Lewis Wolpert arranged a meeting of the examiners in his office ahead of the viva, and, after some discussion and input from each examiner, asked if all were agreed the thesis was of a high standard and there was no question at all of the candidate having fulfilled the requirements for the degree. After this consensus, he called the candidate in, who showed the usual signs of anxiety and fear at having to face the judges. Lewis then opened the discussion by congratulating him and telling him that the examiners had agreed that his thesis was of sufficient calibre for him to have passed the examination. So he could now relax whilst the examiners went through the full process of interrogating him on his research. I was quite amazed at the confidence with which he was able to present his data and to deal with a wide range of searching questions. Whilst I was initially quite surprised at the unconventional approach of Lewis Wolpert, I came away feeling this was certainly a very sensible and humane way of assessing a candidate in the face of a satisfactory thesis.

Joe continued his research on a second three-year grant I obtained from the MRC, but when I successfully got an almost unprecedented third round of support, he decided he had to find a secure post and did not wish to continue in an insecure position in scientific research, with very little opportunity of a definitive university post. This also seemed to be compounded by the fact that his wife, who was also a research scientist, had a permanent position in an MRC supported immunology unit. So without any alternative post to go to, he declined the research fellowship and registered unemployed at the local labour exchange, and took on a temporary job as a grave digger, until he eventually landed a secure and fairly senior position with a medical equipment company, as a senior sales representative. I suspect that what attracted him in particular, apart from the security of the position, was a company car and a designated parking area at the company headquarters, the obvious symbols of having arrived. I did feel a twinge of sadness that the insecurity of the whole scientific research system had lost a good researcher with a lot of fire still in his belly.

After Jan Witkowski left for the USA, we appointed Mike Dunn into the post and our research expanded into a new area to study membrane proteins in normal and dystrophic muscle cells. Mike had been working on a membrane protein called spectrin in red blood cells, in the haematology department at Guy's Hospital Medical School, and was now able to follow a similar study in human muscle. There proved to be some serendipity in this work, which involved two dimensional gel electrophoresis of protein extracts from the muscle and analysing the ensuing snowstorm of separated spots, representing separate proteins, for differences between the normal and dystrophic. The novel protein named dystrophin which was later found to be absent in Duchenne muscular dystrophy after an approach from the genetic end, had an 85% homology to spectrin in its composition.

A further expansion of this work was undertaken by another bright biochemist who joined our group, Mike Capaldi, and used lectin binding to study surface glycoproteins in dystrophic human muscle. He found an absence of one particular glycoprotein in a single biopsy sample, which turned out to be merosin, and once again this may have been an advance detection of a protein related to congenital muscular dystrophy, some ten years or more ahead of its eventual detection and characterisation. Unfortunately Mike Capaldi joined the well-known ICI (Imperial Chemical Industries) laboratories after his three-year grant expired and was lost to muscle research. Mike Dunn also introduced immunological studies and one of his research fellows, Steve Appleyard, made an important discovery of an increased expression of the major histocompatability antigens (HLA) in the membrane of muscle with inflammatory disorders, which had diagnostic importance in muscle biopsies.

A number of other scientists worked with Mike Dunn in ensuing years, and completed PhD theses, including Arthur Burghes, who was very enthusiastic about pursuing research in Spinal Muscular Atrophy, but the Muscular Dystrophy Group was not prepared to support any genetic research outside the small number of designated laboratories, such as those of Williamson at St Mary's or Kay Davies in Oxford, so he upped and offed to the United States, initially working in the laboratory of Ron Worton in Canada, and then establishing his own laboratory in Columbus Ohio, and still continuing in the vanguard of Spinal Muscular Atrophy research up to the present. Another associate was Ketan Patel, who then moved to do postdoctoral research at the Imperial Cancer Research laboratories and now has a definitive university senior lectureship in the Veterinary College in London, and is back in the muscle field with the study of genes controlling muscle development. Thomas Voit also spent some years with Mike Dunn at the bench as a sideline to his clinical work and now heads a paediatric unit in Essen in Germany and is a leading figure in the neuromuscular world.

As the old adage goes, a prophet is not without honour save in his own country, and in his own house. And so it was with

Mike Dunn, who was never fully appreciated by the Muscular Dystrophy Group, who regularly undervalued the proteomics he was doing some ten years or more before it became mainstream. This was perhaps most graphically illustrated when he successfully landed a major grant from the European Union, in collaboration with a physicist and computer scientist at Queen Mary College, of some quarter million pounds, to set up a powerful computing system for the automated comparison and quantitation of gels between normal and diseased muscle. When he wrote to inform the Muscular Dystrophy Group of the fantastic windfall, he got a letter back from Arthur Buller, the secretary to the research committee, not congratulating him, but requesting him to provide reassurance to the Group that he was not distracted by his new development and was still able to fulfil his obligations to the Muscular Dystrophy Group for the work they were funding. Mike was in a state of shock and disbelief when he told me of this. I had to constrain him from writing to the Group resigning from the project they were supporting. So when he was later appointed to a senior post in charge of the research laboratories at the Cardiology Institute, working with the eminent heart transplant surgeon Magdi Yacoub, he felt no qualms about taking all his sophisticated equipment with him, and I had no valid objection to this and was happy to agree a nominal contribution from Yacoub to our laboratory funds. Mike is now a professor of biochemistry at King's College London.

Mike Dunn's successor was Peter Strong, a biochemist from University College, with special expertise in relation to ion channels, who had expert knowledge of scorpion and other venoms, include bee venom, which directly influenced various channels, especially the potasssium channel. Peter's main research interest in specific muscle disorders was in relation to myotonic dystrophy. He supervised the PhD theses of three research fellows, Angela Clerk, Tim Sherratt, and Barry Brewster.

One of my key associates over the years in relation to both our diagnostic and research programme has been Caroline Sewry. She had worked with Everson Pearse on a special three-year training grant Pearse had obtained from the Muscular Dystrophy Group, and joined my group soon after I moved to Hammersmith and has been a mainstay in the Unit ever since. Her expertise has been in muscle pathology, but more specifically the new

Caroline Sewry, expert on muscle pathology and immunohistochemistry

Francesco Muntoni, paediatric neurologist and molecular scientist

technology of immunohistochemistry for immunological recognition of specific proteins with selective antibodies to the proteins. This area has snowballed in recent years following on the recognition of specific proteins in many individual muscle disorders and then raising antibodies to these proteins. This in turn provides a powerful diagnostic tool for identifying the presence, reduction, or absence of the individual protein, either biochemically with gel electrophoresis and blotting techniques, or directly in the muscle biopsy sections, which has been the main approach in our laboratories.

Caroline was originally a BSc graduate in Zoology from Aberystwyth University. She did a PhD thesis on calcium in normal and diseased muscle, using a sophisticated technique of electron microscopic microprobe analysis, which provided localisation at a sub cellular level, as well as quantitation. We had a very enthusiastic collaborator in this work, a very dynamic and somewhat hyperactive pathologist from the Hadassah Medical School in Jerusalem, Rena Yarom, who had been working on this technique in close collaboration with basic scientists at the Rutherford laboratories in Cambridge, and was now keen to work with Caroline on the study of human tissues. She was remarkably productive in turning out high quality papers almost simultaneously with completing the work and was regularly studying a whole range of diseases.

In parallel with the laboratory work we also had an expanding weekly muscle clinic and steadily reorganised things so that we could deal with new patients together with patients coming back for discussion of biopsy results, alternating with follow-up clinics.

We also established a muscle biopsy review session in the labs each week for discussion of biopsies, and I encouraged the clinicians to start taking a special interest by usually calling on one of our new residents to give an opinion of the sections projected on the screen. There was usually a stunned silence until I broke the ice by saying, 'Well tell us what you see. What is the tissue? Do you think it looks like muscle?' 'Yes'. ' How do you know?' And they then found themselves describing the basic features. Next question 'Do you think it is normal or abnormal?'. And so on. Within two to three sessions they were all giving very authoritative commentaries and also feeling part of the system. I also encouraged the laboratory people to join me in the clinic and, subject to approval of the family, it was also important for them to get some idea of the disorders they were researching.

On one occasion we had a site visit from the research committee of the Muscular Dystrophy Group. I had to excuse myself when I had a call from the physiotherapy department to come and see a boy who had just been rehabilitated in callipers. I asked Professor Huxley, Nobel Laureate for his fundamental work on muscle contraction and chairman of the research committee, if he would like to come along with me. He was fascinated with the boy having got ambulant again in callipers after losing the ability to walk. He also confided to me how happy he was to have seen his first case of muscular dystrophy.

PA par excellence

Another key figure in the team was my long-suffering secretary, Val Chalk, who joined me as a part-time research secretary soon after I took up the chair at Hammersmith. She remembered me from my early days in the Pearse laboratory in the late fifties, when she had just started as a secretary with Professor Harrison, the chairman of the pathology department. As her young family grew she increased her weekly sessions until she ultimately succeeded my academic secretary Liz Montgomery, in a full-time capacity. Val was one of the last of a unique generation of all-purpose, multi-potential secretaries, who were able to take dictation by shorthand from normal speech and could type with the then state-of-the-art, golf-ball IBM typewriter at such an incredible speed and accuracy that she had to slow down intermittently for the spinning ball to catch up. She also ran all the affairs of the academic department, kept my diary, and dealt with most of my mail during my extended absences. In addition she helped me with the preparation of my books and was a meticulous proofreader. When she retired in 1986, I had to appoint a full-time administrative PA to succeed her and two junior secretaries to do the day-to-day work.

Photographic records

I was also keen to maintain the photographic work in relation to our clinical and investigative muscle programme, which I had

With Val Chalk, secretary, and Audrey Begent, muscular dystrophy family care officer

Karen Davidson, photographer to the muscle unit, at her retirement party

Sylvia Hyde, head of physiotherapy department, and John Heckmatt, Nattrass Memorial Lecturer

been able to establish in Sheffield. The Postgraduate Medical School had an excellent audio-visual department and I was once again able to build up a collaboration for routine clinical photographic records, I personally continued to take colour slides of all the biopsies, which I personally assessed on my Zeiss photomicroscope, as I had done in Sheffield, whilst Christine Hutson produced a record of black and white prints of the biopsy slides. In relation to the clinical photography, which still formed a routine component of our clinical assessment, I initially got a lot of help and support from the head of the audiovisual department of the school, Bill Brackenbury, and later Doig Simmonds, and his photographers, in particular David Hawtin. As the volume of work expanded beyond their capacity to keep pace, I managed to obtain support for a dedicated photographer as part of our centre grant from the Muscular Dystrophy Group. Amongst the clinical photographers I recruited were Lindsay White and later Karen Davidson, who stayed a considerable number of years and was not only an excellent clinical photographer, who never seemed to picture a sad child, but also actively documented the results of laboratory studies. I was able to write a photographic technician into our centre research grant for several years, partly on the grounds of documenting research data and partly on freeing up the time of the clinicians or researchers who would otherwise be doing their own photographic work.

The longstanding association of Christine Heinzmann (Hutson) came to an abrupt and unexpected halt, after the birth of her twins and their earlier move from South London to the green pastures of Aylesbury. Christine found herself in a cleft stick and unable to get any home help or any support services in Aylesbury, such as a crèche for the care of her infants, and was thus catapulted into an unplanned and reluctant retirement. We only met up very intermittently over the subsequent years, with special occasions in relation to the muscle unit, but had a totally surprise meeting again recently. As a longstanding devotee of the excellent service of Virgin Atlantic airline, I had achieved gold card status in their flying club. From time to time I had invitations to Richard Branson's social events, which I did not take up, until an irresistible one to a dinner at the Cinnamon Club restaurant in the old Westminster library building in central London. Lil and I anticipated a quiet sit down dinner with perhaps 50 or 100 people and were stunned to find a crowd of several hundred, tightly packed into the premises, partaking of a constant service of sumptuous finger snacks and entertained by various musical and other entertainment groups. Lil and I also realised immediately we were totally outside the age bracket and felt our presence had nudged the average age up marginally from around 40 years. And we did not recognise a single soul until I unexpectedly bumped into Christine. We both simultaneously called out 'What are you doing here?' Turned out her question was more appropriate than mine. Whilst I was still an indigent academic, gaining my brownie points with Virgin for my frequent travels in premium economy, Peter had risen to the upper echelon of his pharmaceutical profession as a director in Merck, and was a frequent traveller in upper class. It was the first time that either of us had taken up the Virgin invitation.

Nattrass Memorial Lectureship

One of the major scoops we had for our muscle unit was the Nattrass Memorial Lectureship of the Muscular Dystrophy Group. When Professor Fred Nattrass, a much respected and revered Professor of Medicine at Newcastle University and founder of the Muscular Dystrophy Group, died, the Group launched an appeal to establish a permanent lectureship in his memory. There was an open competition for the award and I was able to make a strong case for a lecturer at Hammersmith, to have a full clinical and research commitment to our muscle unit and to move on to a senior clinical post after completing his training and possibly a higher degree with us. We were successful in our bid, and I was able to advertise for the post and appointed John Heckmatt, who had just completed a full paediatric training in Leeds. When I telephoned my friend and paediatric colleague, Professor Dick Smithells, for a reference he spoke very highly of him; a very congenial person, a very sound clinician, an extremely dedicated person and totally committed to his clinical responsibilities. Only reservation he had, that he was at times a little short on social graces. John proved to be very gentle and kind with our patients and their parents, achieved good rapport and cooperation from them, and also acquired good expertise for doing electrodiagnostic procedures, and also needle muscle biopsies.

John Heckmatt presents a poster at the Medical Research Society on ultrasound imaging of muscle in neuromuscular disorders

Ultrasound imaging of muscle

John Heckmatt approached me unexpectedly one day with a completely new initiative he had thought of. He had obviously become a bit envious of the work of another research fellow I had on the newborn unit, Malcolm Levene, who was doing routine ultrasound imaging on all the newborn babies coming through our neonatal intensive care unit. This powerful new tool was giving us for the first time a window on the brain so that we could routinely identify bleeding or other lesions in the brain, even in infants with no apparent clinical abnormality.

John had thought of applying a similar approach to visualising muscle, in order to detect pathological changes. He had discussed this with Sydney Leeman, a physicist in the medical physics unit, and they then set about doing some exploratory scans with one of the early prototype static B scanners, in the medical physics department, with which one had to move the imaging head to an fro across the tissue to be scanned and to gradually build up an image. This was completely virgin territory and the results were remarkable. In normal muscle there is hardly any echo so that the area remains dark on the image but there is a strong echo from the underlying bone so it appears white. One can also see the demarcation between the muscle bellies caused by the surrounding muscle sheath. In striking contrast, when one looked at a dystrophic muscle, it was like a snowstorm with a tremendous increase in the echo and a loss of the underlying bone image.

So here was an instant screening tool for a muscular dystrophy. They were then able to look at earlier cases and to show that one could already see an increase in echo even before one could detect any obvious weakness in that muscle. As the technology became more sophisticated and the machines more portable, one could rapidly scan several muscle groups of children in the outpatient muscle clinic with a real time linear array machine and get an instant printout of the image.

John Heckmatt was able to publish several papers on ultrasound imaging of various muscle diseases and also to show selective involvement of individual muscles specific to individual diseases. He also completed an excellent doctorate in medicine thesis on the work, and developed a quantifying system for the imaging in collaboration with another expert physicist, which was sensitive enough to pick up changes in symptom free carriers of Duchenne dystrophy. Unfortunately John was neither a good salesman nor a good ambassador for the technique and did not have the fire in his belly to popularise it.

Some years later it was rediscovered in America and some very sophisticated, very expensive machines were produced, but it never found the practical application in the USA it did in the clinics in the UK and also in a number of European centres. This was mainly because the radiologists in the USA had a monopoly on any imaging and it could thus not readily be done as a simple screening tool in an outpatient clinic, performed by a mere clinician, but was looked upon as a special investigation, needing referral to the radiology department and attracting an appropriate fee.

It is thus not surprising that the much more expensive imaging techniques, which could only be done in the imaging departments, such as Computerised Tomography (CT) scanning, and Magnetic Resonance Imaging (MRI), which are also many-fold more expensive, superseded the ultrasound imaging. On the positive side, MRI can provide a lot more information about individual muscles, selectively involved in individual diseases, by imaging a cross-section of a whole limb.

John found a niche for himself in a consultant paediatric post based on community paediatric services with a fair component of rehabilitation work.

Kay Davies, molecular scientist and longstanding collaborator in research on muscular dystrophy and spinal muscular atrophy

He was succeeded in the Nattrass Memorial Lectureship by Francesco Muntoni, a clinician from Sardinia with a specialist training in childhood neuropsychiatry (the standard paediatric neurology training in Italy), who had a longstanding interest in muscle diseases and had also spent a period of research at the bench in our Muscle Laboratories. He was later to succeed me as director of the Muscle Unit and was also promoted initially to senior lecturer, and subsequently to a professorship. With the expansion of the muscle unit, his professorship released the Nattrass Lectureship to which Eugenio Mercuri, a paediatric neurologist from Sicily with a dual interest in newborn neurology and neuromuscular disorders, was appointed. He recently moved to a chair of paediatric neurology in Rome.

A major development for the muscle unit in the 1980s was its designation by the Muscular Dystrophy Group as one of a handful of Muscle Centres nationwide. This was on the basis of clinic excellence in parallel with an active research programme. A new post we were able to successfully apply for as part of our annual centre grant was a trainee clinical fellowship, to train young paediatricians in muscle disorders, so that they could have a comprehensive training in muscle diseases and also complete a research project on a selected area of research, before ultimately becoming a consultant paediatrician. Amongst those appointed to this post, were Jo Philpot, Fiona Goodwin, Alison Sansome, Neil Thomas, and Nathan Hassan.

We were also able to establish a long-term collaboration with Kay Davies in Oxford, one of the pioneers in the search for the gene of Duchenne muscular dystrophy. Having obtained a research grant from the American Muscular Dystrophy Association to initiate research into spinal muscular atrophy, one of the most severe common and disabling muscle disorders in childhood, I stimulated her interest in it and set up a collaborative programme in the search for the gene. Our collaboration has continued to the present day.

Muscle laboratories torched by an arsonist

I was awoken in the early hours one morning in October 1990 by a very distressed Peter Strong and told that the muscle unit on top of the roof of the main hospital was ablaze and completely destroyed. I rushed in to the hospital to be greeted by the scene of complete destruction of our laboratories and the firemen still actively engaged in controlling and confining the fire and preventing it moving to the hospital wards below.

The fire had started after midnight on a Saturday night and had only been discovered by chance after a nurse in a ward on the ground floor below detected the smell of smoke. It turned out to be the work of an arsonist, as we later found the telltale zigzag burn scar on the floor of one of the laboratories, where the arsonist had poured an inflammable liquid onto the floor.

We suspected it might be the anti-vivisection and animal rights group, who were committing acts of violence and attacks on animal facilities and laboratories at the time. Ironically our own research programme was mainly in relation to human disease and analysis and study of human muscle and not geared at all to any invasive animal work. It was also unusual for such protest groups not to publicly claim responsibility, but possibly there was reluctance because it could easily have led to a major disaster if the fire had taken hold and possibly affected the hospital wards below.

Another possibility was someone with a grudge against the hospital, or simply an impulsive arsonist. This possibility was also pursued by the police and suspicion centred on one employee who had been dismissed the previous week, but no connection

Devastation after the arson of our muscle laboratories in October 1990

could be established. The person would have needed to have an intimate knowledge of the building complex, as he came up through a back staircase and got access to the laboratories via a back route.

The scene in the labs after the conflagration was one of complete desolation. All the equipment was damaged beyond repair and a lot of material was lost, as well as archival data. Angela Clerk and Tim Sherratt lost a large component of the data for their PhD theses and Angela was so despondent that she was considering giving up her whole scientific research programme. But she eventually rallied together what material she had and was able to complete sufficient additional work to successfully prepare and defend her thesis. One remarkable survivor of the fire was our −80°C upright storage refrigerator for frozen biopsy specimens. Although the outside was black and contorted the contents were still frozen when the machine was opened.

The Muscular Dystrophy Group rallied to our aid and immediately set up a special appeal fund to help resuscitate the unit. The President of the Group, Richard Attenborough, came to visit us in person within days of the fire and to launch the appeal and provide publicity on the news media. I very much

Muscular Dystrophy Research at The Hammersmith

In the early hours of Sunday 21 October 1990 the Jerry Lewis Laboratories, home of the School's research effort in muscular dystrophy, were gutted by fire. Although arson is suspected there has been no evidence as to who might have been responsible.

The laboratories were built in 1974 with the generous help of a grant from the Muscular Dystrophy Association of America. The staffing and recurrent costs of the research programme have been provided by the Muscular Dystrophy Group of Great Britain and the research unit has become one of the foremost centres in the UK for research into muscular dystrophy and related neuromuscular disorders in children.

Fortunately no-one was hurt as a result of the fire but there has been a substantial loss of research material, some of it irreplaceable. Almost miraculously some written material has been able to be salvaged and some precious patient samples held in liquid nitrogen also survived the disaster. Much was lost however, and much work will be needed to replace the material, where it is possible to do so.

The building was of course insured, as were the contents, and a project team has been set up to ensure the laboratories are rebuilt as soon as possible. In the meantime temporary accommodation has been found for the research team within the Department of Histopathology and this should be available after January 1991.

The Muscular Dystrophy Group of Great Britain has launched an appeal to help meet the inevitable costs that will arise and we hope that together with the insurance money we will be able to put back a significantly better building than its predecessor. Sadly we cannot put back the research work quite as easily.

Brochure produced by the Royal Postgraduate Medical School, after the disastrous fire in the muscle laboratories in October 1990, to launch the rebuilding programme, Project Phoenix appreciated the obvious personal concern of this passionate and humane man. It was very moving to receive so many donations with personal messages from a whole range of people and amounts ranging from a substantial personal contribution from Chris Bland, chairman of the Hammersmith group hospital board, to a few coins dropped into a box by indigent patients. The firemen who had been involved in extinguishing the fire also had an appeal amongst their colleagues and made a substantial contribution.

One of the most touching was a few months later when I was an invited speaker at a satellite muscle symposium in Yokohama, in conjunction with the International Child Neurology Association Congress in Tokyo. The scientists and clinicians participating in the symposium had passed a box around for personal donations and at the closure of the meeting handed me an envelope with a substantial contribution of Japanese yen for our rebuilding programme. I felt very embarrassed and expressed a bit of diffidence in accepting it. But they then explained that this was an absolutely normal procedure in Japan, and if any relative or friend suffered any grievous loss, it was imperative for everybody to gather round and provide financial or other supportive help.

Fortunately our building belonged officially to the Postgraduate Medical School, although located on the roof of an existing hospital building. This meant that it was covered under the general insurance policy of the school and we were thus able to get some insurance funds as well for the rebuilding programme. If it were under the hospital ownership, it would not have been insured at all, as all hospital property comes under indemnity of the Crown, and goodness knows how many decades it might have taken to get a contribution to the rebuilding.

The most important priority was to get back on the road as rapidly as possible and to set up temporary laboratories for the processing of our muscle biopsies from patients and to also try and get various research projects going again. Through the generosity of Nick Wright, head of the pathology department, together with some vacated quarters alongside the children's wards, we were soon back in full activity again. Peter Strong and all the lab team put in a tremendous effort to get things going and also to ensure that Project Phoenix saw the rebuilding of the laboratories on the same rooftop site, but with a much expanded laboratory facility, as rapidly as possible.

The muscle laboratories reopened in due course, with appropriate pomp and ceremony. We had hoped to attract a substantial contribution again from the American Muscular Dystrophy Association, so that we could continue to designate it as the Jerry Lewis Laboratories, but they were not prepared to give more than a token contribution, comparable to various other individual donors, and as the British Muscular Dystrophy Group's special appeal had raised the major part, we decided after consultation to leave it essentially nameless as the Hammersmith Muscle Research Laboratories. Following my retirement, the laboratories were renamed the Dubowitz Neuromuscular Centre.

Neonatal research

In parallel with the steady expansion of the muscle research, we also saw a steady expansion of neurological research in the newborn unit. Lil had initially started doing some infant welfare clinics to keep her hand in and gradually started doing research sessions, with a view to expanding our Sheffield work on assessing maturity of the newborn infant to assessing normality or abnormality of the premature and full term newborn infant. This culminated in the publication of a monograph on neurological assessment of the newborn, which subsequently was updated to a second edition. Lil was also interested in developing methods of assessing and quantifying neurological development of infants beyond the newborn period. There were also a number of subsidiary studies on the development of hearing and of vision in the preterm and full term newborn infant and we were fortunate in having some very skilled and motivated research fellows from abroad including Anna-Lise Fawer from Switzerland, Ana Morante from Venezuela, Sana Lary from Saudi Arabia, and Linda de Vries from Holland. We also obtained a research fellowship to study ultrasound imaging of the newborn brain, to follow the course of bleeding or insufficiency of circulation in the premature and full term infant and appointed Malcolm Levene, who had completed his basic training in paediatrics and was interested in newborn research. We did a prospective study of ultrasound imaging of a series of 100 consecutive newborn infants, as a purely research procedure without any influence on the clinical management, done by Malcolm Levene, in parallel

(Top left) Pamela Davies, in conversation with Harold Gamsu, neonatologist at King's College Hospital
Jonathan Wigglesworth and Malcolm Levene
David Harvey and Peg Castle (former nurse in charge of Neonatal Unit)
Frances Cowan and Mary Rutherford

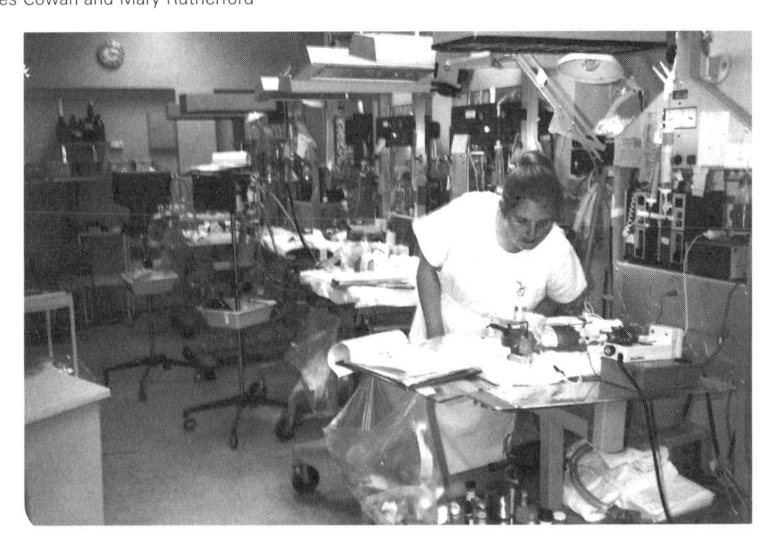

Neonatal intensive care unit with the current charge nurse, Sylvia Watson with a detailed neurological assessment done independently by Lil on the same infants, but recorded separately with no crossing of the data. When the study was completed it was possible to compare the imaging and the clinical data, and two important results came out. Firstly, there were some consistent clinical signs, which related to brain haemorrhage in the premature newborn infant, and secondly one could not predict outcome on the appearance and extent of a haemorrhage, as some neonatologists were doing, but had to take account of the clinic status as well. We subsequently recruited Frances Cowan as a research fellow under an MRC project grant to study cerebral blood flow in the newborn infant by Doppler ultrasound. Frances had been doing basic research in this area in Scandinavia, and this provided another facet to our comprehensive assessment of the neurological status of the newborn infant.

We set up a close collaboration with Professors Robert Steiner and Graeme Bydder, who pioneered the application of magnetic resonance imaging of the brain and other systems, and were able to get in at ground level and were the first to document the maturation of the infant brain on magnetic resonance imaging. This was later expanded to include a detailed study of bleeding and ischaemia (circulatory insufficiency) in the newborn brain

Linda de Vries, recurrent neonatal research fellow, and currently Professor of Neonatal Neurology in Utrecht, and Eugenio Mercuri, neonatal research fellow and later Nattrass Memorial Lecturer, now Professor of Paediatric Neurology in Rome

Members of the neonatal unit and associates in good voice at a party at our home on the occasion of Lil's retirement

and culminated in publication of a colour atlas, in which Lil and I were ably assisted by Linda de Vries, who meticulously collated all the images and data. One of our clinical registrars, Mary Rutherford, became particularly interested in the development of MRI in the newborn brain and made a career of documenting normal and pathological states and was appointed in charge of the paediatric brain imaging programme, and later awarded a personal professorship. She also edited a highly acclaimed textbook on imaging of the newborn brain. Mary has recently been appointed to the newly created chair of paediatric imaging in the department.

Before the advent of the neonatal brain imaging, I was invited to contribute a talk on neonatal neurology at the 50th anniversary meeting of the Association of British Neurologists. I pointed out the difference in approach to the neurology of the newborn and the fact that some of the regular armamentarium of the neurologist, such as the reflex hammer, were unlikely to be of any use in the newborn and might be distinctly hazardous, given that its length exceeded the newborn's. I then demonstrated our special equipment such as a torch to assess visual responses, a bell to assess hearing response, and one's general observation of the infant's behavioural responses.. The one major handicap was that we had no window on the brain, comparable to other organs.

Within a couple of years the whole scenario was to change with the advent of routine imaging of the newborn brain and an opportunity to document imaging changes in parallel with the clinical observation.

Clinical colleagues

After my appointment to the chair, I was very conscious of Jon Scopes' disappointment at not being appointed and I immediately made a recommendation for him to be given a personal chair within the department, which was approved by the university some months later. He was also applying for other chairs and was appointed to the chair at St Thomas' Hospital. To fill the senior lectureship post he vacated, we appointed Simon Godfrey, who had had a scintillating undergraduate career in medicine and topped the list of graduates of the University of London Medical Schools. He had a special interest in respiratory medicine, which opened a new area of clinical expertise within the paediatric service, given the common problem of childhood asthma and related disorders. He also had a very incisive and enquiring research mind and rapidly set up a very productive partnership in collaboration with an experienced technical expert in the medical physics department, Norman Levy. His first project involved the measurement of lung function in small newborn infants in a sealed box in which the whole infant was encased in order to measure the air moving in and out of the lungs. He also refined the oxygen electrodes which had recently been introduced for continuous monitoring of the oxygen saturation in the blood. Simon then conceived a grandiose project, which attracted a substantial five year programme grant from the Wellcome Trust, for setting up a system which would continuously monitor the oxygen saturation in the infant's arterial blood, and would then regulate the ventilator providing the breathing backup for the infant, in order to maintain the oxygen at an optimal level on a continuous and fully automated basis. This was a major programme, passing through several stages, from the initial bench work undertaken by Norman Levy to set up the equipment and test it in the laboratory, through some trials in an animal setup, and finally introducing it into the human situation. Everything seemed to be going very smoothly and coming towards fruition, when Simon was spirited away to a chair of paediatrics at the Hadassah Hospital, Mount Scopus, in Jerusalem. We were able to continue much of the clinical respiratory work in children as well as the newborns, with the appointment of Mike Silverman as his successor, but the very sophisticated experimental work ceased with Simon's departure.

The Neonatal Unit continued to make major contributions in relation to magnetic resonance imaging of the newborn brain, and subsequently achieved a world first in having a dedicated magnetic resonance imaging machine installed on the neonatal unit, so that very ill and delicate premature infants under intensive care on the unit could have their brain imaging done, whilst still under the close surveillance of the neonatal team.

An American visitor is gobsmacked

In the 1970s when Lil and I were working on the neurological assessment of newborn infant, I phoned our audiovisual department at the Hammersmith one morning about the possibility of doing some cine recordings on an infant on the unit. They offered to provide someone the following week on Wednesday! By that time the baby might no longer be with us, having either gone home or perhaps changed considerably in clinical condition, for the better or the worse. So we soon realised there was no alternative to just getting on with it ourselves. So I duly purchased an 8mm cine camera with sound facility and we started to do regular recordings of the preterm and developing infants on our neonatal unit, with Lil demonstrating the clinical features and me at an appropriate vantage point, standing on a chair for the recording, and the two of us having a to and fro discussion on our observations. One morning Laura Ment, a budding neonatologist from Yale doing an extended attachment with Pamela Davies, came onto the unit while we were in action and stood there frozen and open mouthed, watching this unusual spectacle. When we had finished the run, she leaned over to me 'Excuse me professor; is this in your job description?' Quick as a flash I came back 'Indeed; no clinical professor in England can get an academic appointment without a full training in clinical photography!' I guess she is still dining out on some of these quirks of the British system, given that on neonatal units in the

United States at that time, ward rounds were usually conducted in the office or nurse's station and the only one who came anywhere near handling an infant was the junior resident.

8

Family on the move

The growth of my muscle unit in Sheffield in the 1960s was echoed by the growth of my young family, with our four sons, David born in Sheffield in 1963, Michael in 1964, Gerald in New York in 1965, and Daniel in Sheffield in 1969, and the transition from Sheffield to London was in many ways as traumatic and unsettling for them as for the muscle team.

There is often a gradually evolving conflict of priorities between the needs of one's family and the demands of one's department. It is all too easy to concentrate all one's energies on the one, usually the academic, with the neglect of the other. What can be extremely difficult to achieve is an equitable balance between the two, so that neither feels deprived. So I soon found

The four boys in school in London

myself balancing the demands of an active academic and clinical commitment with the needs of my growing family. One of the essentials was to try and identify prime time, which was sacrosanct for the family.

I soon realised that an annual two-week vacation was essentially no vacation at all, as it took me at least a week to unwind from my regular routine, and the last week I was already beginning to worry about the things awaiting my return. So we decided early on in Sheffield to take most of my annual leave entitlement with a four-week break in August, when clinical and academic activities were at a low ebb anyway. This enabled us to plan more extensive travelling and camping holidays. Two of our most successful family holidays, which we were able to repeat in ensuing years, arose out of initial academic contacts.

In the early 1970s, I had an invitation to Finland from a group of clinicians in Helsinki with an active interest in muscle disorders, including paediatricians Marta Donner and Pirkko Santavuori, a paediatric pathologist Juhani Rapola, and an adult neurologist, Hannu Somer. Hannu invited me to come out in the summer to their summer cottage on Saimaa lake (every Finn has a summer cottage on the water somewhere) and I did not give it much further thought until I had a letter from him the following January with pictures of the idyllic place and a suggestion of possible dates. So began a series of most successful family holidays in Finland. I remember coming back on one occasion from an extended holiday and a trip back on a cargo boat, with only a few available cabins and superb service, and bumping into Donald Calne, a neurologist at Hammersmith Hospital, and he was telling me with great gusto of the very successful medical congresses he had just been to and all the exciting new developments and interesting people and activities in Parkinson's disease, his area of special interest. 'And where have you been?' he asked me. 'To Finland'. 'And who did you meet?' 'My family'.

Another very fruitful friendship dating from the 1970s was with Luciano Merlini, a neurologist at the Rizzoli Institute in Bologna, and his wife Claudia Granata, a physician with a special interest in physical therapy and rehabilitation. Luciano initially invited me out to help him set up a muscle unit with full investigative procedures. They were both keen sportsmen and

Holiday at Somer's summerhouse on Saimaa lake, Finland

Fishing

Sawing competition

Judging the sawing results

On one of our recurrent skiing visits to the Selva area in the Italian dolomites with the Merlinis. From left David, Michael, Lil, Gerald and myself

had family links and facilities in the Gardena Valley near Selva in the dolomites, and invited us to join them for a skiing holiday. As both Lil and I had missed the critical period for downhill skiing and thought it potentially hazardous to try and indulge at our advanced stage of life, we opted for cross-country skiing instead and that has continued to be one of our main winter holiday pleasures since. The children understandably were more enthusiastic on the downhill and became very proficient skiers.

We were quite happy to send all our children through the state school education system and did not aspire to private education for any of them. We felt the money was better spent on these trips abroad or providing them with extra tuition in either their academic subjects or extramural activities.

After our move to London, all the boys went through the Brooklands primary school, which had a phenomenal headmistress, Miss Morris, who not only seemed to know all the pupils in her school by name, but was also able to produce the most incisive assessments of their character in the open evenings for parents. This was from personal contact as she ensured she did not spend all her time ensconced in her office but did at least one weekly session with each of the separate classes.

David's choice of secondary school

On reaching 11 years, application had to be made for secondary school and there were various options between, on the one hand, the state-supported grammar schools, the so-called secondary modern schools, with no major academic orientation, and the newly-introduced comprehensive schools attempting to integrate the two, and on the other hand opting for private education in the time honoured, so-called Public Schools.

If one had a choice of which area to live in, this was often influenced by the availability of good schools in the area, which in turn was reflected in the higher house prices.

Inevitably the state schools in an area where many of the parents were highly motivated and demanding professionals were of a high standard and as we had always favoured a state-supported schooling system, having both come from a similar environment in the colonies, we were happy to go for the local grammar school, Christ College. However several colleagues we spoke to were singing the praises of University College School in Hampstead, which had a high rating as a public school, but was also a direct grant grammar school with about ten places subsidised by the state. So we felt there was nothing to lose letting David sit the entrance exam for UCS. It was certainly a very impressive school with a very motivated staff, but had perhaps one drawback for David that it was traditionally much more oriented to the classics rather than the sciences. David won a place, so we left the final choice to him. He decided on Christ College for two reasons. Firstly it had a much better design and technology department, with wood and metal work, technical drawing and design facilities, which particularly attracted him, and secondly it was compulsory to play rugby at University College and he didn't fancy that. It is amusing that some years later when he went to Cambridge, one of his first activities was to join the rugby club. So much for coercion.

At the end of the day, the quality of a school is to a large extent influenced by the quality of the headmaster, and in Christ College there was a superb head in Mr James, who was an obvious inspiration to his staff as well as the students. There were also a number of outstanding teachers in the 6th form who were quite inspirational for the A-level students.

David gets lost on Table Mountain

When we spent a month in Cape Town in 1977, David got a temporary place in the senior year in Herzlia School. Within the first week, he became very friendly with Sydney Jacobs, the son of a local lawyer, who was a very good student and also an all round sportsman and something of a daredevil, who used to go scrambling solo up Table Mountain most Sundays. David asked me if it would be okay for him to go up Table Mountain with Sydney the first Sunday we were there and I said I would first need to know all the details. It turned out they would go up and also down Nursery Ravine, near Kirstenbosch botanical gardens, and as this is rated as an easy hike I agreed. They were also supposed to be accompanied by or meeting up on top at the reservoir with several other scholars from their year.

In the course of the week I became concerned that the arrangements kept changing and in particular their starting time was moved to 11 am, which I thought unusually late for going up the mountain. They duly set off after 11 am that Sunday, a reasonably clear and sunny day. About 6 pm we had an anxious call from Sydney's father that he did not want to alarm us but he was extremely concerned as Sydney was always down by 3 in the afternoon. So he had contacted the mountain rescue service, who said that there was unfortunately nothing they could do as there was a heavy mist on the mountain and it was already getting dark and as they had no idea where the boys might be they could not send out a search party.

They suggested that if they had said they would be coming down nursery ravine the best would be for us to go the trailhead at Kirstenbosch and wait for them there.

A few extremely anxious hours followed and it was well after 9 pm that the two of them finally appeared, not down Nursery ravine but coming along the pipe track. Although they went up nursery ravine, about half way up Sydney said this was a rather boring walk and too easy, so sidetracked laterally and went up an almost vertical rock face, followed by David who was a complete novice on the mountain. They duly got to the top but none of their friends turned up at the meeting place. So after a light meal and a short wait, they decided to head down as a heavy mist was coming over the mountain and visibility was fading. Sydney suggested it would be preferable to go down Skeleton Gorge than back on Nursery as it would be as easy as Nursery, and would provide some variety. There is, however, one section of Skeleton Gorge where there is a fixed ladder, which is easy going up but can be more difficult coming down, especially in poor visibility. What they had not bargained for was a section of the ladder had disintegrated and was missing. There was no possibility of going back and finding an alternative route and it also did not seem practical to stay put, as they had no protective clothing. So their only option was to negotiate this fairly steep rock face where the ladder was missing, without any ropes or gear.

We were all greatly relieved by the safe outcome. The following day, after his shock had settled, and mine, I told David that I had no objections to him hiking up or climbing the mountain but there were some very important basic rules which one had to abide by and he and Sydney had broken them all! I bought for both him and Sydney a copy of the excellent book of the Mountain Club of South Africa on hikes on Table Mountain, which spelled out five basic rules in bold font on the back cover. Essential to always plan full details of the itinerary, to inform friends or relatives the route of ascent and descent and the expected time and to always take protective clothing in case of change of weather.

The following week David was keen to go up with Sydney again. I said this was fine but I was coming as well! Sydney's father had exactly the same response. He also brought along a friend of his, who accompanied him on the fateful evening and 'knew the mountain'. This friend duly arrived for the following Sunday's outing at the trailhead of nursery ravine, decked out in full military dress, complete with a Sam Browne belt and shoulder strap, and revolver in holster. When I asked him why the revolver, he responded with obvious concern, 'Man, you never know when you may meet a snake!' In all my years of hiking up the mountain, I had never encountered a snake, although there certainly are poisonous snakes including adders and cobras about. I guess our friend had probably never been up the mountain before. Moreover, if he tried to shoot a snake there was a greater danger of the bullet ricocheting off a rock and hitting one of us. Our younger sons Mike and Gerald also came along. Sydney was keen to take us up on the same detour up Nursery as the previous Sunday but when we were faced with a 30-foot almost vertical rock face, we insisted he get back to the regular path and his senses. Getting to the top of Table Mountain is always exhilarating and the views in all directions are spectacular. What many don't realise is that the top is a plateau, with easy walks in all directions, and extends from the table face, so familiar in pictures, for several miles toward Constantia in the south and looks down on the Atlantic coastline on the west side. But one needs to have a healthy respect for the mountain and every year several students from the university and others lose their trail and fall down an unexpected precipitous waterfall to their death. In fact, my mother was so concerned at the recurrent newspaper reports of students falling off Table Mountain, that I had to give her a faithful promise never to go rock climbing. The enthusiasm of the boys for the mountain increased and on return to London they joined the local YMCA climbing club in Tottenham Court Road to use the artificial wall. Gerald in particular became completely hooked.

David was a keen sportsman at school but keener on individual sports rather than team ones and became quite a competent swimmer. On one occasion he participated in a charity swim and solicited sponsorship from our friends on a per length basis (25 metres). One of my paediatric colleagues was in a fairly generous mood and gave quite a generous amount, thinking in terms of a final donation based on about 10 lengths. In the event David rose to the occasion and just kept on swimming all afternoon, logging up a massive 140 lengths. As this would have set him back quite a considerable sum, my colleague started bargaining with David for a fixed amount as a compromise. However, I took a firm line and told him that it was very unsporting of him to try and negotiate a compromise deal after David had put in such a Herculean effort to rise to the challenge. He duly provided an appropriate cheque and David was very proud of his substantial contribution to a worthy charity.

David thrived in the Christ College environment and particularly also took advantage of the design and technology facilities.

He was clearly heading in the direction of a career in science with a leaning towards engineering. His final inspiration came from one of the annual Christmas lectures at the Royal Institution that we regularly took the boys to, when lucky enough to get tickets. This one which came at a critical time of David reaching his A-level stage at school was by Heinz Wolf on advances in bioengineering in monitoring human functions and its increasing role in medical research and practice. David was absolutely set on following a career in that direction. So he arranged a visit to Heinz Wolf, who gave him a lot of encouragement and one very sound bit of advice. He would be far better off doing a basic training in medicine and adding on the engineering, and remain in charge of his own programme, rather than qualifying in engineering and running the risk of playing a secondary role to the work of clinicians.

Fantz Box; American optical company patents David's design

Whilst David was still in his A-level class at Christ College school, we gave him a challenge in design. Lil and I had been interested for some years in visual maturation of the premature and fullterm newborn infant, which we had studied with the well-known Fantz box. This is a fairly large structure in which the infant is placed in a seat on one side and the observer watches the infant through a peephole on the other and notes the deviation of the infant's eyes to one or other side, when presented with boards containing two black and white geometrical images alongside each other. If the infant can distinguish between them he will look to the more complex one. One can also test visual acuity with parallel black and white stripes of decreasing width. During a visit to Japan in 1979 for a congress, we had a specific request to demonstrate the system at the neonatal unit of a local hospital in Tokyo. So the challenge to David was to produce a portable Fantz box, which we could take with us. The constraints we gave him was that it had to fold up flat and go into a standard Marks and Spencer carrier bag as hand baggage. He rose to the occasion and produced a very effective unit, the frame of which was of thin plywood and hinged with a piano hinge so it could be readily folded. The innovative part was a bright idea to paste the design cards in pairs onto an aluminium sheet, which slotted into the wooden frame. Instead of a peephole on the box itself, he placed the peephole in the centre of the aluminium sheet. By placing the images on both sides of the aluminium he could provide the six basic variants on a total of only three sheets. The system proved very successful and I encouraged him to write a short report on the new invention, which I submitted on his behalf to *The Lancet*. It was accepted for publication, and duly appeared. When he modestly remarked that it had probably been accepted simply because I had sent it, I had to point out to him that my success rate was not as good as his, and I more frequently had *The Lancet* rejecting my papers. A couple of years later, Lil happened to attend a conference in London on visual acuity in infants, also attended by a well-known expert on visual function in infants, Janet Atkinson from Cambridge. A contributor from the United States presented a paper on a new system for assessing visual acuity in infants, the so-called Seattle method, using cards with pairs of images and a peephole in the centre for quick assessment, identical in format to David's, which they were marketing at 1000 dollars a set. When Janet Atkinson asked the speaker in what way her method differed from that described by David Dubowitz in a publication in *The Lancet*, she responded 'What publication?'

In his final A-level year, David duly applied within the university clearance system, where candidates can select up to five universities of their choice in priority order. He made a lot of enquiries about the best medical schools having an option for some parallel training in biophysics and eventually secured a place at University College London. He then decided to take a year out, which is a very good option within the British university system, where candidates can elect to defer entry to their allocated place for a year. They can then do something of their own choice, such as simply seeing the world or doing some selective work. We always encouraged it as a great asset for maturation and generally becoming more worldly wise, and although initially we had some concerns in delaying their chosen career, in the long term the slight loss of time was more than compensated by additional experiences.

It was purely by chance that David stumbled on an opportunity of spending time at the internationally renowned California

Institute of Technology (Caltech). When a paediatric friend of ours in California heard of David's search for some activities abroad during his year out, and his special interest in bioengineering, she said she would talk to a medical colleague whose partner was on the faculty at Caltech. Not long after David got offered a six-month elective in the bioengineering department under Professor Derek Fender. It had all arisen as a result of a misunderstanding and divergence of American and British English. When David had sent a short CV and said he had just finished school and was taking a year out before taking up a place in university, they thought he was a graduate, who had completed his first degree and was awaiting entry into medical school, comparable to the USA.

It was only when he actually got to Caltech that the confusion was realised but they found a way around and were able to provide him an 'official' position as handyman to the department and he spent time putting up shelves and other odd jobs, and making use of his previous design and technology studies to build small pieces of equipment for them in their workshop, as well as constructing simple electronic devices such as amplifiers for the research projects. He also then had access to the computers, which he instinctively enjoyed tinkering with, and was soon able to help one of the graduates with computer analysis related to his PhD research. This short attachment was to provide a basis for a return to Caltech some years later and to obtain a research position and to complete a PhD there.

But after his six months at Caltech he headed for Australia, where he got first hand experience as a labourer on the road construction and earned enough cash to travel most of the eastern half of Australia and to pay for a full training in scuba diving off the barrier reef.

David had the chutzpah to phone around all heads of admission for the individual Cambridge colleges personally the day his A-levels came out and ask them whether they had any candidates who had not made the grade and if they would be prepared to interview him instead. Many colleges still wanted him to sit the Cambridge entrance exam but he got an interview at Girton based on his A-level results alone. They were sufficiently impressed by him calling them up on his own initiative, and the fact that he already had a research position at

Caltech set up for his year off. They were prepared to consider him for the following year, but it would mean going through the UCCA system, and putting down Cambridge as his first choice, which would at the same time mean releasing his place at University College, and putting them as his second choice. David realised this was too big a gamble to take, as the chances at Cambridge were still small against the strong competition. I advised him to come clean with University College and see whether they would guarantee his place and still allow him to have a crack at Cambridge. He wrote a detailed letter, expressing his total satisfaction with his place at University College but that Cambridge had the unique additional advantage that if he registered for a medical tripos, he would have the option of majoring in any subject in the third year and he was very keen to major in electronic engineering, which Girton College had offered him the possibility of doing. University College were prepared to play ball, so with nothing to lose he applied to Cambridge with University College as his second choice, and he duly got a place at Girton College for the medical tripos. As planned, he eventually left the medics in his third year and joined the third year electronic engineers, and despite a tremendous amount of catching up to do in physics and mathematics, successfully passed the tripos, majoring in electronic engineering. He then had a dilemma of taking up a place in the engineering department, who had offered him an opportunity to do a PhD, or to go back to medicine. He decided if he did the PhD it would be the end of his medical career. So he opted for going back to medicine.

An additional complexity of the Cambridge system was that in view of not majoring in one of the basic medical subjects for his tripos, he was not eligible to join the clinical course at Cambridge but had to look elsewhere. So he secured a place at Oxford and had a very stimulating few years completing his clinical medical training, after which he stayed on for a number of residency posts, including neurology.

David always had a sense of humour as well as a good sense of fun, and was an active participant in the usual student pranks. One of the traditional activities of Cambridge students was to flout the regulations and climb up the spires of the colleges in the dark of night. Extensive mechanical barriers and severe punishments eventually stopped this practice. I was particularly impressed by the appearance of a large banner on Marble Arch to celebrate May Day with the inscription 'May the 4th be with you'. (a pun on the Star Wars catch phrase 'may the force be with you'). Apparently David and a fellow Cambridge undergraduate, Dave Tooth, had managed to scale the high vertical walls of the well-known Marble Arch in the early hours of the morning and attach the banner. They were on their way off after the event, but decided to call the national press from the payphone of a nearby hotel. Shortly after they were confronted by a policeman, whom they reassured that they had just been walking by, when they noted the banner and decided to notify the press. It brought back memories of the stone laying at Lewisham Hospital in 1956.

During one of his summer vacations when at Cambridge, David visited China, going from place to place on local transport. He had intended coming back via the trans-Siberian railway through Russia, but couldn't get a Russian train ticket so decided to fly back via Thailand. At the same time, Michael, who was at Charing Cross Medical School, was having an extended visit to Greece, and having become a bit bored bought a low-priced, special offer round trip fare to Thailand. On a Saturday morning at a busy Bangkok market, David and Michel bumped into each other at the same kebab stand. I wonder what the statistical chances would be of two people buying meat on a stick at exactly the same time in some far flung part of the world, having got there at short notice from diametrically opposite directions.

David eventually got back to Caltech via a somewhat circuitous route, with the usual unexpected coincidences, and joined a group studying neuronal neurophysiology, but working on functional magnetic resonance imaging. He is currently on the faculty of the radiology department of the University of California at San Diego, doing research on functional magnetic resonance imaging of the brain, which has provided a satisfying niche for him to pursue his ongoing interest in bioengineering and medicine.

Michael

When Michael finished his Primary School at Brooklands, there was, as with David, a choice of whether to take up an automatic place, which was available to him at the local grammar school, Christ College, or to pursue, as with David, the alternative route of an assisted place at University College School. We thought that it would be in Michael's interests not to be at the same school, under the potential shadow of his older brother, but to have an opportunity of independent development. He accordingly sat the entrance exam for University College School and although he attained a reasonable level, he missed out by one place.

We were then faced with an unexpected and unusual problem. The local Education Authority decided to make a test case of him and because he had put University College as his first choice and Christ College as his second, they were not prepared to consider him for a competitive place at Christ College, which they could readily fill with all the applicants putting it first and having automatic right to it.

He was accordingly placed at the secondary modern school, which had just become comprehensive and was hoping to cover all levels of ability. This looked like a potential disaster for him and we were concerned that he might not find the necessary academic stimulus in this environment. However, things turned out well, when some three or four academically minded boys found themselves in the same class and provided a micro-environment for achieving a good result at the O-level exams.

He then had an automatic choice for A-levels, as there were available places and opted to move to Christ College, much to the disappointment of the head master at his current school, who was rightly proud of what the school had achieved for some of its pupils. It also turned out to be a less than ideal environment, as he now had to establish new relations with a completely new group of pupils and in addition, some of the examinations they prepared for were the Cambridge Boards rather than the London, with different requirements.

He still managed to get the requisite grades at his A-level exams for entry into medical school at Charing Cross, but may well have had a more expedient passage through his own previous school. Despite our early reservations, Michael was not going to be deviated from his intentions to become a doctor, and eventually sailed through medical school, and proved to be an excellent resident, as epitomised when doing his first surgical residency job with Harold Ellis at Chelsea Westminster Hospital. He had to provide cover for an absentee fellow resident, who had managed to fail his finals at Cambridge and, although taken on as an observer in the post pending his re-writing, was unable to actively take any responsibility for patients. Michael managed a 23-day consecutive on-call commitment without any apparent ruffling of any feathers. Our earlier fears for his choice of career were completely dispelled! He is now a fully-fledged, and fully extended clinical cardiologist.

During the few months prior to taking up his place at medical school, Michael decided to get some work experience and save some pocket money. So he went to the local labour exchange and registered as unemployed. He particularly expressed an interest in working as a dustman. To his surprise he got offered a job soon after. It was very difficult getting part-time or short-term dustman jobs, as there was an apparent closed shop. They must have thought he was a career dustman, perhaps reinforced by his stocky build. He decided not to spill the beans as to his white-collar aspirations. He soon settled in very well with the early morning starts, striking up camaraderie with his workmates and joining them regularly at the local pub after the shift was finished. In fact, one of the incentives for their rapid working practice was to finish their round and make it to the pub before closing time at lunchtime. I was very impressed by the experience Michael got from it and would highly commend it to all aspirant medics as an exercise in communication skills and also insight into other sections of the community.

Mike somehow always seemed a bit accident prone, as we were to learn from a number of episodes over the years. When people asked if we were happy about our boys climbing mountains, Lil was always quick to respond that she was much more concerned about an accident crossing the road or driving a car.

Mike walks into a car and knocks himself out

One day whilst Lil and I were both at a one-day paediatric symposium at Guy's Hospital in southeast London, Mike was on his way home from school in the mid afternoon and, having taken the usual bus to Golders Green station, was crossing the road at the pedestrian crossing when he walked into the side of a moving car and knocked himself out. He has always been a bit of a dreamer, and guess this may have contributed to his lapse of care and attention.

As he seemed to be unconscious, an ambulance was called and he was admitted to the Royal Free Hospital. By that time he was sufficiently *compos mentis* to give his name and address and shortly afterwards a police officer knocked at our door to be greeted by Gerald, aged ten, the only occupant of the house, who had also just come home from school. Being pretty cautious by nature, Gerald refused to open the front door until he was certain of the caller, so conducted the conversation through the letterbox. 'Where are your mother or father?' 'Don't know. I am alone in house. My brother is not yet home from school.' 'How old are you?' 'Ten.' I wonder whether the officer, or possibly even Gerald, was reflecting on the legal negligence of parents leaving a child under 11 alone at home? 'How can I contact your parents; your brother has been in a car accident.' 'I'll phone their friend Louise Scheuer, whose son is my friend.' This he did and the officer explained the circumstances to her and Louise then phoned the secretary in my department at the Hammersmith, with the number provided by Gerald, to get information and we were duly summoned by an announcement in the midst of the symposium and after a phonecall home headed for the Royal Free Hospital.

Mike seemed reasonably alert and awake, although still rather vague about the circumstances of his injury and the period immediately after till he found himself in hospital. He had apparently lost consciousness and presumably was concussed by the impact of his head with the side of the car or the pavement when he fell down.

He was awaiting admission for overnight observation and it was difficult to get any information about his neurological status and examination. He had of course chosen a very inopportune time to have his altercation with the car, as we were flying out to Israel on a long planned trip two days later, and as that was over the weekend, we had to make a decision by the following day whether to postpone our departure by a day or two, to cancel the whole trip, or to continue as planned. Fearing that the neurologists might well just want to keep him under observation over the weekend pending the arrangement of any further imaging or other investigations, I chose to try and short circuit the system by contacting a longstanding senior neurology colleague, PK Thomas, who was professor of Neurology at the Royal Free but not involved in Michael's case. Things remained a cliff-hanger throughout the next day but we were eventually given the option of continuing with the pre-planned travel arrangements, as Michael's condition seemed stable and he was fully alert with no obvious neurological sequelae, despite a rather dramatic facial appearance with two swollen and bruised eyes and side of face. All went well and we all had a very relaxing time, even though Michael bore the facial evidence for his traumatic experience throughout the ensuing week.

Danger on the road

Whilst at medical school, Michael also joined the Charing Cross mountaineering club, which used to arrange regular trips to Wales or the Lake District. On one occasion he told us he was going climbing in the Lake District that weekend. We were rather surprised to get a phone call from him on the Friday evening whether we could come and collect him at Kings Cross station. Apparently the club's minibus had turned over en route to the Lake District. He in fact had a lucky escape as he injured his neck when the vehicle rolled over and a subsequent X-ray revealed a fracture of one of his cervical vertebrae.

Mike disappears into a whirlpool in the Danube

One of our longstanding friendships was with the Denes family in Budapest, and particularly Szusza Denes who had come out to Sheffield in 1963 at the time of David's birth. On one of our many visits to the Denes family we also visited the home of an aunt in Szentendre, and went down to the local bathing place on the Danube. The Danube is very calm in places but also renowned for its strong currents, so needs to be treated with respect, as Lil knew well from her own childhood and being a swimming enthusiast. All seemed fairly calm in the water until Michael got caught in the vortex of a whirlpool and kept bobbing up for a gasp of air and sinking down again. He seemed totally unable to get out of the whirlpool, despite being quite a strong swimmer. Lil rushed to the rescue and moments later was bobbing up and down in unison with him, and both of them seemed to be getting exhausted in their efforts to come above the surface.

Fortunately a local vicar, who was relaxing on the bank, and obviously knew the river well, dived in and managed to pull them out of the whirlpool's current by swimming tangentially to the whirlpool in order to use the centrifugal force of the whirling water to get out of the vortex. In true Michael laid-back style he seemed completely unperturbed and claimed he didn't actually realize he was caught in a whirlpool and was just bobbing up and down to try and touch the bottom to see how deep the river was.

It reminded me of the treacherous rip currents at Llandudno beach in Cape Town, which took unsuspecting swimmers diving into the surf 50 yards or more out to sea by the time they surfaced, and then struggling to get back. Ginger Johnson and his wife pulled several hundred swimmers to safety over the years by moving tangentially with the current and then coming back alongside parallel to it, rather than directly against it.

Up in smoke

During his medical training at Charing Cross, Michael decided to do an intercalated BSc, based at Queen Mary College in the East End of London. He majored in genetics and computing, which later proved valuable in setting him on the course of an academic career in cardiology with a special interest in molecular genetics. During his summer break he applied for a summer post in the laboratories of Dr Kay Davies in Oxford. I was unaware of this application and he was unaware that I had a major collaborative programme with Kay Davies on neuromuscular diseases. She assumed I had pointed him in her direction. He got very valuable hands-on experience in the techniques of molecular genetics and as a *quid pro quo* helped her set up her computer programs and sorting out recurrent gremlins in the system. All seemed to be going very well until the day Michael went off for his lunch break and forgot to turn off the Bunsen burner under a crucible containing radio-active material. Kay rightly decided discretion was the better part of valour and suggested Mike concentrate on the computing and keep clear of the bench work.

I have to add that we did gently dissuade Michael when he subsequently told us he was keen on taking up parachuting, and once again later on when he was keen on flying lessons. While there is no guaranteeing their safety, I think in general it is no bad thing for people who seem accident prone to at least stay on terra firma. On the other hand we were thrilled when he announced he had registered for a training course in sailing, and envisaged leisurely sailing weekends for Lil and myself with him at the helm. However, he did not pursue this sport after duly completing the course.

Mike holds the family record, by a long way, of the number of times his car has been broken into to lift laptop computers and other items he has inadvertently left exposed. But it is not always his fault. Recently sophisticated thieves got into the locked trunk of his BMW car, by a new technique of capturing the code of the electronic locking device and then duplicating it and opening the boot of doctors' cars parked outside the Wellington hospital in St John's Wood. Comparable to the modern crime of thieves stealing credit card details at the bank cash dispensing machines.

Musical interest

A final sequel to Michael's early musical interest was an urge to get a grand piano with the small legacy that an aunt of Lil left for each of the children following her death. As it was a relatively small amount, we were convinced this was pie in the sky for him but told him to search for one himself. This was already during his medical school days. Sure enough, about a week later, he called us urgently on a Sunday, that he had found an advert in the *Sunday Times* for a grand piano which seemed to fit in with his wishes and almost his budget! We accordingly drove out with him on the Sunday evening to an address on the outskirts of Colchester, where a young couple had inherited a grand piano from her deceased mother and could not accommodate it in their cottage. It looked in good condition but we were unable to judge it at all, as all the keys were stuck and unable to produce any sound. As it was a smaller Steinway Grand and they were keen to part with it at a price somewhere in the region of what they

Mike with his saxophone

were offered by the Steinway company, to whom it was of minimal value, as they had to totally recondition it, we phoned Michael's piano teacher Anthea Cohen, a concert pianist, who in turn phoned her Steinway piano tuner, who had only one question, 'What is the serial number?' When we phoned back with the information, we got the immediate response, 'Go ahead and buy it, it is an 1896 original Hamburg production!' The tuner who had been a senior technician until retirement at Steinway's itself, was so enthused by the piano that he offered to personally recondition it, as it seemed to have all the original keys and the only reason it had become somewhat arthritic was because it had not been played for some years. It also had all the original strings and he almost managed to conserve them after replacing the hammer pads and starting to re-tune the strings from outside inwards, until he got to the middle C, at which point it snapped and he had to replace all the strings. Michael still enjoys playing on it as a diversion from his busy career and his progeny, hopefully, seem to have developed an ear for it as well. Michael was also a good clarinettist and during his student years and earned some pocket money playing a saxophone in a dance band on the Saturday evenings for Charing Cross Hospital parties.

Gerald

From an early age, Gerald already showed his ability to organise himself and others and his environment. He took on the role of looking after Daniel who was some three years younger than him and for many years we were convinced that Daniel thought that Gerald was his mother! He has continued to be a natural with children ever since.

His ability to cope with emergency situations and to maintain calm was well illustrated by the episode in connection with Michael's car accident. After the Table Mountain saga with David, all three older boys became interested in rock climbing and we encouraged them to have appropriate training at the climbing wall at the YMCA in central London. Gerald took it much more seriously and within a short period of time became a climbing instructor for young novice climbers. Whilst still at school, he became secretary of the Crag Rats, a group of climbers who used to meet regularly for climbing at various venues. It was at that time that he also became concerned about his intended career in biology, following contact with a large number of unemployed PhDs amongst his climbing friends. He then decided it might be better to pursue his research interests from a basis in medicine rather than in pure biology or science. He was particularly pleased to get a place for his pre-medical training at St Andrew's University in Scotland, which allowed him ready access to the mountains and was later followed by the linked clinical training in Manchester. This was not too far from our cottage in Corris in North Wales in the Snowdonia area, so that he could pursue weekend climbing activities, together with friends.

From the time of his BSc course in physiology at St Andrews University in Scotland, Gerald developed a special interest in high altitude physiology and this formed the basis of his research career to date. He obtained a research grant from the British Heart Foundation which enabled him to purchase sophisticated computerised portable ultrasound equipment for echocardiography, in order to study blood flow dynamics and effects of altitude on the cardiovascular and respiratory systems. He accompanied two British medical expeditions to the Himalayas, one to Everest in 1994 and one to Kangchenjunga in 1998.

As with so many events in our life, Gerald's meeting with his future wife, Debby Miller, followed directly from a series of unlikely events and coincidences. We had been on a visiting professorship to the University of California, embracing various centres within the State University, including Los Angeles, Irvine, San Diego and also San Francisco. I had a fairly hectic lecturing schedule in all these centres and we arranged for the three older boys to fly out direct and join us once we got to San Francisco, and managed to get a place for Daniel at a music camp near Irvine, the start of my lecture tour, through the help of my host paediatrician, Beverley Morgan. Although Daniel was initially very averse to the thought of a music camp, which he looked upon as an extension of his music lessons, it turned out very well for him and he subsequently went back again, of his own accord, on a number of later occasions.

When I got to San Francisco, I already had a very full programme but had a very persuasive invitation from a paediatrician at the Letterman Military Academy Hospital in Golden Gate Park. He and his colleagues were very keen for me to give them a talk on one of my favourite subjects, 'The Floppy Infant'. I told him that I reluctantly had to decline the offer, as I did not have a single free spot as I was already committed to visiting Stanford, the University of California at San Francisco (UCSF) Hospital, and also the Oakland Children's Hospital.

He then tried to persuade me to have a breakfast lecture with them on the morning prior to my other activities. I was still reluctant until he produced an irresistible carrot. I already told him we could not extend our time in San Francisco, as we were heading for a family camping holiday in Yosemite. He informed me that they had a family cottage in Wilsonia, a small private enclave that had remained within the King's Canyon National Park, and as a *quid pro quo*, I would be welcome to have the use of it in return for my lecture. I promptly agreed.

At Wilsonia there was a small provision store for the benefit of the residents there. Whilst doing some food shopping, Lil was looking down into the freezer compartment alongside another shopper, who then turned to her and said, 'You will not known me but I attended your talk on newborn care at Irvine last week. I am Jessica Miller, a respiratory nurse.' A few moments later, her daughter Debby appeared and she and Daniel took one look at each other and simultaneously yelled out, 'Oh no, not you!' They had apparently been in the music camp together. Debby was a keen clarinettist and had attended previous camps.

She and Gerald must have exchanged eye contact at that time as well, because Debby was then trying to persuade her parents to allow her to stay on with us to go hiking together. Well, as they say, the rest is history. After a 13-year courtship, the two of them decided to tie the knot with a wedding at the Ahwahnee Hotel in Yosemite, their happy stomping ground over the years and dream venue. As fate would have it, Yosemite Valley was struck by the most devastating floods of the century in January 1997 and the park had to be closed for months on end. There seemed to be no firm date that the authorities could give an assurance of opening again, but Debby and Gerald stood firm with their plans and refused to be moved by alternative back-up suggestions of other more formal venues from Debby's parents. Fate was on their side as the Park eventually opened on Saturday 15 March, just in time for their wedding on the Sunday, which was duly attended by many of their close friends and relatives. They then went on a two-year honeymoon working at various places of interest around the world and always combining their work with sporting activities, mainly climbing and skiing. Debby is also medically trained and now heading for a career in paediatrics.

Gerald and Debby have also volunteered their services on several occasions to the Himalayan Rescue Association. They also inspired Lil and myself to do our second Himalayan trip in March 1998, along the Everest highway, from Lukla through Namche Bazaar as far as Pheriche at 14,000 feet, where Debby and Gerald were spending three months as volunteers at the high altitude Himalayan Rescue Centre. We convinced our friends Kati and Peter Vamos and Clarice Friedman to join us on the trip.

During our weekend in Pheriche, Gerald laid on a spectacular display for us, when he needed to summon a helicopter from Kathmandu to evacuate two seriously ill climbers with mountain sickness. The helicopters have to keep the props turning whilst

Human and Yak transport on the Everest highway

Clarice Friedman, Lil, Kati and Peter Vamos and our Sherpa guide trekking along the Everest Highway near Namche Bazaar

Sharing the trail with yaks

At the Mt Everest Documentation Centre at Sherwi Kangba near Namche Bazaar, George Lowe shows us the route and relates some of his personal experiences with the first successful ascent of Everest in 1954

Lil and I arrive in Pheriche (4240m.)

Local infant with grand-mother

With Gerald and Debby at the Himalayan rescue centre in Pheriche

Gerald and Debby await arrival of helicopter for evacuation of two hikers with severe mountain sickness

Hiker scrambling onto helicopter

they hover above the ground, as they might have difficulty taking off again at the high altitude if they were to stop. All the local people were crouching behind the wall, whilst the helicopter was hovering a few yards away and I managed to get an interesting photograph by stepping back a few yards behind them and capturing the patients entering the helicopter and the props also freezing with a V-shaped frame to the snow-covered peak in the background.

Eaten by a bear

During one of our many camping holidays at Tenaya Lake, an idyllic, walk-in campsite with only 30 places and now closed for several years because of the fragility of the environment, I did a three-day hike with David and Gerald from Tenaya lake to Yosemite valley via Clouds Rest and Half-dome. We slept overnight at designated camping areas and followed the strict backcountry rules of hanging up all our backpacks and provisions on a branch of a tree at least ten feet above ground and ten feet out from the tree trunk. During the night I was a woken by a commotion, which I instantly recognised as a group of black bears in the tree. I woke the two boys, who responded by promptly crawling deeper into their sleeping bags. There was insufficient moonlight to be able to see what exactly was happening but in the morning we found all our packs on the ground and all the provisions devoured and the wrappers of sealed salami and other foods neatly piled in a heap. In addition, one of the bears had bitten into David's aluminium container for his toiletries and directly into one of his contact lenses.

As required by regulation we duly reported the 'bear incident' to the ranger station at the visitors' centre in the valley, and were given a form to complete with the most inordinate questions such as the size of the bear ('couldn't see'), the sex of the bear ('couldn't inspect') and so forth. Apparently the bears, which have exceptional intelligence and ingenuity, had worked out a system of pushing a bear cub out onto the branch holding the backpacks, and as it moved further out it had more difficulty with sustaining its balance and position and consequently shook the branch quite vigorously, thereby dislodging the suspended articles.

Hike with David and Gerald from Tenaya lake via Clouds Rest to Yosemite Valley

Remnants of our supplies after bears had ransacked our backpacks overnight

View of Yosemite Valley from top of Half Dome

When I got back to England I duly filled in an insurance claim for David's contact lenses, which had a special cover for loss or irreparable damage. They paid out in full without any query about my answer to the question, 'how did the damage occur?' 'eaten by a bear'.

Gerald completed his clinical training at Manchester University, and made good use of our cottage in Corris, North Wales, to pursue his climbing activities in Snowdonia. He is currently completing his training in anaesthesia at the University of California in San Francisco, in parallel with a continuing research programme on high altitude physiology, and recurrent trips to the mountains.

Daniel

Daniel was still at the nursery school stage when we moved to London, and on the recommendation of Max and Clarice Friedman, we placed him at an excellent nursery school a few blocks down the road from us at the North West London Reform Synagogue in Alyth Gardens, where he became very friendly with Daniel Friedman. He subsequently also went to Brooklands School followed by Christ College, which by this time had become a comprehensive school.

Musical interest

Daniel also demanded to have music lessons at a relatively early age, soon after we came to London, and was insistent on the violin. We feared this would be apocalyptic and the end of peace and quiet in our household. Fortunately our enquiries pointed us to a very talented violinist, Felicity Lipman, who taught the Suzuki method. Suzuki was a Japanese baseball star who also had an interest in music and felt that music was for the masses and that all children could be taught to play a musical instrument if they learnt it by ear, as one does a language. He accordingly popularised the Suzuki method where young infants around 18 months could already be introduced to a mock violin to learn to hold a bow and instrument and listen to the music, starting with the well-known 'Twinkle, twinkle, little star'. One of the most amazing things about this method is the sound these children

Suzuki concert with about 200 young violin enthusiasts at all levels, including Daniel, being led by Suzuki himself on a visit to England

produce is tolerable and they do not produce the usual out of tune screeching sounds so familiar in budding violinists. All the children continue to play the early tunes as they graduate to the next level and eventually end up playing the Bach double violin concerto entirely by ear. It is also an amazing experience to see an assembled mass of some 300 Suzuki enthusiasts at all levels playing together and the younger ones gradually dropping out, as the groups became more advanced and smaller in numbers. Finally the group playing the double violin would be divided into two for the two parts and could switch from one part to the other at the flick of a finger. Contrary to expectation, these children, although very proficient at what they achieve, never learn to sight read adequately and don't seem to achieve professional status as individual soloists.

Daniel got about half way up the Suzuki ladder and from an early stage was a keen performer and showman to any of our guests at home. One of the things these Suzuki children do acquire early on is a sense of being performers and they are also taught early on to take an appropriately deep bow at the end of any performance. Once he left school, he seems to have lost it all and I cannot recall him every lifting up his violin again. We still have a very nice half-size French violin he used in the early stages, which has done the rounds of some of his nieces and is now waiting for further activity from any enthusiastic grandchild.

From early on we realised Dan was a typical 1960s child of the Spock era. We also subsequently learned for the first time what all the parental anxieties were about adolescents. We had not really had any experience of adolescence with our first three boys but Daniel certainly made up for them. As the boys themselves remarked, there was probably a bigger generation gap between them and Daniel, than between them and us.

By the time Daniel reached his O Level stage at school, he was already expressing interest in getting on with his life and enjoying it, rather than pursuing any further academic activities. He had also already developed a special interest in photography, which he was keen to pursue as a career. We managed to gently persuade him to head for a more formal academic training and he chose architecture.

A career in architecture

After taking a year off and having fun mainly in the Far East and Australia, he secured a place in Sheffield University and completed his architecture training there. He always had completely different visions of architecture to simply the construction of buildings and one of his main dissertations was of a philosophical nature of the interaction of man and his environment.

For his main project when graduating, he produced a conversion of a disused slate mine at Cwmodyn in Wales (near our cottage in Corris) into a research centre and constructed a scale model in solid slate from the area, to represent the mountainside and the mine and various additional components. The examiners had quite a problem in deciding, on the one hand whether he deserved honours for a very innovative and unusual project, and on the other hand whether he fulfilled the requirements for graduating in architecture. In the event, the former won the day and he also was selected as one of the Finalists for the President's Award at the annual exhibition of the Royal Institute of British Architects (RIBA).

He subsequently formed a partnership with another Sheffield graduate in architecture from the previous year, Matt Baker, who

One of Daniel's more fanciful student projects in Sheffield university, converting disused cooling towers into a crematorium, on display at the London Royal Academy of Arts summer exhibition in 1994

had trained as a stonemason and sculptor in stone and was now pursuing a career in that direction in relation to architecture, whilst Daniel was heading more in the direction of photographic images in relation to architecture, and particularly conservation. They formed a syndicate named 'Heisenberg', to reflect the improbability theory and did a number of collective works, including 'Bodies Through Space', and subsequently the identification of various derelict sites in Glasgow during the year of architecture. They produced a series of larger-than-life-sized human forms in fibreglass, which should have ended up with a red colour but turned out to be orange and where colloquially called the 'Orange Men', rather than their official designation as 'Journeymen'. They used these to draw attention to various projects, trying to revitalise various disused buildings and other structures of special interest, always using the 'Journeymen' as props for the event. On one occasion they had the 'Journeymen' in St George's Square in the centre of Glasgow for a particular event, and it happened by chance to coincide with the beginning

At the exhibition of the final year architecture students' work in Sheffield, with Dan's project of converting a disused Welsh slate mine into a research centre

of the marching season of the Orangemen of Northern Ireland and also Scotland. When interviewed by a reporter from *The Glasgow Herald*, Dan was asked whether he did not consider it to be a little insensitive having these 'Orangemen' on parade at the beginning of the marching season. He instantly responded, 'I'm afraid I'm only a simple Jewish boy from Golders Green and am totally unfamiliar with all these deep-rooted conflicts.'

It was perhaps also not surprising that Dan and his longstanding partner from his Sheffield student days, Jenny McCready, decided to have their wedding in Corris, and a pretty unconventional one at that. They probably scored a first with a wedding ceremony under a traditional Jewish Chuppah, in a Welsh chapel. The chuppah is a square-shaped canopy under which the

Dan and Jenny on their return from a visit to East Africa

bride and groom stand and are betrothed by the rabbi, together with the parents, and held up by four vertical poles, traditionally held by four pole holders, who were close male relatives or friends. The vicar had spent some time in Israel and was happy to stretch the rules a bit for the occasion. After the wedding ceremony the bridal couple walked up the road from lower Corris towards upper Corris and then up a path to Cwmodyn for the reception. En route the traffic had to be stopped for the procession, and as we passed one of the cars, the driver leaned out of his window and demanded to know 'What sort of a ceremony is this?' Without a moments thought, I reflexly answered 'Pagan', and left him to reflect on it.

We had a tremendous wedding feast on the hillside overlooking the town, which went on well past midnight, partly in the open air and partly in a large marquee open on one side, for the serving of the food and resting on chairs rather than rocks. Quite

Michael, Gerald and David catering for our 25th wedding anniversary they organised in 1985

Family in 1990 on occasion of Lil's 60th birthday

Family reunion on occasion of Gerald's wedding in Yosemite in 1997, together with Les and Jean back row at right

Four consecutive weddings
(upper row) David and Miriam Scadeng (left) and Michael and Jackie Hudd
(lower row) Daniel and Jenny McCready (left) and Gerald and Debby Miller

Nine grandchildren from top, Jenny and Becky, Andy and Alex, Ben and William, Eva, Rubin and Zac a spectacular large-scale barbeque of lamb on a spit in addition to the usual grills.

As always with such events there were a few cliff-hangers in the week before, when, in addition to the usual permission for gatherings from the local council, extra permission had to be obtained from the Forestry Commission to use land under their jurisdiction. At the eleventh hour the question was raised by the commission of who was responsible for the public safety, given the large attendance and the presence of ruined buildings and also some precipitous edges, which might not be readily visible to inebriate Welshmen in the dark. So the regulations had to be met by nominating a safety officer from amongst Dan's organising friends, and also to put a cordon around the site and notices of danger. Full toilet facilities also had to be provided, which the functioning architects managed very well, and in addition to laying on water from the local mains, someone with a sense of modern art and of humour also erected a urinal basin halfway up an adjacent tree (with apologies to Marcel Duchamp).

9

‘Retirement’: new pastures

OUT AND ABOUT

Muscle bound

Victor Dubowitz, professor of paediatrics at the Hammersmith Hospital, has been elected president of the World Muscle Society.

From the mid 1980s the universities introduced a very attractive incentive to encourage academics in university posts to take early retirement. The fundamental objective of the exercise was to save money in the long-term by not refilling the posts, and the initial objective was probably aimed at encouraging relatively inactive and unproductive academics in longstanding personal chairs and similar positions to take retirement. The carrot was to provide a pension commensurate with what would be obtained if one worked till the obligatory retirement age of 65. The pension was based on the number of years in academic posts, divided by 80. So if one had 40 years (maximum) of employment one would retire on half one's current salary. In addition, one could be re-employed in a part-time capacity by the university for up to four sessions, which then made up another four-tenths of salary. One also got a lump sum at retirement equivalent to a year and a half of salary. Investment of that could easily provide another one tenth. So in effect one could retire on a full salary but only be committed to nominally four sessions of work, and the pension scheme provided the rest.

I had not personally given any consideration to the recurrent circulars on the system, as I thought it was not aimed at senior academics with chairs of a department. However, when my friend Professor Peter Scheuer, head of pathology at the Royal Free Medical School, told me that both he and PK Thomas, head of neurology at the Royal Free, had taken early retirement under the scheme and were reemployed into their posts, I began to see the many advantages of the scheme and accordingly discussed it with the dean at the RPMS, David Kerr, who thought it an excellent idea, and advised me to pursue the formalities further with the school secretary, Neil Gershon. I was thinking of working towards it in the next academic year, so that I could plan the necessary reorganisation within the department and make way for a new chairman of department. That was in August 1989. A couple of weeks later I had a call from Neil Gershon that if I wanted to go ahead with the scheme, I had better do it right away, within the current academic year, as there could be no guarantee of it being available in the next academic year.

So I had all of about two weeks to make a momentous decision and set the whole ball rolling. In the first instance, I discussed it with the most senior person in the department, Mike Silverman, to see if he would be prepared to take on the position of acting head of the department, pending the appointment of a definitive new professorial head. He agreed to do this and I then convened the whole department to discuss my plans and to ensure a smooth transition, without any disruption of any of the department's clinical or research activities, and make it clear that I still intended taking an active share of responsibilities in relation to my four sessions of reemployment.

There are of course always two sides to every coin, and in addition to all the benefits of any such move, one also has to look at the flip side. A major change would be the loss of executive power and ability to take executive decisions and action on what one wished to do. Lil kept asking me if I would be able to adapt to this and I felt it was a reasonable concession to have to make in return for all the potential benefits.

With hindsight, I think the decision was undoubtedly the right one for me at the time, as I have been able to start a number of new initiatives, which I would never have been able to even consider, given the considerable commitment I had to running the department, in addition to my personal clinical and research interests. The major bonus has been the opportunity to continue doing the things that I most enjoy doing, right up to the present time.

The major hurdle in ensuring a smooth transition from a fully extended, fulltime, academic life to one of selective activity and 'retirement' was to ensure that one retained sufficient activities of personal interest to still keep oneself fully active. There was no way I could envisage a retirement of leisure and inactivity. I was particularly fortunate that a number of new initiatives arose in the ensuing years, which provided a new challenge for me. These followed three main channels, launching and editing new journals, getting involved in the activities of various societies, and becoming president of some of them.

Birth of *Neuromuscular Disorders*, 1990

In the late 1980s, in the course of one of my regular visits to Bologna, Luciano Merlini brought up the question of a need for a new muscle journal to provide a vehicle for publication of the major molecular genetic and other advances in the neuromuscular field. There had been a well-established journal in the field, *Muscle and Nerve*, launched in 1978 by Wally Bradley, a neurologist in Newcastle and later in Miami, with a special interest in neuromuscular disorders. Unfortunately in the mid-eighties it ran into the common problem faced by freestanding journals to make ends meet, given the high cost of production and personal subscriptions, and a decreasing number of library subscriptions with the falling university budgets. The only easy solution to expand the readership and pool of subscribers is for the journal to be adopted by a society with a large membership. So *Muscle and Nerve* came to an arrangement with the American Association of Electrodiagnostic Medicine, to become its official journal, with a *quid pro quo* of providing a substantial amount of its space for publications from members of the society. This rescued the journal from a financial point of view, but at the high cost of now having a predominance of papers of very little interest to a multidisciplinary readership of clinicians and researchers in the mushrooming neuromuscular field.

Luciano did a very careful inventory of all papers on neuromuscular topics published over a two-year period in the major general medical and neurological journals as well as the specialised scientific journals. This showed a very wide scatter over a large number of key journals and with no predominance in any specific journal. A case for a new journal dedicated to neuromuscular disorders was clearly made. We then wrote to many of the key players in the neuromuscular field about the need for a new journal, and with only two exceptions, of senior establishment figures who were not quite convinced, there was universal support and interest.

The next problem, which was a major one, was to convince a publisher to underwrite the project, starting from scratch, and usually needing an outlay of some £30,000 for such a launch till it became profitable after a period of some five years. As this was totally jungle territory for me, with no previous experience in the field, I took the opportunity of consulting a longstanding friend from my Sheffield days, Norman Chigier, a fuel technologist with an international reputation, who was already doing much research for NASA in his Sheffield days and eventually took up a prestigious Mellon Professorship in Pittsburgh. Our family spent a few summer vacations at his summer house on the shores of India Lake in Pennsylvania, and one of these visits coincided nicely with our new venture.

He had been successful in convincing Robert Maxwell, an entrepreneurial publisher owning Pergamon Press, which had launched some 600 or more new scientific journals, to publish his. And I was very impressed that Norman had settled the deal over a single lunch with Maxwell. When Norman asked him about the finances he got the simple answer, 'You look after the science Norman, I'll take care of the finances'. I later learnt that in the first year the new review journal on fuel technology attracted only one subscriber! But Maxwell was happy to launch new journals at a continuing loss, underwritten by well-established profitable ones. Norman's journal subsequently thrived and became the official journal of a large international society.

So I wrote to Pergamon, direct to Richard Marley, the publishing editor dealing with Norman's journal, and spelled out my discussions with Norman and wish to launch a new journal in the muscle field to meet a big new demand in an expanding field. They expressed interest and did a lot of their usual market research, contacting many of the leading people in the field, a list of whom I provided for them. But then things went quiet and when I telephoned the publishing editor was told they had not launched any new journals that year, but would keep the option on the table. The following year I was told they might launch one or two new journals and that *Neuromuscular Disorders* was still under consideration. In 1989 they confirmed that our journal was one of two they had decided to launch that year.

We now had the task of getting it off the ground as soon as we could. I personally had not entertained taking on board the role of editor-in-chief, as I already had enough on my plate with the sole authorship of a major clinical textbook on muscle disorders and another on the pathology. But my good friend Luciano (as they say, with friends like that who needs enemies?) was quite emphatic that there was only one person for the job and that was me. In fact, he felt I had an obligation to do so. And that was that. How could I possibly refuse? We then set about trying to set up an editorial board, looking initially to a small group of associate editors, who would cover both the multidisciplinary neuromuscular field and also bring some geographical spread. We envisaged that the associate editors might take on some of the responsibility for handling papers from their geographical region.

After sounding out a lot of senior people in the field for suggestions we gradually got a team of associate editors together comprising Luciano Merlini (Italy), Fernando Tomé (France), Richard Edwards (UK), Bob Brown and Steve Ringel (USA) and Ikuya Nonaka (Japan), backed up by 30 invited editorial board members (including the original two dissenters!).

We then planned to launch the journal at the four-yearly international muscle congress of the World Federation of Neurology, due to be held in Munich in September 1990. In our enthusiasm to get the journal off the ground, and with a totally unrealistic optimism, we somewhat rashly also planned to start publication in early 1991, and to go for six issues a year. With hindsight it would have been more realistic to go for four issues in 1991 and then move up as the volume of papers increased with time. In the event we did actually have over 50 papers submitted by the time we went to press with the first issue, which surfaced in June 1991.

Deciding on a suitable cover also posed quite a challenge. I initially thought we might use a well-known painting depicting something appropriate for the subject and was enthused by one of Picasso's early paintings of a toddler taking his first steps. However, it soon became obvious that we would land in a quagmire of bureaucracy with any such endeavour, and although this particular painting was at Yale University, the copyright for reproduction lay with the Picasso estate and it turned out the royalty they extracted was quite prohibitive.

So we just set about designing our own cover. I was keen to have something of instant recognition to the muscle fraternity and thought the well-known Gowers sign of the child with muscular dystrophy getting up from the floor by climbing up his legs with his hands would be an appropriate one. I had a number of sequential slides I had prepared of the manoeuvre, and it was thus easy to select a few of them. However, it somehow did not

Launch of a new muscle journal, *Neuromuscular Disorders*, in 1990

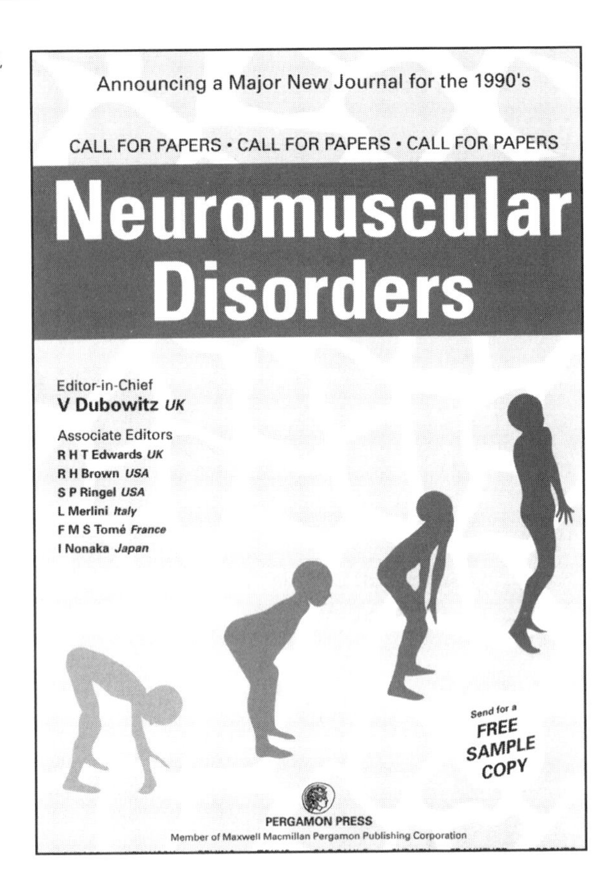

Announcing a Major New Journal for the 1990's
CALL FOR PAPERS • CALL FOR PAPERS • CALL FOR PAPERS
Neuromuscular Disorders
Editor-in-Chief
V Dubowitz UK
Associate Editors
R H T Edwards UK
R H Brown USA
S P Ringel USA
L Merlini Italy
F M S Tomé France
I Nonaka Japan
Send for a FREE SAMPLE COPY
PERGAMON PRESS
Member of Maxwell Macmillan Pergamon Publishing Corporation

First meeting of the foundation editorial board in Munich, September 1990
From left: Brooke, Tomé Angelini, Fardeau, Di Mauro, Gros, Davies, Jerusalem, Sugita, Cornelio, Nonaka, Rowland, Dubowitz, Merlini, Emery, Rudel, Brown, Somer, Henriksson, Hausmanowa-Petrusewicz, (Poortman), Walton, Van Ommen

Launch of *Neuromuscular Disorders* in Munich, 1990. Myself with Richard Marley (Pergamon Press) and Luciano Merlini

Meeting of senior editors of *Neuromuscular Disorders* with the publishing editors in the ivory towers of Elsevier in Amsterdam, 2004. Clockwise from left, Victor Dubowitz, Thomas Voit, Peter Bakker, Elly Tjoa, Fernando Tomé

seem to work until our senior physiotherapist, Sylvia Hyde, came up with a simple solution of putting the sequential figures on an angle upwards, rather than in a straight line. I then filled in the background with a picture of the muscle histology in muscular dystrophy. As a logo for the journal I did a stick figure of the intermediate stage of the Gowers manoeuvre and did a double helix around it.

I tried out many different colours for the cover and eventually settled for a dark chocolate brown. But as the end product can be a bit of the luck of the draw, the first few volumes turned out a somewhat faeculent orange, not very palatable for a paediatrician, and it took some further trials to get an acceptable solution. After a few years there was some agitation to change the cover to something less clinical and reflect its multidisciplinary nature. I was reluctant to lose the Gowers, so ended with a compromise of a multi-topic background of several different techniques and results, taken from publications within the journal. I personally doubt many readers have even noted the details.

In order to maintain a dynamic viability to the journal, I had a regular acquisition of a few new young researchers to the editorial board each year and also dropped one or two in less active areas. We also had some changes over the years in the associate editors to reflect changes in emphasis in the neuromuscular field. The idea of sharing the load between the associate editors on a regional basis never really worked and most papers ended up in the editor's office for final decision anyway. So it became easier and more expedient to just handle the whole load though the editorial office and channel papers to the relevant experts on the editorial board or beyond.

Editorial assistant *par excellence*

I have long been aware that the efficient running of any academic department is a direct reflection of the efficiency of the secretary or PA of the professor. I was equally aware that it would not be possible to run a journal without an efficient and dependable editorial assistant. So having got agreement from the publishers for the appointment of a half-time editorial assistant ahead of the launch of the new journal, I set out to try and find one. I planned a number of advertisements in the appropriate sections of some

Jane Miller with the ubiquitous Fernando Tomé, and Peter Bakker, current publishing editor of *Neuromuscular Disorders*

of the national newspapers and ahead of that also sent a personal circular to all departments at the RPMS, with details of the new post and a few keywords such as 'bored with your current job?', 'looking for new challenges?', 'a new initiative', 'flexitime'. When I got back to my office from my regular Friday morning muscle clinic, my secretary told me there had been a phonecall from a secretary in the renal unit, who had seen my notice and was interested. She had arranged for an interview at 2 pm. We hardly needed an interview. When I was awaiting the candidate to be ushered in, I heard peals of quite infectious laughter coming from my secretary's office down the corridor. 'That's my gal', I thought quite instantly. One needs a sense of humour to take on such a thankless and demanding task as editing a new journal. I was immediately convinced Jane Miller was just right for the job. And we soon got on to flexitime, as she already had a problem with the interview as she had to collect her older child from school and also had her younger one, aged eight months, in the hospital crèche. 'Don't worry,' I said, 'you go off now and collect your eight monther first. I'll entertain him whilst you go and collect your daughter from school, and you can then come back to complete the interview.' That was in 1990, and Jane has been running the journal ever since.

Birth of the World Muscle Society 1995

In 1995 Luciano Merlini opened up a new debate. Looking at the statistics for the journal, it had now reached a plateau and there was little chance of further expansion without being adopted by a society. But there was no society to adopt it, so the only option was to form a new society. In parallel with the question of the journal, there was also a general feeling within the neuromuscular fraternity that the four-yearly muscle congresses organised by the World Federation of Neurology, were too large, too expensive and usually located in distant venues not readily affordable by the young researchers in the field. In addition, the whole field was advancing at such a rapid rate that the four-year interval between meetings was much too long. There thus seemed to be an inherent need for a new multidisciplinary society to meet on a more frequent basis and to direct its objectives more to the active research community rather than the established icons, who were recycled from one meeting to the next in the WFN congresses. We were still at a stage of informal discussions when things took a leap ahead for a totally unpredictable reason.

In February 1995 Lil and I had planned a trip to Verona to combine with my standard package of an academic visit to Bologna and a skiing trip to Selva. All the details were planned and clinics arranged for the Bologna visit. Unfortunately, the week before the visit Lil tripped over an African chief's chair in our lounge, which then swung back and hit her shin, producing a large subperiostial haematoma the size of a golf ball. Apart from the pain and discomfort, it was slow to settle, despite cold compresses, and a senior orthopaedic colleague at Hammersmith advised it would be extremely unwise for Lil to fly as arranged. So we cancelled our trip and I agreed to still come out to Bologna on my own.

Instead of a regular airline ticket at a preposterous price, I bought two back-to-back apex tickets, and selected a nominal three days in early march for the two return halves. As the time approached, I decided to utilise them for a free trip and arranged with Luciano Merlini a meeting together with Giovanni Nigro in Bologna on the Monday, 6 March to discuss the formation of the new society.

The meeting was a very productive one and we worked out a strategy of writing to a list of about 60 people worldwide, active in the muscle field, asking two questions, 'do you think there is a need a for a new international muscle society to arrange more frequent interdisciplinary meetings; and would you be able to attend a foundation meeting of the new society in London on Sunday 4 June, 1995?' The three of us had a celebratory dinner to toast the conception of the new society that evening.

All but two of the 65 people approached responded positively, and 15 agreed to attend the foundation meeting in London, including two from Japan, one from the USA, one from South Africa, and the remainder from various European countries with three local people from the UK. So I finalised arrangements to hold the meeting at the Novartis centre in central London, which also had residential accommodation for out of town participants.

A few weeks ahead of the meeting I was faced with a serious personal crisis and dilemma. My second son Michael phoned late one Sunday evening to say he had just sent me a fax, which I should read and respond to. I went down to my basement to collect it. It read that he and his partner felt that their dog, Mungo, needed a stable home life, and they had decided to get married. And the only weekend they were both free from clinical duties was the weekend of the foundation meeting of the muscle society. The wedding was scheduled for the Saturday and it was expected we would stay over Saturday night and have a champagne breakfast together on the Sunday morning. Matters were complicated further by my brother in the USA and sister in Australia deciding to come over to join us for the celebration. Lil was quite clear in her ultimatum 'it's quite simple, you have to decide between your family or your society!' and there seemed no way I would be able to slip away on the Sunday. But things eventually resolved themselves, when both my brother and sister suggested they would like to come back to London on the Sunday. So I was duly released on Sunday morning when we all returned to London and we were able to start our foundation meeting at 10 am.

The foundation members attending were Corrado Angelini (Italy), Victor Dubowitz (UK), Laszlo Dux (Hungary), Lars Edstrom (Sweden), Robert Griggs (USA), Hyam Isaacs (South Africa), Jean-Claude Kaplan (France), Luciano Merlini (Italy), Giovanni Nigro (Italy), Eijiro Ozawa (Japan), Georges Serratrice (France), Hideo Sugita (Japan), Michael Swash (UK), Fernando Tomé (France), and Greta Vrbova (UK).

The World Muscle Society is conceived in Bologna, Monday 6th March 1995. Celebratory dinner with Luciano Merlini and Giovanni Nigro

Foundation meeting of the World Muscle Society, at CIBA [now Novartis] in London, Sunday 4 June 1995. From left back row Dux, Angelini, Griggs, Vrbova, Swash, Serratrice, Nigro, Kaplan, Ozawa, Merlini; front row Isaacs, Edstrom, Sugita, Tomé, Dubowitz

Limitation of time helps to concentrate the mind. By 6 pm we had completed our business, agreed a name for the Society, World Muscle Society, as well has its credo 'An international multidisciplinary society for the promotion and dissemination of knowledge in the neuromuscular field for the benefit of patients.' An executive board was elected comprising me as President, Merlini as secretary and Nigro as treasurer plus eight additional members, Kiichi Arahata (Japan), Laszlo Dux (Hungary), Robert Griggs (USA), Eric Hoffman (USA), Francesco Muntoni (Sardinia), George Serratrice (France), Fernando Tomé (France) and Thomas Voit (Germany). The executive board agreed to adopt *Neuromuscular Disorders* as its official journal and I offered to host the first annual congress of the Society in London in September 1996. It also elected an international advisory board of some 68 clinical and basic scientists worldwide, who had expressed interest in the formation of the society. We then set off for a celebratory dinner at Chez Gerard, a French restaurant nearby in Charlotte Street.

First congress of the World Muscle Society

My offer to host the first conference of the World Muscle Society within a year of the society's foundation proved to be a pretty tall order, and I soon realised I may have bitten off more than I could chew. All we had was a nascent society, with no members yet, no budget, no venue and no guidelines for the congress. So we had to ensure that the congress would be self-supporting from the income from registration, which had to be at a reasonable level to be affordable for active young researchers, together with some sponsorship. I initially approached some congress-organising agencies but these were prohibitively expensive, so we were soon in a potential cul de sac of going it alone. A possible solution presented itself, when I discovered that Elsevier had a department that organised conferences in relation to some of its journals and their associated societies, so I pursued this option and had a lot of help from the person in charge of this section at the Oxford-based wing of Elsevier, Penny Moon. We discussed and visited various potential venues, and settled for the Commonwealth Institute, which had good facilities for a meeting of around 200–300 participants, had a good ambience and a commonwealth-oriented display museum as a backdrop to an opening reception, and most important, was reasonably priced. It was also fortuitous that the Association of British Neurologists, of which I was a member, would shortly be having their annual meeting there, which I attended in order to get a first-hand perspective of the venue. We also discussed having a banquet as a special and important component of our congress in order to promote some social integration of our new society. I accordingly paid my £40 for the ABN dinner held at the Science Museum, a potentially interesting venue for us as well. The venue and the dinner were fine; the only problem was that only about 40 people attended, defeating in many ways the objective of an official dinner. The majority of neurologists ended up at conflicting dinners hosted by pharmaceutical companies.

That was an important experience for me and I decided there and then that our own dinner would be attended by all our participants, and the cost would be inclusive within the registration. Another firm objective we had from the beginning was that the conference, unlike most international congresses of established societies, would be directed at the active young researchers and not the establishment icons. We thus worked out a novel approach based on the concept of the European Neuromuscular Centre (ENMC) workshops, of selecting three major topics that were currently active in the muscle field and devoting one of the

Core organising committee for WMS congresses. Fernando Tomé, myself and Luciano Merlini, Bologna 1996

three days to each topic, with a small number of invited keynote speakers on each topic to summarise the current status of that topic from a clinical and research perspective. The rest of the day was devoted to contributed papers on the selected topics, partly by oral presentation but mainly by poster, all of which would be fully discussed with two co-chairmen. We also invited contributions across the neuromuscular field, which would be presented by poster only, with selective discussion as time allowed. This core structure has remained the pattern in all our ensuing conferences to date, with a lot of fine-tuning on the way. It proved to be especially popular with the young researchers, who felt they were given good exposure of their research as the posters remained up throughout the meeting and the individual discussion sessions were organised with the same vigour as were the oral presentations. We also had a very convivial and successful banquet on board a boat sailing up the Thames, notwithstanding the inevitable London weather with incessant rain.

There were innumerable hiccoughs on the way, many of which looked like a death knell for the congress, but as in the theatre we just plodded on in the hope that all would be all right on the night. Amongst the major hurdles we had to contend with was that Elsevier decided to move the management of our journal from Oxford to Amsterdam, with almost instant effect, which meant a whole change of scene and control and starting afresh with a new publishing editor, Tatjana Fischer-Driessen, based in Amsterdam, to take over with immediate effect from Paul Carton in Oxford. To add further fat to the fire, the production of the journal was now moved to a totally new team, with no experience of medical publishing, in the Elsevier production centre in Shannon, Ireland. In no time the journal, which had been running a month ahead of schedule was three months behind. And as if that were not trauma enough, the final straw came as we were starting to get the abstracts coming in, when I had a cold call from a very pleasant but completely unknown American lady in Cardiff, who told me that she did part time editorial work for Elsevier and had been retained by Penny to oversee the publication of the abstracts for our conference. Could she arrange to meet me in London to get some information on what the conference was all about? I was almost apoplectic. I immediately got on to Penny, with whom I had already spent countless hours on all the arrangements for the publication of the abstracts, who told me it was their normal policy to farm out the actual work to individual helpers. No surprise then when the proofs of the abstracts eventually arrived that they were in a state of total disarray and I spent countless hours copy editing them myself to at least get them into a reasonably acceptable state.

We finally made it, by a hair's breadth. The congress duly opened, had a good attendance, and the journal supplement of abstracts duly arrived, on the morning of the opening day of the congress. I guess my blood pressure must have had a commensurate rise of at least ten points, not to mention my stress index.

WMS Congress

The important thing in life is always to learn from one's experiences. Having ended up doing most of the work for the congress ourselves, we decided in future years just to organise our conferences ourselves, and control our own finances, so we set up a core programme committee for the society, comprising the president, secretary and one additional member of the executive board, who would work closely with a local convenor, who in turn would organise a local team of colleagues to assist with the organisation, and also as required a professional organisation to handle some aspects of the registration and facilities.

We have not looked back since and the conferences have gone from strength to strength each year. We have also looked for venues that were interesting in themselves but, more importantly, off the main stream of major congresses, such as the eastern or western seaboard of the United States, so that we could negotiate reasonably priced packages for our young and active participants, who did not have access to lavish travel funds. All applications are discussed by the executive board, following presentation by the local convenor, and to date we have had our congress in successive years in London, Tunis, Naples, Antalya (Turkey), The Kruger National Park (South Africa; millennium meeting), Snowbird (Utah, USA), Rotterdam, Szeged (Hungary), Göteborg (Sweden) and shall have our tenth anniversary meeting in 2005 in Iguassu (Brazil). All our conferences have provided a good combination of academia and social activity and at the

Organisers of the first 10 annual congresses of WMS, left column from top down, Giovanni Nigro, Naples 1998; Faycal Hentati and Mongi Ben Hamida, Tunis 1997; Haluk Topaloğlu and Beril Talim, Antalya 1999; John Rodda and Gail Scher, Kruger National Park 2000; right column from top, Kevin Flanigan, Snowbird 2001; Laszlo Dux, Szeged 2003 and Nicolette Notermans, Rotterdam 2002; Anders Oldfors, Göteborg 2004; Mariz Vainzof, Iguaçu Falls 2005. Not pictured, Victor Dubowitz, London 1996

Excitement for the WMS president. Lessons in belly dancing, Antalya 1999; Shangaan chief, Kruger Park 2000; 'Happy Birthday Mr President' (70th), Snowbird 2001; Old Master, Rotterdam 2002

Snowbird congress I dubbed our society the Triple E Society (Education, Enjoyment, Excitement) and every congress since has had a good measure of each.

In addition to the exciting new developments in the muscle world presented at each conference, there has also been much informal interaction and many collaborative research programmes have evolved out of people from different disciplines, working on a similar muscle disease, meeting up personally for the first time at a WMS congress.

The credo of the society, which our founding fathers spelled out at our very first foundation meeting in June 1995, have been more than met by each of our congresses.

Given the close interrelation of the journal and the society, Jane Miller also got actively involved with many of the aspects of WMS and at the third Congress in Naples, I arranged for her to attend and to act as a nominal minutes secretary to the executive board, in addition to attending our annual meeting of the journal's editorial board, which we were now routinely having at the WMS meeting each year. I regularly introduced her as 'This is Jane Miller, my boss on the journal.' At the lunch hour meeting of our editorial board, I usually open proceedings with asking people round the table to introduce themselves. We went all the way round from my right and ending finally with Jane on my left 'I'm Victor's boss' came a spontaneous, almost reflex response. For a split second she did not seem to have realised what she had said until the spontaneous burst of laughter round the table.

She has attended all the WMS congresses and the NMD editorial board meetings since and become very much part of the society and also found it very helpful to be able to put a face to a name when corresponding with authors or reviewers on journal articles, apart from practising her nascent French, German and Italian.

It came as a complete surprise to her, as well as myself, when the Conte Committee in 2004 awarded to her the prestigious annual Conte Medal for 'Social' contribution to neuromuscular disorders. The Conte Foundation was established by Nigro in Naples, following the discovery that muscular dystrophy had been described by the Neapolitan Physician, Gaetano Conte, in 1836, way ahead of Duchenne. He instituted an annual medal and award in each of three categories, clinical research, basic research, and social contribution. The latter usually involved an

Myologists on the move
Fernando Tomé and Michel Fardeau; Yukio Fukuyama and Pirkko Santavuori; myself and Susan Iannoconne; Kiichi Arahata and Eijiro Ozawa; Val and Byron Kakulas; Bob Brown and myself; Makiko Osawa and Kayoko Saito; Eijiro Ozawa (centre) in fine voice for Neapolitan songs in Naples in 1998. To left Coşkun Özdemir, and Lucia Comi, and at right Pervin Dinçer

Myologists photocall. Irena Hausmanowa-Petrusewicz; Gerta Vrbova
Reinhardt Rudel; Andy Engel

individual actively involved in some aspect of supportive work for neuromuscular patients but on this occasion, the Committee decided to extend the definition of 'social' to include the tremendous impact Jane had made in relation in social integration of individual members of the World Muscle Society and her active contribution as well to the Journal.

Presidency of newly established European Paediatric Neurology Society

The European Federation of Child Neurology Societies (EFCNS) evolved out of the annual meetings which Ronnie MacKeith, a paediatrician at Guy's Hospital, organised at St Edmund's Hall in Oxford and usually including a selection of invited paediatric neurologists from an individual European country. The federation had very productive and enjoyable meetings, hosted in different European countries and attended by a small number of representatives, chosen by each member

The foundation officers of the newly constituted European Paediatric Neurology Society, from right Dietz Rating (treasurer), Philippe Evrard (secretary) and myself (president), 1993

country, in relation to the particular topics chosen for the meeting. In many ways it still had the atmosphere of a closed and friendly club. As the specialty expanded throughout Europe, the Executive Board of the EFCNS, which comprised the current president and secretary of each member country, discussed the possibility of expanding into an open society with eligibility for membership of any paediatric neurologist in those countries, who in turn would be at liberty to attend the biennial meetings. This finally came to fruition during my presidency of the British Paediatric Neurology Association in 1993, and I was elected by the current board as president of the nascent European Paediatric Neurology Society, with Philippe Evrard as secretary. One of the board members, Shaul Harel, offered to host the first congress of the new society in Eilat, in Israel in 1995.

I worked closely with Shaul Harel in choosing the venue for the congress and coming to terms with organising a meeting for a society, which had just been born, had no official membership, and no finances! But Shaul Harel was a past master at organising meetings and established for me a completely new definition of the famous Yiddish word 'chutzpah' which has in recent years crept into the English vernacular. Like so many expressive Yiddish words it is difficult to translate but embodies a combination of cheek, audacity, and nerve, and the classical example

Shaul Harel, organiser of first EPNS congress, Eilat 1995

Paediatric Neurologists on the move. Clockwise from top: Trying to stay on a camel at the first EPNS congress in Eilat; Philippe Evrard; Keith Brown and Neil Gordon; Bengt Hagberg; Franco Guzzetta; Jean and Jeanne Aicardi; Stuart Green and John Stephenson at BPNA 2000, Glasgow; Isabelle Rapin and Werner Isler.

quoted is of the young man who murders both his parents and then pleads for mercy in court on the grounds of being an orphan. That is sheer chutzpah. Well, I think Shaul matched that one when he negotiated with the managing director and the head of marketing of the Isrotel chain of hotels in Eilat, and said he had a tremendous proposition for him to put Eilat on the international congress map.

'Tell me more!' Came the response. 'Send me a plane ticket and I shall come down to Eilat to discuss it further with you.' So Shaul travelled down to Eilat, all expenses paid, met up with Daniel Rogers, head of marketing, and outlined his plans for having an international congress of paediatric neurology in Eilat, centred on the luxurious Royal Beach Hotel, which had excellent congress facilities but to date had only organised national meetings but never an international one, which usually gravitated to Jerusalem or Tel Aviv. The remaining four hotels in the chain could provide back-up accommodation at a range of lower budgets. He grabbed the bait and expressed interest. Till it came to the details. 'Tell me about your society. How many members do you have?' 'Well, strictly speaking we have no members, as we have just been formed. But we potentially have a vast potential for members from all the paediatric neurology societies around Europe who have previously supported the federation of societies.' 'And what about your budget?' 'Well, we don't really have a budget, being a nascent society. That is why I came to you with the proposition. You provide the budget, I shall ensure a good attendance, and you can keep all the profit, or carry the risk of any loss' And it was agreed. Moreover, we were able to get a special rate for the 5-star Royal Beach hotel at about half the tourist rate.

In the event, the congress proved an unqualified success, with over 400 participants and a tremendous social programme in addition to the excellent academic one, including a special *son et lumière* in a nearby hillside location, for the one free evening, sponsored by Jaffa oranges, who provided an unlimited supply of freshly squeezed orange juice from a giant 'orange' dispenser, in addition to a sumptuous meal.

If I were asked what is the most important attribute for success, apart from the standard ones of intellect and drive and initiative, I would say enough chutzpah, to battle your way over all the hurdles of academic life.

Birth of the *European Journal of Paediatric Neurology*

One of the hot potatoes that had recurrently come up for discussion at the board meetings of the EFCNS and now spilled over into the new EPNS, was the question of adopting one of the two European-based paediatric neurology journals. *Developmental Medicine and Child Neurology*, was a British-based, infant-development oriented journal, which was the original brainchild of Ronnie MacKeith and had evolved out of the *Cerebral Palsy Bulletin*. The other was *Neuropaediatrics*, a more broadly-based paediatric neurology journal, founded by Frans Schulte and published in Germany, and currently edited by Thomas Voit. The committee was completely deadlocked with a split almost down the centre, largely on nationalistic, chauvinistic or emotional lines. Neither journal was ideal and each had pros and cons.

At the meeting of the executive board in Eilat I tried to bring things to a final resolution by getting board members to debate and vote on two basic questions.

1. Did the Society wish or need to have an official journal, and if positive,
2. Which option would it prefer between one of the current journals or a new journal of its own.

There was almost unanimous support for having a journal, and a majority in favour of a new journal, rather than aligning with either of the current, not quite ideal journals. Some members of the board added a proviso, that they would only support the launch of a new journal if I were willing to undertake the groundwork for the launch and negotiation with potential publishers.

In discussions with a number of publishers, I made it clear that the society would only consider offers if two basic requirements were met, namely that (1) the ownership and copyright of the journal would rest with the Society and (2) the Society would share a substantial component of the income of the journal. A third important negotiating point was also a favourable level of subscription to the journal for the members of the society.

After serious discussions with five potential publishers, I was about to reach a final arrangement when the publishing editor of

Saunders put in a last minute bid, after broaching the subject at a celebratory dinner that week on the publication of the second edition of my muscle disorders book. Not only did he cap the previous best offer, but also agreed to my request (almost a condition) to appoint as production editor Jane Duncan, with whom I had the pleasure to work on my muscle disorders book, and who was quite outstanding; in fact in a class of her own. Following approval of the Executive Board, the Secretary and President then signed the contract on behalf of the Society, with effect from 1 January 1997. In relation to the *European Journal of Paediatric Neurology* I had already worked with Sean Duggan at Saunders for many years through various books, and it was a great pleasure to come into the friendly Saunders fold with the new journal.

The next major problem was identifying an editor to get the journal off the ground. I had not envisioned doing this myself as I already had my hands full with being sole editor of *Neuromuscular Disorders*. After further discussion with the executive board, I agreed to consider it if I could find an additional two co-editors. I called for offers from any members of the board and subsequently approached several individuals personally, but only got one firm bite from Paul Casaer, a long-standing colleague and friend in Leuven, Belgium. So after further discussion we agreed to co-edit the journal and have two editorial offices set up, one in London and one in Leuven, with the appointment of an editorial assistant in each. A great bonus for the journal and me was that Jane Miller was prepared to move from a part-time commitment to the muscle journal to a fulltime commitment taking on the additional sessions for the new journal. What we had not foreseen was that salaries in Belgium were about twice those in the UK, no doubt spiralled up by competition with the European Parliament in Brussels and all its associated bureaucracy. So Jane was employed for twice the number of sessions and before long a major part of the day-to-day work on the new journal was channelling through our London editorial office. I had planned to step down after five years, once the journal had reached equilibrium, but inevitably this quite imperceptibly became seven.

In October 2000 Elsevier announced the purchase of Harcourt Medical Publishers, which already embraced Saunders, Churchill

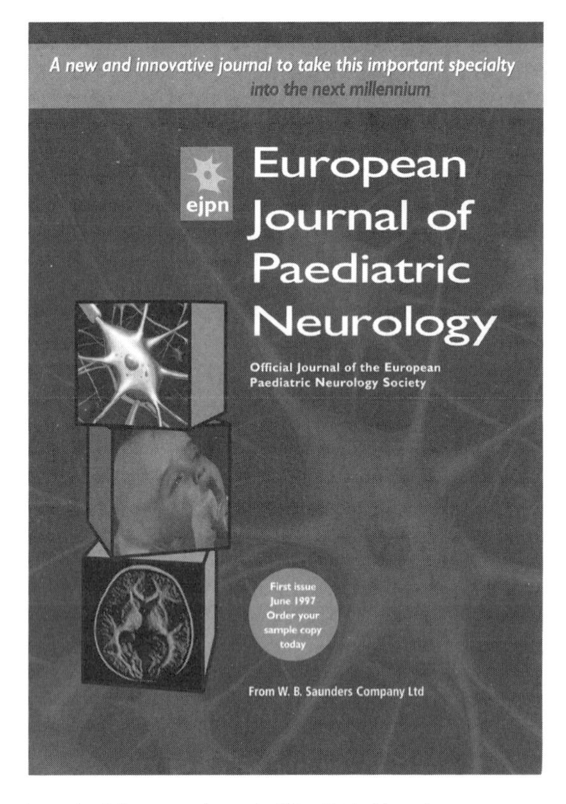

Launch of *European Journal of Paediatric Neurology*

Foundation production editor Jane Duncan

Paul Casaer, co-editor EJPN, president EPNS 1997–

Livingstone, Mosby, Academic Press and others. This eventually brought the *European Journal of Paediatric Neurology* and *Neuromuscular Disorders* into the same Elsevier stable of neurology journals produced through their Amsterdam office.

BPNA goes bananas

I was a foundation member of the British Paediatric Neurology Association in 1974 and have attended most of its annual meetings since, and was president from 1992–1994. In the course of the annual meeting in Oxford in January 1997, which I attended, a motion was put forward at the annual general meeting of members, with the support of the then president, Richard Robinson, and the executive board of the BPNA, that the EPNS be requested not to go ahead with its plans to launch a new journal of paediatric neurology as this was considered counter-productive to paediatric neurology in Europe.

I pointed out that the decision to launch a new journal for the Society was not mine to decide but had been made by the executive board at their meeting in Eilat in 1995, and had asked me to negotiate with publishers for the publication. Moreover, things were already a long way down the road of launching the journal. Nevertheless, I would be happy to communicate to the

EPNS at their next board meeting the wishes of the British Association. The executive received the details of the motion carried by the BPNA with an obvious sense of incredulity and there was no support at all for reconsidering the decision of the Society to start its own journal.

It was reassuring to find at the next meeting of the Society in Maastricht two years later, that there was now a large British contingent and increasing membership of the Society, and in contrast to the initial efforts to boycott the European society and even consider starting a separate European society, they formed an appreciable cohort on the next executive board and have been active contributors to the welfare of the society. Indeed, in line with my own predictions, rather than undermining the existing two paediatric neurology journals in Europe, which felt threatened by it, the new journal actually strengthened them by attracting more high quality papers into the European journals which would previously have been submitted to the corresponding American journals.

Rubbing noses with publishers

One of the sidelines of writing books or editing journals is that one comes into contact with a highly motivated group of people, often with a scientific background and qualifications, who stood apart from the bureaucracy of the tight-fisted and hard-nosed administrative echelons, who usually had completely different and one-track objectives, and spoke a very different language to the scientific community. These publishing editors of *Neuromuscular Disorders* included Richard Morley, working with Pergamon at the birth of the journal, and with the usual musical chairs within the publishing world, he is now with Oxford University Press, as is his successor on the journal, Janet Boullin. We subsequently had a longstanding and friendly relationship with Paul Carton, based at the Oxford branch of Elsevier, which had earlier already taken over Pergamon in an agreed deal with Maxwell. Then at fairly short notice Elsevier decided to shift production of the journal to Amsterdam, with publishing responsibility passing to a young medical graduate, Tatjana Fischer-Driessen, who was still cutting her milk teeth in the publishing world. She decided to grab the bull by the horns and jump in at the deep end, literally akin to a bull in a china shop. At the same time the production was moved to Shannon in Ireland, who had not had previous experience with medical publications. So it took a good year to get back into equilibrium again and to establish a good working relationship with Tatjana. A few years later she was elevated within the Elsevier hierarchy to cyberspace and electronic publishing, to be succeeded by Peter Bakker, with whom we have been on the same wavelength since the start, and I think has been tremendously helpful in seeing things from the point of view of the editor as well as the publisher. And he fortunately has an excellent sense of humour to come back at me on my regular digs at the ivory towers of Elsevier. He is still trying to convince me that the motto of Elsevier, *non solus* does not mean 'without a soul', which I have always considered very appropriate for avaricious publishers.

On a positive note Peter Bakker was very supportive of our idea that the Journal owed a lot to the World Muscle Society in consolidating its subscribers and readership and also generating high quality papers, and in turn it would be a reasonable gesture for the publishers to provide some monetary return to the Society. After a protracted period of negotiation, he managed to secure for our World Muscle Society a contract with Elsevier, who own the copyright of the journal and are happy to pocket all its revenue, which provides for the society a royalty on the gross income of the journal each year. This in turn has enabled the Society to open an educational fund to provide fellowships for young researchers to attend the annual meetings. In the first year of the new arrangements we were able to provided 20 fellowships of 500 euros each, and the following year had 35 applicants competing for it, based on the scientific content of their submitted abstracts for the annual congress. Hopefully this will continue to increase as the journal expands.

We were thus able to reinforce the very close interrelationship between the journal and the World Muscle Society, and although the journal had preceded the society by some five years and the two had developed independently of each other, it was extremely helpful to have an overlap between the three of us, Luciano Merlini, Fernando Tomé and myself, as editor and associate editors of the journal, and also on the executive board of the society, so that we could negotiate in both directions with our respective hats. We also had a good opportunity for this at the annual one-day get-together of the three of us together with the publishing editor and his close associates, at the Elsevier headquarters in Amsterdam.

European Neuromuscular Centre (ENMC)

The European Neuromuscular Centre was an initiative generated in 1990 by the combined efforts of the various European Muscular Dystrophy Associations, to promote collaborative research programmes. Two of the main driving forces in the formation of ENMC were Giovanni Nigro, who was active with the Muscular Dystrophy Association in Italy, and Reinhardt Rudel who was similarly involved in Germany. Alan Emery was elected as their first Scientific Director, and played a pivotal role in establishing scientific workshops, bringing together multidisciplinary experts on a particular neuromuscular disease for a weekend workshop to set goals for research on the molecular genetic basis of the individual neuromuscular diseases and promote collaborative work.

ENMC Workshop on Congenital Muscular Dystrophy
14-16 May 1993, The Netherlands

First ENMC workshop on Congenital Muscular Dystrophy, Naarden, 1993

Individual workshops were convened by a person or persons with an interest and expertise in the particular disease entity applying to a multidisciplinary research committee of the ENMC, which vetted all applications. I served for several years on this research committee and also convened two workshops, one on congenital muscular dystrophy in 1993, and one on the use of corticosteroids in the treatment of muscular dystrophy in 1996. By my definition, workshops comprise only participants and no passengers, so all the selected participants have a contribution to make. Consortia are established after the first meeting and can then meet at regular intervals to review progress and plan further research. The congenital dystrophy consortium recently had its ninth workshop and no less than ten individual genetic disorders have been defined within the group. The same has applied to many other neuromuscular disorders.

Alan Emery presided over these workshops, with the convenor acting as chairman, and I personally participated in many of them. Alan and I had a great time provoking speakers in order to promote discussion and often setting up an argument between ourselves on a particular point, as we both felt that free discussion was much more important in these workshops than the actual presentations of the individual participants.

A few years ago the ENMC executive board started a new initiative on therapeutic workshops in addition to the basic clinico-genetic ones, aimed at bringing together groups of experts to plan therapeutic interventions in individual muscle disorders and also discuss supportive therapy for the complications of the diseases and prevention of such secondary complications. I was invited in 1999 to fill the new post of Director of Therapeutic Studies to have a comparable role to that of the Director of Scientific Studies.

To celebrate the 100th workshop in 2000, the executive board were keen to have a special meeting with an emphasis on therapy, and asked if I would organise it. I agreed on two conditions. Firstly that it take the form of the usual workshop structure, rather than a regular type of conference structure, and secondly that we confine it to therapeutic possibilities in Duchenne muscular dystrophy and bring together the international experts at the cutting edge of new technology such as cell and gene therapy, together with clinicians with expertise in the potential treatment of these patients. The meeting was a very productive one and resulted in the publication of full proceedings of the meeting as a supplement to the *Neuromuscular Disorders* journal, in addition to the standard report, which is regularly published in the journal highlighting the main contributions in the individual workshops.

I enjoyed the new initiative of promoting workshops in relation to therapeutic advances in the various muscle disorders, bringing together clinical and basic scientists, and held this position for three years from 2000 to 2003, when the ENMC executive embarked on a further evolution to setting up Cochrane reviews on the treatment of individual disorders and promoting therapeutic trials, and Professor Richard Hughes was appointed as mediator in these studies. I have been elected as an honorary member of the research committee, which has one major advantage of giving me landing rights to participate in any workshop that I wish to attend, a prerogative members of the research committee have always had.

Meryon society

I first became interested in the meticulous and voluminous writings of the London physician Edward Meryon on childhood muscular dystrophy in the 1850s, when I first started pursuing the early literature during my time at Queen Mary's Hospital for Children in the 1950s, and spent many an interesting hour with the historical collection in the library of the Royal Society of Medicine.

Some ten years ago Alan Emery and his wife Marcia, a former librarian, undertook a very detailed study, not only of the scientific contributions of Meryon but also the fascinating background of his Protestant family, who were Huguenots who had fled to England from persecution in France in the seventeenth century. They wrote a very scholarly book on the whole history of Duchenne muscular dystrophy, including a detailed section on the contributions of Meryon, and established a Meryon Society with an annual Meryon lecture, concurrent with the annual Oxford muscle meeting. As a result of their further efforts they were recently able to convince the Westminster

Alan and Marcia Emery at the inaugural meeting of the Meryon Society at the Royal Society of Medicine in London, coincident with the first congress of the World Muscle Society, September 1995

Meeting of the Meryon Society, Oxford 2001
From right John Pearn (Brisbane, Meryon lecturer), Alan Emery, John Walton, Victor Dubowitz, and David Gardner-Thorpe

Council to put up one of their blue plaques on Meryon's residence at 14 Clarges Street in Piccadilly.

Dubowitz prize

To mark my official (obligatory) retirement in 1996 on reaching 65 years, the RPMS library put on an exhibition of a selection of my photographs on the theme of 'Children around the world', together with some sculptures and a display of the 8 books I had authored or co-authored. Following a number of unexpected requests to purchase some of the pictures, which I had no intention of parting with, I agreed to provide additional framed copies and to donate any proceeds to muscle research. This resulted in a windfall of £600, which I offered to the muscle laboratory. As they could not identify a particular item to purchase, I then decided to establish an annual prize of £100 plus

Annual Dubowitz prize for the best scientific paper published in the previous year by a young researcher in the muscle unit
Clockwise from bottom right: Matt Dunkley 1998, Jo Philpot 1999, Leigh Skordis 2002, Cheryl Longman 2003 and Martin Brockington, three times winner 2000, 2001, 2002 (joint)

a framed certificate, for the young researcher in the muscle unit, either clinical or laboratory, publishing the best paper in the previous year, to be decided by an outside multidisciplinary panel of judges. In support also of the principle of having to sing for your supper, the prize-winner each year gave a short presentation of the award-winning work, followed by an informal reception. After expiry of the initial six years, I offered to continue supporting it on an annual basis, *sine die*.

10

Anxious moments

I suppose there are occasions in every person's life where they are faced with situations which produce a feeling of impending disaster, and a great sense of relief afterwards that one has got away with it. The following are some that I have had over the years.

Winter crossing of Iseran Pass

In October 1957, my classmate from medical school, Jules Smith, who was also doing residency posts in London, and I set off for a tour of France and the west coast of Italy in my Ford Anglia car. On the way back we decided to go via Grenoble and then cross the Iseran Pass, the highest in Europe at something over 10,000 feet. As we approached the pass, in brilliant sunny weather with clear skies, there was a freestanding notice in the centre of the road, with *Fermé* on it. As it did not seem to be an obvious barrier across the road, we assumed it was not a complete closure so decided, without much depth of thought or discussion, to proceed. The views were quite spectacular going up and the conditions good, and we were also struck that we had the road to ourselves and did not meet a single car in either direction. When we got to the top of the pass, I tried to get out of the car to take some photographs, only to find there was such a gale blowing it was impossible to open the door. It was also becoming a bit misty and overcast so we pressed on. The journey down was a complete nightmare. Visibility was becoming poor and there was a fine snowfall in addition to ice patches on the road. And we were driving a light, two-door car with regular tyres. We eventually made it down to the bottom, but I still have nightmares of us stranded on the top and not being dug out again till the snow thawed out in the spring.

Anaphylaxis on the Acropolis

In 1959 I visited South Africa over the Christmas holidays. Those were the days when jet aircraft were not yet in regular use and most long distance flights were by the four-engined turbo-prop DC6 aircraft, which usually needed three or four stops for refuelling. They also seemed to have a propensity for flying through every thundercloud in Africa.

On the way back I had a stopover in Athens and duly headed for the main tourist attractions. Strolling around the Acropolis I was attracted by some very interesting seed cake slices, composed entirely of sesame seed. This was an interesting new experience for me both in taste and in effect.

Within minutes of eating it, I developed generalised urticaria (hives) with associated itching, followed by swelling of my face and a spasm in my chest with associated wheezing. I also had an acute abdominal pain suggesting to me I may have a perforating ulcer. My first craving was for some milk to relieve my abdominal pain but the stand owner tried to offer me soda water instead, which was the last thing I needed. I rapidly took stock of my situation and realised I was on a bit of a precipice, with an incipient full-blown anaphylactic reaction and already had visions of laryngeal oedema and choking to death on the Acropolis! What a way to die. But what to do in Athens on a Sunday afternoon with no knowledge of the language? I decided that to get to a doctor or hospital might be difficult so opted for getting to a pharmacy and trying to reverse my acute symptoms with antihistaminics.

So I rushed for a taxi at the nearby taxi rank and wheezed as loud as I was able 'pharmacia' whilst I clasped my throat. He got the message and within minutes we were racing across Athens to the apparently only pharmacy open for emergency on Sundays. He crossed several red lights and one intersection with a traffic policeman on a raised stand in the centre controlling traffic. At the pharmacy I recognised some standard antihistaminic tablets and after trying to assure the pharmacist I was a doctor, managed to get a supply which led to a gradual abatement of the acute symptoms.

I was somewhat amazed by this seemingly isolated allergy to sesame seeds, as I had no sensitivity to any other nuts, although

I had once had a laryngeal spasm following my first tasting of a well known black porridge in South Africa called Maltabela, during my obstetrics residency as a medical student. A couple of years later I had a reaction with swelling of the face, tightness of the chest and a sensation of swelling of the ears, after eating halva in Israel which is also produced from sesame seeds.

One of my registrars at Hammersmith later told me of a severely ill patient her husband, who was a respiratory physician at University College Hospital, had admitted through the casualty department the previous night, with an anaphylactic reaction to sesame seeds. I offered to add my own case history if he wished to publish it.

In a thundercloud on Mount Dana

During one of our camping holidays at Tenaya lake in Yosemite Park, I went with Michael and Gerald on a guided hike with a park ranger to the top of Mount Dana, the highest peak within the park at around 14,000 feet. Tenaya Lake itself is already at an altitude of 9000 feet. About halfway up Michael developed severe headache, an early sign of altitude sickness, and headed back. Gerald and I made it with the rest of the group to a point a couple of hundred yards from the top, where the ranger set up his camera and tripod to do some photography and about five or six of us continued on to the summit. It had become a bit misty but we did not give it much attention. I then started

Static electricity and hair standing on end in a thundercloud on Mount Dana, Yosemite National Park (14,000 feet)

experiencing a crunchy feeling and sound from my boots as I stepped from rock to rock. When we got to the top, an Austrian in our group handed me his camera to take a picture and I experienced a nasty shock from static electricity. I then noted that people's hair was standing up vertically. The ranger was meanwhile also heading up and when we shouted to him that our hair was standing on end, he shouted to us to come down immediately. We had been totally oblivious that we were actually within a thundercloud and in dire danger of being struck by lightning. Perish the thought of disappearing on Mount Dana in a whiff of smoke!

Too close for comfort

In 1985 I was guest speaker of the New Zealand Paediatric Association at their annual congress in Hamilton, followed by a lecture tour of the main university centres at Dunedin, Wellington, Christchurch and Dundee, and we included an extended tour by car of both the north and south islands, including the spectacular sights around Rotarua and along the west coast of South Island. As we flew out via Los Angeles, we decided to have a stopover on the way back the first week of September and join Gerald and his fiancée Debby Miller, who were spending the summer in Irvine, for a camping trip to Sequoia National Park. True to form, Gerald had everything organised down to the last detail and we set off for the winding 29 mile road from the south of the park, ending at the trailhead at Mineral King, whence we planned to hike up to Pear and Moose Lakes, for three days camping. We had intended reaching Mineral King before noon, but in the event only got there after 3 pm, so decided to camp the night and to head off early the following morning. Lil and I had a small two-man bivvy tent. During the night I woke up repeatedly, partly because of the marked drop in temperature but mainly because Lil seemed unusually cuddly and was crowding me out of the tent, as my space seemed to get steadily less. When we finally woke at daybreak the reason became obvious. There had been a heavy snowfall during the night with some two feet of snow, which was halfway up the sides of our tent. The scene was quite spectacular, after we had dug our way out of our tent, with a crisp clear day. And it certainly looked as though the

Digging out after an unexpected overnight blizzard at the campground, Mineral King, Sequoia National Park, September 1984

winter had arrived and was set to stay. Our pleasure at the scenery was soon overshadowed by our intense anxiety on how we were going to get out, in order to make it to our return flight to London from Los Angeles on the Friday. We met up later in the morning with the ranger, a stocky American Indian, who seemed to have a permanent ear to ear smile and kept repeating, 'snow, what wonderful snow, enjoy . . .' He couldn't understand how anyone would want to consider leaving such paradise. But it soon transpired we were not the only ones needing to go back and caught unawares, without snow tyres or chains, and the nearest supplier of chains was in Silvermine, a small town about ten miles down the somewhat winding, single-track mountain road. Eventually the ranger organised a caravan of some seven cars to follow him down the road in first gear and at minimal speed under the rather inhospitable road conditions. I was happy to leave the driving to Gerald, who seems to relish this sort of challenge. In a state of some exhaustion we stayed the night at Silvertown and headed down along the slightly better road, which had also had the snowploughs on it. By the end of the day the temperature had risen to well above freezing, and the snow began to melt very rapidly. Perhaps the ranger was right that we should have just laid back and enjoyed it for a day or two before heading down.

Mugging at Swiss Cottage

One does not expect to be mugged coming out of a crowded cinema on a Saturday night in a quiet north London suburb. As we were walking towards our parked car on the other side of the open space alongside the Hampstead Theatre in Swiss Cottage, we were rushed by a group of youths, who bumped against us and almost knocked us over. I initially thought they were just larking but they then rushed back again, separated us and started attacking us. Lil instinctively flopped to the ground as a protective action. I remained standing and soon realised they meant serious business when one of them swung around a lamppost and kicked me on the side of my face, fracturing a tooth and also causing some bruising to my retina. Another started hitting me repeatedly on the head with a wine bottle. I suddenly had a fear that they could easily cause me permanent brain damage or even kill me, so I tried to plead with them that I was a doctor and I thought they had had enough. Soon after they stopped. Lil was also pretty shaken but not as severely injured physically. They had also ripped off all my trouser pockets with the contents and also taken my wristwatch. Lil also lost her watch and also a large sculpted pendant hanging round her neck on a chain, which I had bought for her in Amsterdam some years back and was a sort of talisman to her.

Although I was quite dazed I struggled to a restaurant round the corner to call the police. I explained the situation to the local Hampstead police station and also that the thugs who attacked us seemed to have gone into the leisure centre adjacent to the theatre, where there was a reggae party going on. It took a good 20 minutes for a policeman to arrive and after he had taken a full story he was reluctant to go into the dance hall for fear of his own safety and mine, and called for a colleague. When a second policeman arrived, they asked me to accompany them into the entertainment hall and try and identify some of my attackers. This proved extremely difficult. Firstly, the organisers at the door denied any knowledge of any youths coming in. I was still quite dazed and feeling in a state of shock and it was extremely humiliating being paraded around the large number of youths gathered around in a circle and obviously leering and mocking at me, with no obvious sign of any sympathy. Even if the perpetrators were in their midst, I doubt anyone would have been prepared to point a finger at them. The police called an ambulance to take us to the emergency room at the Royal Free Hospital. After a wait of some two hours for attention, no fracture was found on X-ray and we were allowed home.

It turned out from the press reports in the local Hampstead and Camden newspapers that week, that the group of violent black youths, possibly high on drugs, had attacked eight consecutive couples. One girl had her nose broken by a blow and her companion, who was a heavyweight boxer, was powerless to either defend her or himself against the concerted attack. I was particularly angry as well with the editor of the Hampstead newspaper who gave details in the report of a doctor in Middleton Road who was attacked. Given that they had stolen my wallet as well as my bunch of keys, including my house and car key, which was an obvious Volvo key, I thought this was highly irresponsible as it would be no major effort for them to check what Volvos were parked in the short street and to allow themselves easy entry into our house. So the first action I took was to replace the front door lock. I telephoned the editor who sympathised with my situation but said it was 'in the public interest' to reveal this information, which presumably was supplied by the police department. What absolute garbage!

In order not to be thrown off course by this sort of intrusion into one's equilibrium and daily life, I decided to go along the following week to the symposium on muscle disease convened by the Muscular Dystrophy Group at a hotel in the Holborn area, belonging to the father of a boy with muscular dystrophy attending my clinic at the Hammersmith. I thought my sunglasses satisfactorily concealed my bruised face with two very swollen black eyes, but word had got around and I was strongly encouraged to take myself home after the first session and to relax at home for the rest of the week.

We felt a tremendous aftershock after the next weekend and decided to go away for a few days of total relaxation and change of environment. Some days after our return we had a letter from a local counsellor asking whether we needed help on post-traumatic stress following our experience. We felt we had got ourselves sufficiently together by this time and declined the need for any immediate help but said we would come back to her if we felt the need. We also had a series of forms to complete in detail to apply for financial compensation following traumatic attacks of this type and I needed to obtain medical certificates in relation to the trauma to my teeth and eye and also provided some clinical photographs, taken for my own record.

Although it took a considerable time for the compensation to come through, following on detailed confidential reports from the medical attendants direct to the compensation board, it did arrive at a very appropriate time when we were just in the process of planning a visit to the Himalayas, following on the postponement of the South American meeting we were going to after a Tokyo paediatric neurology congress. After her cardiac bypass operation a couple of years earlier, Lil had made a list of the places she most wanted to visit before she died; and the Himalayas were top of the list.

Although we were sure that the culprits would never be brought to book, given the obvious ineptitude of the police service to take any constructive action in the acute phase, and were resigned to the loss of Lil's pendant, which was the most important personal and sentimental loss, we subsequently felt that the tremendous pleasure we got from our trip to Annapurna sanctuary in 1990, which was just about covered by the compensation award, provided a reasonable *quid pro quo* to draw a line under the whole traumatic experience.

God does not want me to go to Copenhagen

It took an unusually prolonged effort to find a mutually convenient date to give a special lecture to the Danish Paediatric Neurology Society. A few weeks ahead of the due date, I had an unfortunate experience of the rupture of my Achilles tendon, whilst examining in Hong Kong for the Royal College of Physicians of London. This occurred with minimal stress whilst trotting up a few steps at the university's postgraduate residence, where I was lodging.

Instead of opting for an operation locally by a senior university surgeon, experienced in dealing with the same injury in competitive squash players, and having a leisurely recuperation, compliments of my travel insurance, I opted rather irrationally for flying home immediately, at great inconvenience and discomfort to my partially plastered leg which needed to be constantly elevated, in the vain and somewhat unrealistic hope that I would still be able to make it to Copenhagen in a few weeks time. Instead my friendly orthopaedic colleague in London duly repaired the ruptured tendon, but trussed me up in a full-length plaster cast from hip to toe and left me essentially immobilised and a prisoner in my downstairs lounge for the best part of six weeks, given the difficulty of ascending or descending the staircase on my bottom.

I thus had no option but to postpone and renegotiate a date for the visit to Copenhagen some four months ahead. Two days before the due date, I was driving back from Cambridge to London in atrocious weather with heavy rain and a gale force wind, when I had a lapse of concentration and suddenly found myself completely out of control and off the road and trying to avoid oncoming trees, before finally impacting into one at about 20 miles per hour. My last thoughts as I saw this massive tree directly in front of me was 'What a stupid way to die! Nobody is going to believe it!'

A few moments after the impact I realised I was still alive, but was not sure, so I felt my pulse and it seemed to be beating. I then undid my seatbelt and stepped out of the car, which was firmly imbedded against the tree. Although I had a tremendous pain on the front of my chest from my impact against the steering wheel, I realised my seatbelt had saved my life, or I would certainly have suffered a severe impaction of my chest or gone flying through the windscreen.

I walked to the road to thumb a lift, but forgot my briefcase in the car so went back to collect it. Numerous cars passed me but none stopped, so I walked to a nearby roundabout where I was able to hail down a truck. I had great difficulty raising myself into the truck owing to pain at the front of my chest, and realised I must have fractured my sternum. I asked the driver if he could take me to a nearby hospital but he sensibly took me to a nearby ambulance station. The local ambulance men were on strike, and sitting around a brazier of glowing coals, but immediately obliged to take me to the Barnet General Hospital, a few miles away.

A very sensible and caring senior casualty officer explained to me that I seemed to be stable but had obviously fractured my sternum. He was going to arrange an immediate X-ray to ensure I had not damaged my lung with an ensuing leak of air into the surrounding cavity (pneumothorax), which might build up pressure and compromise my breathing, and also an urgent CT scan as there was a risk with this sort of injury that I might have damaged my main aortic artery, and if that ruptured he would need to get me to the cardiac unit at Hammersmith pretty damn quick. At that point I gave one of the nurses the various telephone numbers for my wife and my son in London and my department secretary to get a message to them that I was in the emergency department of the Barnet General Hospital.

I was duly wheeled on my hospital trolley direct to the radiology department and CT scanner, along an open bumpy path across the hospital grounds. I still recall the discomfort of that ride. I had to wait a while outside the scanner unit as another patient was in and I kept reflecting on the potential rupture of my aorta. Suddenly I started feeling faint and my pulse became thready and I told the nurse keeping an eye on me I thought I would pass out and could she call for help. In no time flat, the medical team were on the spot, checked my blood pressure, which had fallen through my boots, and had two bloodlines flowing in my two wrists. My main concern was that I might pass on without seeing my wife or family.

After about ten minutes I came round and felt stronger and more *compos mentis* again and relieved it had probably just been a vasovagal (fainting) attack and nothing more sinister. This was borne out by the ensuing CT scan, which showed no evidence of any bruising or bleeding around my aorta.

My wife and number two son Michael duly arrived, in a state of some anxiety and shock, as they were still unaware of the full story, and were relieved to find me in reasonable shape. After a good night's rest, I was feeling reasonably well the following morning but still in pain from the fractured sternum and having some difficulty with breathing. I was given unequivocal instructions from the senior physician that I was going to be staying put for at least a week and was going to have active physiotherapy to ensure that my lungs were fully expanded and functional. I should also just forget about any ideas I still had for going to Copenhagen.

So I suggested to Lil that as I now seemed fairly much out of the woods, she should go ahead to the meeting in Copenhagen as planned, as she was also giving a lecture, and for her to take a personal note from me to the neurologist who was organising the meeting, which read simply 'Sorry, God does not want me to come to Copenhagen'. I am not superstitious by nature but somehow felt I had got the message and thus made no attempt to reopen negotiations again for a third time for fulfilling my lecture commitment in Copenhagen.

Bleeding to death in the casualty department of a London teaching hospital

In April 2001, my consultant urologist advised me it might be prudent to have another prostate biopsy, given the fluctuation in my blood PSA level (prostate specific antigen, a marker for prostatic malignancy). As he was pretty conservative in his approach anyway, and thought like a physician rather than a surgeon (a thinking doctor rather than a cutting doctor), I was happy to go along with it. At least the previous two procedures had given me the reassurance that there was no evidence of malignancy (the commonest cancer in men) and the prostatic enlargement was a benign hypertrophy, and the pain and discomfort with the procedure itself was pretty transitory, and well worth it.

Everything went pretty smoothly, undertaken again by the same senior radiologist who had extensive experience of the procedure. However, shortly after, as I was about to leave, I felt the urgency to empty my bowels and passed a large clot of fresh blood. I alerted the radiologist and he advised me to wait until it had settled. In all the many hundreds of prostatic biopsies he had done, he had never experienced any significant bleeding after the procedure. About half-an-hour later I had a further similar episode so remained in the radiology waiting area for a further hour, when it seemed to have settled, so I headed for my car in the hospital car park to drive home. I telephoned Lil to say I was about to come home and explained my two-hour delay. She firmly advised me, in fact ordered me, not to drive home under the circumstances but would come and collect me. So I agreed and thought I would wait in my car till she arrived. Shortly after I had an urge again to go to the toilet, so headed for the paediatric department. I then passed a large amount of blood, possibly a half pint. Enough was enough, I thought, so I took myself to the casualty department of the hospital. I introduced myself to the senior nurse in charge, told her the sequence of events, and that I was concerned I had lost an appreciable amount of blood, and thought it prudent to be under their watchful eye. Could I also just make a quick call to my wife first? She put me on a couch in a side room and on my request also provided me with a bedpan should I require it. Shortly after I passed two further large blood clots into the bedpan and managed to alert a passing nurse that I would need another bedpan. She was about to remove the existing one and I requested her to leave it in case someone was interested in the amount of blood I had lost.

Shortly after that, the surgical resident on call came to see me and spent an inordinate amount of time on irrelevant details to complete her systematic medical history. I told her I was getting pretty anxious about the situation and could she alert the urology registrar. She told me she had to go through the normal protocol of first contacting the surgical registrar on call. I then took a firmer line and tried to pressure her into getting some urgent advice or I would have to phone up my consultant urologist personally. I was at least relieved that she put up an intravenous line before heading off again. I must have been in isolation on my own there a good twenty minutes (or so it felt) when the senior nurse popped her head round the curtain and asked, 'Anything you need?' 'Yes please. Could someone just pop in from time to time, as I am feeling pretty woozy, and could you let me have a bell to call should I need help'. She apologised that this was not a formal casualty room with full facilities but only a transitory room for keeping patients in, and thus there was no bell available. I was not quick enough to respond that a glass and a teaspoon would probably suffice, before she disappeared again. At some point, the surgical director of the Casualty department also popped his head in and said 'I am the consultant in charge of Casualty; everything OK?' A rhetorical question as he rapidly moved on again.

A very cheerful and chatty Australian nurse then popped in to check my pulse and blood pressure, which she carefully charted. To my great relief, and apparently also that of the nurse, my wife appeared at that moment and the nurse told her, 'I'm glad you have come. We are a bit short-staffed and busy at the moment, so could you just keep an eye on him for us.' I think I must have told the nurse, 'This is my wife, who is also a doctor.'

By this time I had practically filled the two bedpans and would estimate I had lost the best part of two pints of blood. Shortly after, I told Lil to call for help as I was feeling pretty faint, and I then passed out. I have to give it to the Hammersmith crash team that when there is a real emergency, like a cardiac arrest, they really are tops. One just has to be careful not to exodus on the trolley before they get to you. So I came round from my period of unconsciousness on an operating table in the casualty department under the glare of the overhead searchlights and with blood flowing rapidly into both arms. I was certainly feeling a lot better than immediately preceding the episode. Sitting alongside me was a senior surgeon, who had been called in and in fact knew who I was from his training rotation a decade or so back, which also involved some paediatric surgery. He had meanwhile also spoken to one of the senior surgeons at St Marks Hospital, a renowned postgraduate centre specialising in surgery of the lower bowel and back passage, and they had never had any experience of a serious haemorrhage into the rectum of this nature, following on a prostatic biopsy. They advised that a possible management was to pack the rectum with bandaging under general anaesthesia to try and arrest the bleeding by pressure. If this failed, open surgery seemed the only alternative. The surgeon was also keen at this stage to do direct visualisation with a large metal tube (proctoscope) to check if he could see the bleeding point.

I was not well pleased with the prospect of massive packing under general anaesthesia and also concerned about the proctoscopy possibly aggravating things. So I told the surgeon I had just come back from a rather unexpected trip to the Elysian plains, and was still feeling a bit shocked by the whole experience, so could we perhaps give it a few hours rest and then review the situation. In any event I did not have the sensation that there was any more accumulation of blood in the rectum, so perhaps it might just be prudent anyway and give nature a chance to try and resolve things. He agreed to leave it at that and I suspect was possibly also relieved himself not to have to rush in.

I was then admitted to the ward for observation and soon passed into a deep sleep, as one usually does after a state of complete exhaustion. I did not wake till about six in the morning, accompanied by a hearty fart, which seemed to resound around the ward. I can still remember my supreme delight and reassurance that greeted this episode, as it instantly indicated for me that I had just evacuated a rectum loaded with flatus rather than blood, and marked the end of my bleeding saga. It crossed my mind that perhaps it is indeed true that every cloud has a silver lining and for me the exsanguination as a result of my two hours of neglect may have lowered my blood pressure and blood flow to the extent of stopping the bleeding and allowing a clot to seal off the breach.

I was minded to write to the senior administrator of the Hammersmith Hospital Health Trust and inform him how lucky we had been to spare him some embarrassing headlines in the morning newspapers, along the lines of 'Hammersmith Professor bleeds to death in the casualty department of his teaching hospital' in the broadsheets, or perhaps in the tabloids 'London teaching hospital fails bleeding professor'. But after some reflection I thought, 'What is the point?' One could anticipate the usual sequence of events as the bureaucracy grinds into action. 'Thank you for your letter which is receiving attention.' A week later 'Your letter has been passed on to this office for further consideration. Can you please send us a detailed account of the timing and sequence of events you have drawn our attention to.' 'The Chairman of the hospital trust has asked the executive committee to convene a special committee to look into the circumstances of the events to which you have drawn our attention.' And perhaps after a suitable period of some three months, a final letter 'our special committee has looked carefully into all the circumstances of your experience in our casualty department and interviewed all the nursing and medical staff involved. After careful consideration of all the facts it has concluded that no individual staff member is to blame but it was an unfortunate combination of unusual circumstances that led to the your unfortunate experience. Our committee also added that it was perhaps the inappropriate decision of the professor of paediatrics to have walked into the casualty department without any prior notice, at a time that the unit was extremely busy and somewhat understaffed, that was a major contributing factor. Meanwhile on behalf of the Trust can I congratulate you on your rapid recovery following the very efficient treatment you received from the emergency unit team.'

Daniel has thunderclap headache; the worst and the best in the National Health Service (a father's story)

When I returned from a visit Budapest, a few days ahead of Lil, on the evening of Tuesday 26 February 2002, I telephoned Dan to say hullo and to get an update on his major Gorbals project in Glasgow, and left a message on the answering machine. At 10.30 pm his wife Jenny phoned me to say that Dan had been admitted to hospital, having had a most severe headache, coming on suddenly at 5 pm that day while sitting at his desk, which he described as if someone had hit him on the back of his head with a plank.

He asked Jenny to collect him as he did not feel fit to drive. He then slept for about an hour and a half in a darkened room but this did not alleviate the headache. Jenny then phoned Mike who suggested taking him straight to the emergency room of the nearest hospital, as it sounded pretty ominous. So they headed straight for the Royal Victoria Infirmary.

In addition to the persistent headache, Dan also had severe photophobia, with marked intolerance to light, and could not even bear the streetlights and had to cover his eyes with a scarf. After getting to casualty he vomited profusely.

The casualty officer suspected a brain haemorrhage, and arranged an urgent CT scan, to be followed by a lumbar puncture (spinal tap) to check for blood in the spinal fluid. The CT scan proved to be normal and by 10.30 pm the headache had eased but was still present in low degree. He slept quite well through the night.

When I called Jenny in the morning, she told me they were considering discharging Dan and that the consultant physician would be doing a wardround at 9 am, so I telephoned him personally after the round. He said nothing had been found on CT and he thought this was probably an atypical migraine and he was content to discharge Daniel.

I felt very uneasy about this. Dan slept intermittently through the Wednesday and that night woke up at about 2 am with a very severe headache again, took some paracetamol and eventually got back to sleep. He woke up normally at about 8 am and the headache seemed to have settled but not completely gone.

I was particularly concerned that the initial history sounded a lot more ominous than a severe migraine and my own thoughts were 1, subarachnoid haemorrhage (imprinted from my undergraduate medical student days for a sudden onset excruciating headache), 2, meningitis, and 3, very low down on the list, an atypical migraine. I was also concerned the physician had given them no instructions for coming back if there were any recurrence or persistence of symptoms, or indeed just for a routine check perhaps 24 hours later.

I phoned my friend Nat Blau, a neurologist with expertise on migraine, and he said this did not sound like a migraine, and needed further review. The only person he knew personally in Glasgow was Professor Graham Teasdale, head of neurosurgery, and suggested I contact him. Graham Teasdale was extremely helpful on the telephone, despite being about to rush off in 10 minutes for a plane to London. He thought further investigation was necessary and in the course of the afternoon Daniel was admitted to the Southern Hospital Neurosurgical centre.

The following morning the consultant recommended doing an angiogram to show up the blood vessels of the brain. I then headed for Glasgow on the next available flight. When I reached the hospital around 7 pm on the Friday evening, the neurosurgeon (Mr Vacus Papanastassiou) was at the tail end of a detailed discussion with Dan and Jen. The initial 'normal' CT scans from the Infirmary showed an unequivocal bleed around the circle of Willis area and the arteriogram revealed an aneurysm on the anterior communicating artery. The two options were direct surgery or a non-invasive imaging approach with arterial catheterisation and ablation of the aneurysm. They could organise the surgery the following morning, whereas the ablation procedure would have to wait till the next radiology session on Tuesday, with the added concern of a further bleed in the interim.

Despite his obvious anxiety about the thought even of a craniotomy, Dan and Jen had already decided on the direct surgical option. The surgeon also explained the lengthy procedure of around five hours and the need for about three weeks in hospital and a further three weeks in convalescent and rehabilitation hospital.

I was extremely impressed by the empathy of the surgeon and the dedication of all the nursing and associated staff on the ward, who all seemed to have an obvious dedication and commitment; an oasis of the highest quality of basic medical care and support in the context of one of the most highly rated neurosurgical units in the country.

On Saturday morning Dan was very composed and relaxed (at least on the surface), considering that on the previous evening he had written out his will, written a letter to his partner that he should take personal executive action on all further arrangements in connection with the Gorbals project, and also digesting the good news that Jenny had just realised she was pregnant.

Dan went off to theatre at 9.30 am, emerged in the late afternoon and was ready for us to visit him in the intensive care unit at 7 pm. Although still very dopey, he was rousable and responding to us. The operation had gone well and the aneurysm clipped.

After a fairly stormy and stressful postoperative period over the weekend, he was considerably better by Monday morning and even recalled that he had mistakenly given Jenny's birth date in place of his own when initially admitted. By the following Sunday he was mobilised and had a prolonged Jacuzzi bath, and was discharged home on Tuesday. Although still feeling very tired and having intermittent headaches, he was fit enough a week later to visit a house up the road that had just come on the market, and was the first they had seen after two years of house-hunting that seemed ideal for them. They made a successful bid for it.

Dan was advised by the surgeon to lie low and maintain a relaxed profile for at least three months (easier said than done!) and not to go back to work for at least six months. This was extremely beneficial on the one hand for allowing a full convalescence and recovery, but created difficulties on the other hand of adapting again to the competitive world of trying to find a niche as an artist/photographer in relation to the regeneration of important buildings under threat of neglect and decay.

Within a year he was back in the fray, working on the regeneration of the Ancoats cotton mills in Manchester, where the industrial revolution started in the nineteenth century, and which had been abandoned in the 1960s following the decline of the British cotton manufacturing industry in the face of competition from the Far East. This resulted in a display of ten large photographic exhibits on the platforms of the metro link section of the Piccadilly main station in Manchester. This was followed by an exhibition in the cathedral of St John the Divine in New York in December 2003 of a series of stunning photographic recordings of three sanctuaries that had been listed architectural gems and were now in a state of abandon and neglect and decay. They included the Catholic seminary at Cardross in Scotland, the Gorton monastery in Manchester and the church of Saint Gimignano in Italy. Thanks to modern technology, one can have a 'virtual' tour of the two exhibitions at Dan's website www.civicworks.net.

11

Clinical casebook

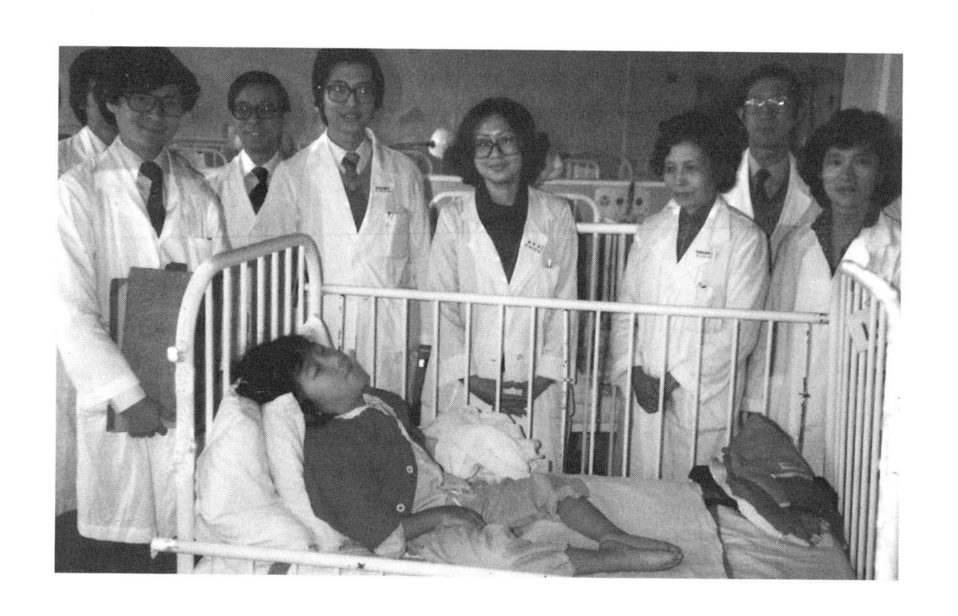

After graduation, it was obligatory to do a six-month residency as a junior house officer, in both medicine and surgery, in order to become eligible for registration with the medical council as a medical practitioner. I was fortunate to obtain a post at Groote Schuur Hospital on the medical unit under the combined care of Dr Helen Brown, a superb clinician and very practical and methodical, with both her feet firmly on the ground, and Dr WPU (Peter) Jackson, who had a very active scientific mind, was very interested in endocrine and metabolic disorders, and had been a pioneer in the recognition of pre-diabetes, particularly in pregnant women. Much of the time he had his head in the clouds and his feet some way off the ground.

I recall one occasion when I admitted a 22-year-old young lady, who was a trainee nurse at one of the smaller Cape Town hospitals, with a somewhat bizarre cluster of features, including some clouding of her concentration and swinging of her blood pressure. Peter Jackson listened attentively to the story when I telephoned him about her and thought she might fit in with a newly recognised condition of hyperaldosteronism (excess production of the hormone aldosterone), which had just been documented in *The Lancet* journal the previous week. I presented her in detail on our regular morning wardround with all the consultant and resident staff, and Peter Jackson made a strong case for the diagnosis of hyperaldosteronism. Helen Brown then reflected on the whole presentation and asked if I had checked the blood barbiturate level, as she had a suspicion she might have taken an overdose of barbiturate tablets. She proved to be absolutely right.

During my surgical residency with Professor Jannie Louw, we were not only expected to be on almost continuous duty to clerk all our admissions to the ward, but the professor also did a regular wardround on Sunday morning to review the progress of patients operated in the major theatre session on Friday and to discuss any new admissions going on to the surgical list on Monday. On one occasion, I had been given a special dispensation to absent myself from the Sunday morning round in order to attend a family celebration. I did, however, ensure that I clerked up all the patients being admitted for surgery on the Monday. I recall having had quite a busy load of new patients, many of whom came from far afield, including one farmer who was being admitted for a partial gastrectomy (removal of the stomach), for a duodenal ulcer, a popular operation in those days to reduce the acidity of the stomach and enable the ulcer to heal, before the modern era of effective drugs. He was my final patient and it was approaching somewhere around four in the morning.

I carefully examined his abdomen and thought I was able to palpate a small firm lump on the back of the abdominal cavity. So, I stuck my neck out and wrote under diagnosis at the end of my detailed case notes, '? Carcinoma of the pancreas (reconsider gastrectomy)'. I also left a personal note for the surgical registrar to review the case prior to surgery and to defer any operation on the stomach. I then headed off for the weekend.

When I returned on Tuesday morning the surgical registrar informed me my diagnosis had been correct and both the patient, and the professor, were happy he still had his stomach intact, and that they had been able to remove the malignant lump which was still fairly confined to the head of the pancreas.

Tetanus in a white infant; a case of reverse apartheid

Pat Smythe, who was one of the doyens of paediatrics at Cape Town, achieved international recognition for his novel approach to tetanus in the newborn, a common problem amongst the black population who had a tradition of applying cow dung to the umbilical cord after it was severed. There was a 100% mortality, which Smythe had succeeded in bringing down to 50% by a vigorous programme of intervention and particularly paralysing the infants with medication to prevent the muscle spasm and giving them full ventilator support till they recovered from the illness itself. There was a state-of-the-art intensive care unit with top rate nursing staff dedicated to this programme. Of necessity it was located in the non-white half of the Red Cross Children's Hospital, in those days of absolute apartheid and separation of the races.

The condition was practically unknown in white infants, given the different circumstances of their birth and the appropriate hygiene in the delivery and postnatal period. On one unique occasion a baby, who was born at the Rondebosch Maternity Hospital, a small private hospital facility, developed suspicious symptoms in the newborn period and Pat Smythe was consulted and confirmed a diagnosis of neonatal tetanus. This had apparently resulted from contamination of some instruments. Pat was now faced with an unusual dilemma. Without ventilator and intensive care the infant would certainly not survive. If he admitted him to the intensive care unit on the White section of the Red Cross Children's Hospital, his chances would not be much better, as the nursing staff were inexperienced in ventilator care, which in those days was not yet a standard practice in newborn intensive care units for premature babies. The only hope for the baby was to admit him to the non-white section of the hospital, which is what he decided to do, following an informal discussion with the superintendent of the hospital in order to defuse any possible political backlash. The infant made a full recovery. A rare benefit from apartheid in reverse.

Elusive muscle problems

It is always a bit frustrating for a medical practitioner to find himself in a bit of a *cul de sac* when unable to establish a firm diagnosis of an underlying problem in a patient. I have had a few such experiences over the years and in each case two important clinical principles emerged. Firstly, the importance of taking a detailed history. This is often overlooked in the new age of increasing technology. The second principle, particularly in paediatric practice, is to always believe the mother (until proved otherwise). She is usually correct.

My first experience was soon after I took up my post at Queen Mary's Hospital for Children in Carshalton. I was reviewing an eight-year-old girl, whose mother had been concerned about her gait, but several doctors had not been able to find any abnormality and had labelled the mother as over-anxious and neurotic, and subsequently also the child as neurotic. On listening closely to the mother a very striking story emerged. She had been worried about the child's gait since she was about two. It often was unsteady and ungainly. It was particularly in the mornings that she had most difficulty. In recent years she very obligingly used to get up early in the morning in order to make tea for her parents in bed. She was so stiff on waking she could scarcely get out of bed and practically stumbled down the stairs. By the time she had made the tea, she had no difficulty coming up the stairs again. She was also keen on competitive running at school but often got left behind at the starting line and took a while to get going but then steadily caught up. On examination her muscles were well developed and prominent and she had no weakness at all.

The history was very suggestive of a condition called myotonia, which causes marked stiffness of the muscles with rest and difficulty in moving them. This can often be demonstrated by closing the fist tightly and then releasing it with a slow opening. But she did not show that. I then decided to sleep on the ward one night and got the nurse to wake me ahead of the child. I was able to confirm the difficulty she had on waking and how it gradually resolved with movement. I was also able to demonstrate percussion myotonia with a gently tap with a finger on her tongue, leading to a marked notch on the side of the tongue, with the contraction of the tongue muscles in response to the tap.

Some years later, I was able to make a similar diagnosis at the Hammersmith Hospital, in a nine-year-old girl with a similar muscular appearance, who had also been dismissed by several doctors as having nothing wrong. The father gave a very clear history, suggestive of myotonia, when I asked him what he thought was her most striking difficulty he had observed. 'Well, it's like this doctor. We often travel by tube train from Neasden to Wembley, which is only one stop, but she is unable to get off the train, she is so stiff. After a few minutes she is walking normally again.'

The most unusual presentation of this same condition was a 16-year-old schoolboy, who had been referred to me at my Hammersmith clinic by a neurologist friend, with no specific diagnosis. When I asked the lad about his symptoms, he told me he thought he had myotonia congenita. I was surprised and asked him how he came to that conclusion. He had found a copy of a 1930s edition of *The Home Physician*, a popular book on medical disorders for the lay readership, which had belonged to his grandmother. On reading through it he had come across the description of this condition that matched his own. He was absolutely right. I commended him on his astute observations. He subsequently went on to study medicine at Bristol University, and I was pleased to meet up with him a few years later at the College of Physicians, when he had successfully passed the membership examination.

A six-year-old girl, who was referred to my muscle clinic in the mid 1980s, provided a good example of the value of John Heckmatt's newly introduced ultrasound imaging of muscle as a routine procedure in our clinic and also the advantages of needle muscle biopsy. Her only complaint was that she had difficulty keeping up with her classmates with games at school. Her local paediatrician had been unable to find any muscle weakness or functional deficit. I was convinced that her story reflected a minimal but definite underlying muscle problem and although she had no apparent problem with all the usual test manoeuvres on clinical examination, I thought she had minimal difficulty getting up from the floor and momentarily putting her hand on her knee in the process. Ultrasound imaging of her thigh showed a completely clear picture in the main central muscle in the front, the rectus femoris, but a marked increase in the echo in the underlying vastus lateralis muscle, suggesting a dystrophy. John Heckmatt was able to do a double needle biopsy under local anaesthetic through the same small skin incision, first taking a sample from the rectus and then from the vastus. Histology showed a normal picture in the rectus but a very dystrophic one in the vastus.

This single case was a very important example of the value of routine ultrasound imaging as a screening tool in our clinic, which had almost completely replaced the traditional needling electrodiagnostic testing, to the great relief of our young patients. It also showed that needle biopsy was not only as efficient in routine biopsies as the traditional open biopsy, with the much larger and unsightly scar, compared to a small almost invisible skin stab, but might even have advantages in picking up an affected muscle, whereas an open biopsy of the rectus would have shown a normal result. On the strength of this we had a paper accepted for publication in the journal, *Muscle and Nerve*, of our experience to date of some 50 cases, despite the reluctance of neurologist reviewers to support it, and we achieved a somewhat unprecedented personal commentary from the editor, Wally Bradley, as a footnote to our publication that this needle biopsy technique may hold some advantages in paediatric practice, but was unlikely to gain much support amongst neurologists. Amazing how blinkered and rigid members of our profession can be at times. Small wonder that needle biopsy has still not been introduced in muscle clinics in the United States, although widely practised in Europe.

We continued to follow this patient over the ensuing years and she continued to show minimal difficulties with various activities. As she passed into adolescence and adult life she developed some rigidity with a limited range of movement of some muscle groups, a condition for which I had coined the term rigid spine syndrome in my Sheffield days, and she now, in her mid-twenties, resembled the Emery-Dreifuss type of muscular dystrophy. In view of the major advances in recent years at the molecular genetic level, she agreed to another needle biopsy, which showed a deficit in a specific nuclear protein called lamin. Interestingly, her selective muscle involvement has also been shown by one of my latter-day colleagues at Hammersmith, Eugenio Mercuri, to be a consistent pattern in this particular form of muscular dystrophy, elegantly shown by a series of magnetic resonance imaging of the muscles. He proudly presented these important new developments in muscle imaging at the 2004 congress of the European Paediatric Neurology Society's congress in Sicily. I felt honour-bound, as chairman of the plenary session, to also mention the modest contribution that the ultrasound imaging had made in the field, and indeed the very case he was quoting had already been earmarked by the ultrasound some 20 years earlier.

Hysterical paralysis

In my early years at the Hammersmith in the 1970s, I saw a number of children referred with major muscle disability and in some instances having been unable to walk at all for up to a year or more. On clinical assessment they all had in common a disproportionate loss of function in relation to any detectable muscle weakness. In each instance the disability had been preceded by an acute illness, often of a relatively mild nature. It became clear that the disability was a psychological overlay or conversion, superimposed on the previous illness, comparable in some ways to the so-called hysterical paralysis, classically described in young adults.

There was very little on the subject in the paediatric literature and practically no advice on treatment or management. Indeed the neurologists seemed quite content to pass the buck to their psychiatric colleagues, as clearly spelled out in the classical paediatric neurology textbook of Frank Ford, a neurologist at the Johns Hopkins Medical School in Baltimore, 'This is a psychiatric problem and if the neurologist is not prepared to undertake this responsibility, he should place the patient and parents in the hands of the best psychiatrist available. It is my custom to follow this course and to wish both the patient and the psychiatrist the best of luck.' Unfortunately the psychiatric literature was no more forthcoming in any guidance on treatment.

So I contacted Dr Lionel Hersov, a very levelheaded psychiatrist attached to the Maudsley Hospital, who also did clinical sessions at the Hammersmith, and was also a fellow South African expatriate. We worked out a practical strategy for the management of these children and defined a few basic principles and guidelines. Firstly, a rigid policy of no further investigations; a philosophy of 'cure them first; diagnose them afterwards'. Secondly, getting the parents on board; no point in saying 'there's nothing wrong; it's all psychological, just snap out of it'. That just does not work. As anyone can see, there *is* something wrong, they cannot walk, and whatever the reason, they themselves are not aware of the mechanism.

So I started off by saying 'I know you are having great difficulty with your walking and it may take some effort and time to get better; I also realise you had a serious illness before which started it; but my assessment of you suggests that the original condition you had is now fully resolved, but that your muscles have not yet fully recovered from the insult, and need some help with retraining and getting them fully functional again.'

It was difficult to get our physiotherapists to go along with this approach, as they could still not get to grips with a major deficit in function without any demonstrable muscle weakness. So I would get one of our residents to take responsibility for a daily session with the patient, encouraging them to work through step by step of standing unaided, walking with support, and gradually walking unaided. We then got the child onto a treadmill (in the cardiac department) and by very slowly increasing the speed were able to get them back to full activity.

Remarkably, and contrary to my own expectation, we achieved this in weeks rather than months. One interesting clinical sign many of these boys showed was that after they were back to standing and walking, they could stand on one leg but were unable to hop on one leg. When trying to do so they were able to gyrate quite actively, with active movement of the arms and the body, but remained firmly stuck to the floor on the one leg. I coined a term 'glued to the floor sign', which was unique to this situation.

Once we were able to rehabilitate them physically, we then also tried to understand the mechanism for it and invariably there was initially some background illness in these children, such as a myositis (viral illness with muscle pains) or some joint pains, and also some general upheaval in the background environment, such as moving house, or changing schools, which created anxiety. In addition most of the children we saw were very bright and doing well at school. Another major factor seemed to be the anxiety of the attending doctor to get to a diagnosis and embarking on a whole range of investigations, many involving needles, and raising the possibility of all sort of nasty diseases, which terrified the patient as well as the parents, and further reinforced the problem.

The child then got into a sort of 'sick role' status, where he was getting a lot of input and attention for his illness and had progressive difficulty getting out of it. So we had to work out a careful strategy to try and get around it. The first was to provide confident reassurance to the child we were going to rehabilitate him completely. The next was to protect him from the doctors. So there was a total ban on any more investigations, which only served to reinforce the anxiety of underlying dreadful disease. The next was to protect him from his parents, who were also very anxious about the possibility of his becoming a life-long invalid in a wheelchair. So we insisted that the child had to be admitted to our unit for intensive daily treatment (voluntary 'parentectomy'). And the next and probably most important step was to provide for the patient an escape route to get away from the illness with honour, and not being accused of it all being psychological. So we developed the strategy of 'escape with honour,' by constantly reinforcing how aware we were of the real physical problem the child was experiencing but at the same time were fully confident we could overcome it.

In fact not only were we able to get remarkable response and return of function, often within days of commencing the regime, but some of them continued with the exercise programme and eventually ended up as competitive athletes. One of the difficult transitions we had was the step of going home from the structured and fairly consistent daily programme of reinforcement in hospital to the environment at home that might precipitate recurrence. So we carefully prepared the child for this, once we thought they were ready, by discussing it and getting a response on when they felt happy to go home. In some cases, where there was still an obvious sense of insecurity and anxiety, we let the child home for a weekend initially and then a week, in order to leave open the possibility of coming back to the ward.

And finally one of the most satisfying outcomes, to our relief, was that the constantly repeated fears of psychiatrists, that if you treat one behaviour disorder in a child, you may open the door for another, which might be a lot worse, did not apply at all and none of these children looked back after their recovery. Perhaps it was because in each case we were able to identify the possible precipitating factor and to discuss it openly with the child as well as the parents. And in every case there was no suggestion of any previous behaviour or personality disorder.

I would like to illustrate two particular cases, with a somewhat unusual presentation, which took some time and a bit of careful detective work to get to the bottom of. The first case was a problem of ambulation, but a most unusual one, perhaps unprecedented in a muscle unit. This 12-year-old boy presented with inability to walk normally and only able to walk on his knees. The presenting picture was reminiscent of the devout Christians in Mexico, who will cover the 100 yards or more approach to the shrine on holy days on their knees. The story was a brief and fairly clear-cut one. The patient and his younger brother were sent home from boarding school after a three-day illness of fever and malaise and aches and pains in the legs. The younger child's symptoms soon subsided and he was back to normal within a few days. However, the pains persisted in the older brother and he remained unable to walk. He did, however, manage to crawl around actively or tried to hobble on his knees. When seen by the local paediatrician two weeks after the onset, his condition was unchanged. His blood tests, including muscle enzymes were normal. A diagnosis of resolving myositis (inflammation of muscles) was made. Two weeks later he was unchanged and referred to my muscle clinic at Hammersmith. On examination he was unable to stand or walk, complained of pain in his calves, and had 'excruciating' tenderness on palpation of the calves; in fact it was even difficult to get near his calves to touch them. In contrast, he was able to raise his legs against gravity when lying supine, and on detailed clinical assessment I was unable to detect any weakness. I thus concluded that this was a case of so-called 'hysterical paralysis', which was a sequel to the presumptive myositis. So we set in train our usual programme of escape with honour, with full understanding of the physical disability, and gradual physical rehabilitation. He initially continued to move around actively on his knees but we were gradually able to get him back to full normal ambulation, and reinforced our optimism for a full recovery with both him and his parents.

We were initially at a loss to explain the reason for his persistent problem, as there was no evidence of any previous behavioural problems or any immediate precipitating factor, apart from the initial myositis. We were gradually able to tease out a potential explanation. The parents had been very keen for both their sons to have a traditional, high quality, public school education (equivalent to fee-paying private school). The younger boy had settled in quite well, but the older was extremely unhappy in boarding school and pleaded with his mother to come home. She was sympathetic towards his wishes, but his father was insistent on the importance of the public school education. After a detailed discussion with the parents, they were prepared, with some reluctance, to accept that the anxiety of going to the public school had precipitated the boy's apparent paralysis and sick role situation, as he fully realised that no public school was going to accept a 'cripple', who could only walk on his knees. They were opposed to any psychiatric referral from the beginning, but promised to review the schooling situation. They subsequently did not attend for two successive follow-up review appointments but wrote to say that all was well and the boy was walking normally and back to full activity. No mention at all of a decision on the schooling. Perhaps the very process of being able to draw attention to his problem and then to escape with honour was sufficient to open the dialogue with the parents and get the attention, sympathy and understanding for him to even face up to the rigours of residential public school education.

Paediatricians need to always have an open mind under such circumstance of the possibility of two major problems children may face, of bullying or child abuse, both of which can be extremely difficult to bring into the open.

My next experience, a non-muscle one, was a rather complex and also delicate situation, as it involved close friends who were both also medical. We went out together one evening to a concert at St John's, Smith Square, and they also brought along their two children, an older girl and younger brother, both of whom had an interest in music and were having tuition. After the concert we arranged to join them for a meal at their home and were rather surprised that the mother and daughter took the car but father and son had to go by underground tube train, as the boy was so intensely allergic that he could not tolerate the upholstery or carpeting in the car and got intractable sneezing. When we eventually all met up in their home, the boy was unable to join us in the living room owing to his allergy to the carpets, which induced an instant paroxysm of intractable sneezing at an amazing repetitive rate of perhaps 100 or so per minute. As soon as he came into the kitchen it stopped instantly. I have been a severe hay fever sufferer myself all my life, with sensitivity to pollen in the summer, but had never experienced or indeed witnessed anything like this before.

I discussed it further with the boy who explained that he had had a relatively mild allergy, which had become exacerbated when their carpeting was re-laid on the staircase, and had subsequently become acute. They had seen a leading allergen physician at one of the London teaching hospitals, who had done a series of skin sensitivity tests and found that he was particularly sensitive to house-dust mite. He had prescribed various medications, which did not seem to have any influence. I was extremely puzzled by the whole story and particularly by the instant switching on and off of the attacks when moving from one room to another. It somehow rang a bell with me that it was somewhat akin to the children I had seen with the hysterical paralysis.

So I arranged with the parents for me to go round and chat to the lad on his own one afternoon when he got back from school. I duly met up with him, and discussed with him in detail what set it off and tried out various environments to see if there was a common ground. Going from one room to another in the house precipitated instant and continued attacks, entirely in relation to the presence of carpeting, and the only safe place was the kitchen and his bedroom which had been stripped of all carpeting and also down pillows and other likely sources of house mites.

I discussed with him the sensitivity to motorcars and once again he had an almost instant and universal reaction when entering a car, presumably related to carpeting or other source of allergens. I offered to try out my car with him and once again he was anxious about entering the car and as soon as he did, had instant sneezing. I pointed out that in fact my car had only rubber mats and no upholstery at all and perhaps if one waited a little while it might settle, which it did shortly after.

I then had a detailed discussion with him, using the same tack as I did with my muscle cases, that I thought he had a severe allergy and this was probably due to the house dust mite in the carpeting which had been lifted on the staircase. However, I felt that by this time the causative agent should have settled and the reason for his continued attacks was not the further exposure to the mite, but that his body had not yet been able to adapt again to the absence of the mite. I suggested we try and see if he could perhaps tolerate a little bit of exposure at a time in the rooms of his house. So we went from the safety of the kitchen to a very short visit to the lounge and to come out again after a minute or less. No problem. I gradually exposed him for slightly longer periods and he became gradually more tolerant. This was very reassuring for both of us. His parents then came home and I decided to defer any further efforts for the moment but said we had worked out a scheme for gradually readapting to the exposure to carpets and so forth and he was going to continue with it and I would be coming round again in a few days to review things with him.

On our next meeting his sneezing had completely resolved. I expressed my pleasure and congratulations to him on how well he had done. Having gained his confidence, I started chatting with him about his schooling and general activities and it rapidly became clear to me that he had developed a severe anxiety, because of the relative success his sister had at school and also with her musical ability, and that he was concerned at how much more attention she was getting from the parents and that he felt he was failing them. When I broached the subject with the parents, they were reluctant to accept there could be a psychological basis to the problem, and indeed became quite aggressive about it, which seems to be a common initial response of parents in this whole group of problems, in accepting it as an explanation. But when I went into the details with them, they realised that his anxieties were probably well founded and, having seen the remarkable cure within days of a problem that had been going on unabated for several months, they also agreed to consciously try to give him more attention and praise and reinforcement.

There was no further recurrence of the problem, indeed of any allergic problem at all, and a few weeks later the parents sent me a very nice letter of appreciation together with a few bottles of wine.

Nearer the bone, closer to home

I guess it is not altogether surprising that doctors may be blind to, or perhaps turn a blind eye to, problems in themselves or their family members, that they would have no difficulty diagnosing in their patients. We had already had such an embarrassing experience in not realising Daniel had severe deafness due to glue ears, until his infant school teacher very diplomatically drew it to our attention.

At the age of around five years Daniel woke up one morning and found himself unable to stand or walk, owing to excruciating pain in his leg. In fact it was so severe that I could not get near him and he was reluctant to move the leg at all. He had also had a mild fall on the stairs the previous evening. I gradually got round to touching the leg very gently and at least localising the pain to the tibia bone, but not any more focal than that. I was also able to convince myself that the joints seemed freely mobile and not painful and that there was no obvious muscle weakness. It all looked a bit incongruous and his disability seemed disproportionate to any actual problem I could identify in the leg itself. But I felt I had to give him the benefit of the doubt and arrange a few routine investigations. So I telephoned a senior orthopaedic colleague at the Hammersmith and told him the story and that I personally could not find any evidence of a fracture or any localised tenderness to suggest an infection such as osteitis (bone inflammation) but would be happy to have his assessment and perhaps an X-ray to exclude a hairline fracture.

He did a very careful examination and agreed with me that there was no obvious sign of fracture or inflammation. The X-ray was also clear. I then had a personal discussion with him that it looked to me like some form of anxiety overlay and I would prefer him to give Dan some reassurance and that we would observe his progress at home, rather than admitting him to hospital and perhaps putting him at bed rest and leg traction, which is a common ploy of orthopods, to improve the patient, and give themselves time to think about the diagnosis. I felt that this might only consolidate Dan's problem, whatever the underlying nature and cause. So we duly followed this strategy and took him home and allowed him to rest and make his own attempts at remobilisation, with our supportive encouragement.

The following morning Dan was able to get onto his feet, and with great effort and difficulty take a few tentative steps. Later that afternoon things looked much better and he came out with a classical remark, in response to my enquiry how he was doing 'I am limping much better now!' Within a further few days it all resolved completely. The whole episode was a bit of a mystery until the underlying anxiety that had precipitated it emerged. The father of one of his closest friends at school had died suddenly a few weeks earlier of an unexpected heart attack. He was only 45. My own birthday was coming up in a couple of weeks and I was also in the process of finalising travel plans to New York soon after for a conference. Dan became extremely anxious about me going to New York and somehow drew an association with dying at 45 and had a fear that it was a vulnerable age to die, and he was thus making an effort to prevent me going to New York. We were then able to talk the whole chain of events through with him and to give him the necessary reassurance.

Hysterical itch

Out of the blue on day, Lil developed an intractable itch of the scalp and neck, which became quite disabling, as she found herself continuously scratching whilst on the neonatal ward rounds or in the midst of other activities. She duly consulted the dermatologist at Hammersmith Hospital, who could find no evidence of any skin disorder and started probing her personal life and tactfully enquiring whether perhaps she was being beaten up by her husband, or the like, as he was suspecting a possible hysterical basis for the itch as a response to some deep-rooted psychological trauma. He advised Lil to consult a psychiatrist and she duly arranged an appointment. However, the matter resolved itself before the appointment materialised, when Daniel brought a note home from school, that there had been an outbreak of head lice at the school, which always spreads like wildfire, and would she ensure an appropriate medicated shampoo was obtained for it. So both Lil and Daniel duly applied the medicated hair wash, and Lil was completely cured of her itch, without recourse to the psychiatrist. I couldn't resist writing a short annotation on hysterical itch for *The Lancet*, in the hope of drawing the attention of the medical profession to it and sparing their patients a psychiatric probe.

Thallium story; Agatha Christie to the rescue

One Sunday morning in 1977, I had an unexpected phonecall from Dr Usha Bhat, a paediatrician from Bombay who had spent a couple of years in our unit at Hammersmith on a Commonwealth fellowship, and was now in practice in Qatar. Would I be able to see a rather unusual infant, who was unsteady on her feet and had some rather complex and variable symptoms? I said I would be delighted but could we postpone it to the following week as I was examining all week in the membership examinations of the College of Physicians. A bit of a problem as the family were already at the airport, about to board a flight to Heathrow! So there was no alternative but to phone my resident house physician on duty and ask him to arrange for a bed to be available for the pending arrival and to let me know as soon as he had assessed the patient. His call finally came through close to midnight.

It was a very bizarre and complex situation as this 19-month-old child was semiconscious and unresponsive to speech or commands, although she did seem aware of someone speaking to her. According to her parents, her illness had apparently begun some ten days earlier with a major convulsion, lasting about five minutes and associated with a fever of 40°C. The temperature settled spontaneously within 24 hours and then remained normal. Over the next three days she became increasingly clumsy and lethargic, and developed slurring of her speech. She was hospitalised in Qatar, where a large number of investigations proved normal. By the seventh day of her illness, she was unable to sit, stand or walk, and had difficulty with swallowing. The following day she had a further convulsion, lasting about five minutes. At that stage she was transferred to us.

A number of episodes in her recent history seemed of possible relevance. One month earlier she had fallen off a fairly high cupboard and struck the back of her head on a concrete floor. How she got onto the cupboard remained a mystery. Four months previously, when aged 15 months, she had almost drowned in her bath, while left unattended by her mother for a short period. She was rushed to hospital and resuscitated, without any apparent sequelae.

There was no history of obvious contact with poisons or drugs, but she had been found with a fertiliser bottle on the kitchen floor about a week before the onset of her symptoms. Apparently she often wandered about the house on her own and had access to several low-level kitchen cupboards, where various domestic substances were stored.

Examination after her admission was not very helpful. She had some drooping of her eyelids, no defensive blink, and the optic discs were pale. She was generally floppy with poor muscle tone and poor head control when pulled up to a sitting position, and was unable to maintain the sitting position unaided. There were continuous movements of her arms and legs whenever handled or disturbed. Her reflexes were brisk and the plantar response extensor. She had a 3-cm bruise on her left upper arm, which her parents ascribed to a bite by her five-year-old brother.

With a tentative diagnosis of possible encephalitis, we repeated her previously normal spinal tap and the fluid was again normal, as were a series of routine tests on the blood and urine. Skull X-ray showed an old occipital fracture but a full skeletal survey showed no additional fractures. A full metabolic screen on blood and urine were also normal as were viral studies. A routine toxic screen on blood and urine was negative apart from a trace of benzodiazepine, presumed to relate to the treatment of her convulsion. An EEG recording the day after admission showed diffuse abnormality with excessive slow activity throughout, suggesting diffuse encephalopathy.

We were still at a complete loss for a diagnosis, and during the ensuing four days, her condition showed a slow but steady decline. On the fifth day she had an unexplained episode of high blood pressure, associated with a rapid heart rate of 200/min and cyclical breathing, lasting some 18 hours. She seemed to become more moribund at this stage and the question of possible respirator support was mooted. The decision was a thorny one, as we did not have a firm diagnosis and could thus not predict if the deteriorating level of consciousness was potentially reversible of not. In the event, her breathing spontaneously improved again and her serial blood gas levels never became sufficiently deranged to give cause for anxiety.

The following morning, during my routine ward round, after we had completed our discussion of all the possible diagnoses in this mysterious child, the nurse who was 'specialling' the child, who was under 24-hour surveillance, peered over the top of the book she was reading and said 'Excuse me Professor, but could the child have thallium poisoning?' I was completely bowled over, and in response to my surprised reaction, and question of her reasons for the suggestion, she pointed out that the Agatha Christie thriller she was reading, *A Pale Horse*, related to a series of cases of thallium poisoning, and that the symptoms were remarkably similar to those of the child and equally bizarre. In particular, the one consistent feature stressed in the book, namely loss of hair, seemed to be developing in the child that morning.

Indeed on inspection of the child's scalp, clusters of hair seemed to be coming away spontaneously or with minimal traction.

Thallium was not one of the toxic substances included in the screen of the national referral laboratory at Guys Hospital, to which we had originally sent the samples, and they were still unable to do it on our specific request but suggested we contact Scotland Yard. They in turn were able to channel us to a specialised forensic laboratory who were able to oblige. A urine sample contained 3.7 μg per litre, which is more than ten times the permitted maximum level. On further discussion, an expert at Scotland Yard drew our attention, rather tongue in the cheek, to an international expert on thallium poisoning in our own health district!

Graham Young was serving life imprisonment at Wormwood Scrubs prison, next door to the Hammersmith Hospital (and indeed a much more impressive building, often attracting my visitors from abroad, who were surprised I was unknown at the enquiry desk). He had an interesting, if somewhat unconventional scientific career. Having studied, whilst still at school, the effects of various poisons, and in particular thallium, on his pet rabbits, he became a bit more ambitious and extended the experiments to his father and sister and a school friend, all of whom became ill but survived. He was convicted in court as a juvenile and sent to Broadmoor prison for the criminally insane, with a recommendation to serve at least 15 years. But he was released after only eight years to a psychiatric clinic in Slough, where he attended a job-training centre. He subsequently obtained a job at a photographic instruments factory in Bovingdon, where he provided tea for his colleagues. Two previously healthy men died after a mysterious short acute illness. Several other members of the staff also had severe acute symptoms, from which they gradually recovered. Young was subsequently arrested and the presence of thallium found in the body of one of the men who had died after it was exhumed, and in the ashes that had been kept in a casket after the second man had been cremated. At that time thallium was still used in the photographic industry. He was sentenced to life imprisonment in 1971 and also admitted responsibility for the death of his stepmother.

To return to our patient, detailed discussion with her parents suggested that the most likely source of the thallium was domestic poison to eliminate cockroaches and rodents in the drains and septic tank in their home. This is apparently common practice in the Middle East. A reappraisal of her clinical features by Dr Peter Rudge at the National Hospital for Nervous Diseases, Queen Square, who had had the opportunity of studying some of Graham Young's victims, revealed white Mee's lines on her fingernails, and her hair also showed the dark band of thallium deposition. These suggested she had probably been exposed to thallium over a long period, but we were never able to establish how she managed to ingest the poison. A decision was made to treat her, even at this late stage, although the prognosis is usually thought to be pretty hopeless once neurological symptoms have set in. She was given oral Prussian Blue (potassium ferric ferrocyanide), a chelating agent, which combines with and solubilises heavy metals and helps in their excretion.

Over the next 14 days her clinical state remained fairly static, although her urinary thallium levels were falling and after three weeks of treatment became immeasurable. She then began to show obvious clinical improvement, took an interest in her surroundings, regained a defensive blink of her eyes and started to swallow. At this stage she returned to Qatar. When she came for a follow-up review four months later, there was remarkable improvement. She was sitting unsupported and able to stand and walk with help, although still ataxic and unsteady. She appeared to be alert and responsive and took an interest in her surroundings. She did not come back for any further review and we were unable to obtain any further information on her progress.

The final question was how did Agatha Christie have such profound knowledge of a condition that perplexed the medical profession? A bit of further detective work revealed she had worked as a nursing orderly on the dermatology wards in University College Hospital in the 1920s. At that time thallium was still widely used in dermatological preparations and she would thus have gained personal observations on the clinical sequelae of thallium poisoning.

I wrote a report on this case, with my registrar Tom Matthew, as a potential bit of light entertainment for the Christmas issue of *The Lancet*, under the title of Diagnostic Mousetrap. The editor obviously didn't read it, as he came back shortly after with a standard regret letter of pressure on space and unable to accept the paper.

I then thought in order to get a large and receptive audience, a good place would be the *British Journal of Hospital Medicine*, a free journal sent to hospital doctors with a series of interesting review and other articles. It was the only journal I regularly looked at each week, on arrival in the morning, before *The Lancet* and *BMJ*. The editor phoned me a few days later that he had enjoying reading it and was sending it to press right away.

Most medical and general scientific weekly journals are published on a Friday and the national press have prior access to them earlier in the week with an embargo on any publication till the day of issue of the journal. On the Thursday evening of that week, my home telephone started ringing at about 11 pm and continued incessantly until about 3 am. I was initially completely puzzled at what was happening as they were all from the national daily press and were asking a similar question 'Did Agatha Christie really save your patient?' I replied in the affirmative and provided some of the background details. In the morning it became obvious what had happened. The medical correspondent of *The Times* had spotted the article, read it in careful detail, and had a full column on the front page of the morning edition headed by the title 'Agatha Christie rescues child'. Apparently all the daily newspapers read each other as soon as the first edition is published, so that a scoop by one paper is often shared by all of them in the final morning editions.

But that was not the end of the story. They were also pursuing Nurse Maitland, to whom I had given a special acknowledgement at the end of the article for keeping us up-to-date on the literature, after acknowledging the excellent and perceptive clinical descriptions of Agatha Christie. I could not provide any detail for them and eventually the senior nursing officer at Hammersmith Hospital thought she could close the matter, after the persistent telephone calls, by telling the press that Nurse Maitland was in fact no longer at the hospital, but had completed her training and returned to Canada. Later in the morning there was a call to my office from the Canadian Broadcasting Corporation to speak personally to me. My secretary said I was not available and they requested to phone me at home at 6 pm my time, which I agreed. A very animated interviewer came through on time that evening and asked a few direct questions such as was it really Nurse Maitland who had made the diagnosis.

I confirmed this absolutely, adding that without her we were completely puzzled and stumped for a diagnosis and it would certainly never have occurred to us. The conversation went on a good ten minutes. A few days later I had a call from David Goldberg, an old colleague from Sheffield days, currently in Toronto. 'What a surprise Victor; how nice to hear your voice on the programme *As it happens* which goes out live each day!' I had no idea at all that I was giving a live interview with the Canadian national radio.

The whole experience was very educational for me and a tremendous insight as to how the world press works. By that weekend most of the Sunday supplements had the story in them and I received in ensuing weeks cuttings from as far afield as Sydney and Melbourne, Los Angeles, Hong Kong and various other countries. What fun to fire the imagination of the lay press. As my friend Peter Scheuer remarked sardonically on reading the headline and article in *The Times*, 'strange really that I have never seen them comment on your excellent work on muscle histochemistry!' *C'est la vie*.

Dubowitz Syndrome

In 1963 I saw an unusual child at my outpatient clinic in Sheffield. She had been born at full term but was nevertheless extremely small in size and had remained considerably below the normal range. She also had an unusual looking face, which seemed quite distinctive. Two other predominant features were a very severe eczema and sensitivity to sunlight.

Of special interest was a similar infant born earlier, who had possibly also been born prematurely and died of an infection in the neonatal period. The mother thought there was a remarkable facial resemblance. I reviewed all the relevant medical literature on low birthweight infants and could not find an exactly similar description or facial appearance. So I wrote a short case report with illustrations in the *Journal of Medical Genetics*. This caught the eye of Dr John Opitz, in Germany at that time, who saw a very similar looking child and wrote a report on the similarity to my case. He subsequently moved to Madison, Wisconsin in the USA and rose to pre-eminence in the genetic field. He continued a special interest in what he labelled the 'Dubowitz Syndrome' and was able to review a larger series of personal cases. His interest has continued to the present and a few years ago I experienced an unusual coincidence in Salt Lake City. We were visiting our eldest son in Pasadena, and had a prior letter from a neurologist in Salt Lake City, Kevin Flanigan, who had recently restarted a muscle clinic there. A family of three affected boys with a congenital muscle disorder that I had seen in a visit to Salt Lake City in 1986, had recently come back to the clinic, more than ten years later, and had enquired if there was any possibility I might be coming back to Utah as they would like to consult me again. So I duly arranged to visit Salt Lake from Pasadena.

Whilst there, who do I bump into in the corridor, but John Opitz, who is particularly amazed to see me, as he had been trying to get me on the phone in London that week. Apparently the support group of families with Dubowitz Syndrome, which I had heard from when they were established some years earlier, had been very active in the USA and he was just in the process of arranging the first clinical session devoted to patients with Dubowitz Syndrome in Salt Lake in two weeks time and had been trying to contact me to see if I might be able to fly over from London to join them. So I duly got release from my family to do another short trip to Salt Lake city from Los Angeles two weeks later and had a most illuminating day seeing some 12 new cases with suspected Dubowitz Syndrome and also meeting up with some of the established cases.

Hospice movement in USA

During a three-month 'sabbatical' in 1999 to Boston, spent mainly at the Boston Children's Hospital and in the lab of Lou Kunkel, pioneer in the discovery of dystrophin in Duchenne dystrophy, I also attended the weekly neurology rounds of the combined hospitals and gave a lecture at one of them.

If there was a spare fifth Wednesday in any month, the grand round was dedicated to a social aspect of medical practice and this occasion was an interesting review of the American hospice system. Unlike the UK, America does not have separate residential hospices, but the services are provided on a domiciliary basis in the main hospitals themselves. After an overview by the current director of the hospice services, an individual case was presented in detail to illustrate the process. This was an 86-year-old man with an advanced prostate cancer, who had had all the usual therapy, including surgery and radiotherapy. He then developed an inoperable cancer of the bladder, which was beyond any radical treatment and was accordingly offered palliative care under the hospital's hospice services. After the presentation of all the medical details by a physician, the social worker assigned to him gave a detailed report on all the background circumstances. He had always lived independently in his own apartment and had three children who were very caring and supportive, especially since the loss of his wife some years earlier. They very actively encouraged him to stay in hospital and accept the hospice care but he flatly refused and was adamant he wished to go home to his apartment. There seemed no possibility of any compromise, so special arrangements were made by the hospice movement to provide regular nursing support at his apartment and also to help with his shopping needs and in addition the social worker would call regularly to provide support.

After this very detailed review of the patient, they then arranged for him to come in. One was anticipating a bedbound elderly invalid in the terminal stages of cancer. Instead, in walked a sprightly 86-year-old, who hardly looked his age. He was surprisingly alert, and happy to respond to any questions raised by the assembled audience of doctors.

'What has the hospice movement done for you?' someone opened with. 'It saved my life,' he responded. 'If I had stayed on in hospital, as suggested, I would have died, probably in a short space of time, as I had no will to live under such circumstances. Once I was back in my own apartment I had full zest for going on.' 'How are you coping with day-to-day life at home?' 'I manage most of the regular activities on a day-to-day basis, and also some of my daily shopping needs at a store on the corner. Once a week the social worker does my main shopping for me at the supermarket and helps to sort out any special needs.' 'Do you have any pain?' 'I have had a lot of pain in the past but at present am well balanced and comfortable with sufficient pain-killing drugs, including morphine, administered by the nurse under the supervision of the medical team, and this has kept me relatively pain-free, and also sufficiently alert and awake, as I became tolerant of the medication.'

And so the dialogue continued and it was now just over three years, since the diagnosis of the inoperable bladder cancer. Finally one of the doctors asked 'You seem so happy and content; do you have any worries about the future?' 'Sure I have,' came an almost instant response, 'I have been following my favourite baseball team, the Boston Red Sox, for many years. I am extremely worried that if they continue to play as badly as in the past season, they will soon be slipping away down the league.' This was one of the most educational medical hours I had had for a long time. One can often learn more in an hour from one patient than in 24 from the medical literature.

Chairman's round; an American clinical tradition

On one of my visits to the Children's Hospital of the Long Island Jewish Hospital complex, where my South African contemporary and friend, Phil Lanzkowsky has been the longstanding Director of Service and chairman of department, he asked me if I would like to take the morning's 'Chairman's Rounds'. This is a traditional clinical practice in academic units in the United States, where the residents meet the departmental chief in his office first thing in the morning, usually at 8 am, to discuss all the new admissions to the ward overnight. After an overview by the chief resident of all the cases, a few individual cases are selected for more detailed discussion. One of the junior residents gave a very impressive account of a young infant, which had various presenting features suggestive of congenital HIV infection, transmitted by the infected mother. This was in the early days of the AIDS epidemic and novel for me. I was rather disappointed that after an excellent presentation of the clinical features, she did not proceed to discuss the diagnosis and the possible implications, but went off at a tangent to a very detailed review of recent literature on the subject, which she must have spent most of the night accessing. I listened attentively until she had finished, complimented her on her excellent clinical description, and then said I had one specific question to ask her. 'What is the half-life of material you read in the medical literature'. She looked at me silent and somewhat puzzled. So I provided my own answer. 'I would say on average I have forgotten about half of what I had read within a week and most of the rest in the weeks following. Now what is the half-life of a patient that you have personally clerked, and got involved in and discussed?' Silence. 'Well I can tell you, it may be a lifetime, and I can still give you full details of some of the patients I clerked during my time as a medical student. I hope you will rapidly learn to have confidence in your own observations, and what you learn from your own experience, and capitalise on it, in addition of course to any supplementary information from the experience of others.'

American medicine; technology reigns supreme

Another exposure to American medical practice, which indicated the way technology has come to dominate clinical practice, occurred some years earlier when I was on an exchange professorship for a month between the RPMS (Royal Postgraduate Medical School) and UCLA (University of California, Los Angeles) in 1976. My host at UCLA, Bob Neerhout, asked me if I would be prepared to be the 'Attending' during my visit. This is a period of time when members of the consultant clinical staff, are on call for special medical problems and also entails a routine round, usually on a weekly basis, with the chief resident, who has usually had some years clinical experience, and in essence runs the paediatric unit on a day to day basis, together with a cohort of residents and fellows. The residents presented for discussion a toddler with progressive hydrocephalus (excess fluid in the brain ventricles or cavities), presumably due to some obstruction in the normal flow and circulation of the fluid. After a brief clinical summary they proudly showed me a series of three successive CT (computed tomography) scans of the brain, showing the progressive increase in size of the ventricular cavities. I placed a finger on top of the child's head and noted that the fontanelle, which all infants have open at birth and eventually closes completely just after a year of so, was still widely open and under some tension. Do you have any head circumference charts to show me to see how the head has grown in comparison with the normal growth lines in relation to age? Stunned silence. Not a single head circumference measurement in the case notes. Now this was a very interesting situation historically, as the CT scanner had been developed in the UK by Hounsfield, and he had in fact had close discussions with a senior radiologist at the RPMS, Frank Doyle, who had a good knowledge of physics, and was impressed by the validity of all the observations of Hounsfield. The large industrial company EMI had produced these pioneering new instruments, which were to provide the first visual image of the brain. The paradox of the situation was that at the time we did not yet have a CT scanner at the Postgraduate Medical School, but there were already three in Los Angeles, one in the children's hospital and two in private practice, working round the clock and having already paid off their investment costs.

So I started off by thanking them on behalf of EMI for supporting British industry and exports. To their amazement we did not yet have a machine of our own at the RPMS. However, in our paediatric department, I informed them, we had a fairly useful, and considerably cheaper instrument, called a tape measure, and we routinely measured the head circumference of any infant with a progressive hydrocephalus on a daily basis, and by comparison with the standard charts were able to get some idea of progression, although we were aware of some of the limitations of this approach and the care needed in interpretation.

Of course this is not to underestimate the tremendous contribution that brain imaging has made to the non-invasive investigation of brain abnormality. Indeed our newborn unit helped to pioneer the application of simple ultrasound scanning, already widely used in obstetrics, for the assessment of the presence of bleeding and other changes in the newborn brain, which as clinicians we were able to do routinely on our unit, without the need to refer the fragile infants to the radiologists. The later advent of Magnetic Resonance Imaging (MRI) added a whole new dimension and quantum leap in the imaging of the brain throughout life, and Hammersmith was the first neonatal unit in the world to have a specially constructed scanner installed on the unit for the imaging of newborn infants.

The main anxiety of traditional clinicians like myself was that technology was taking over and becoming the master of the clinician rather than the servant. This was well illustrated by a trend in the USA, soon after the advent of the CT scanner to classify headaches into 'CT scan positive' and 'CT scan negative' headaches, on the basis of the CT imaging, almost before a detailed history of the headache was documented by the clinician. I initially thought it was a joke or at least an exaggeration, but I soon realised it was for real, and in many branches of medicine, clinicians were beginning to pay more attention to the technological data, rather than the clinical observations.

A horse named Dubowitz

One of my most unusual and unexpected experiences relates to an eight-year-old boy I saw in the mid 1980s, from Tipperary in the southern part of Ireland, who had had a diagnosis of spinal muscular atrophy made at the age of 18 months by an eminent neurologist. The basic diagnosis was correct but the neurologist gave the prognosis straight from the textbook, rather than looking at the child, and related it to the severe form of SMA, so-called SMA1 or Werdnig Hoffmann disease, and told the parents that the infant was unlikely to survive beyond two years. Well, as so often happens in clinical practice, the child had not read the textbooks and he not only survived his second birthday but also the third, and the fourth, and the fifth, and the sixth, and the seventh, and was still showing no signs of imminent death. And the parents of course were becoming more and more puzzled and confused. I was able to reassure them that although he did indeed have SMA it was not the severe type 1 form, but the milder type 2. Moreover, although he had never been able to stand or walk, I thought there was a good chance of getting him ambulant with long leg, lightweight braces, given his excellent ability to maintain a sitting posture.

He not only got fully ambulant with his orthoses, but coming from horse country (Tipperary is equivalent to the Kentucky of Ireland) his father, who was a racehorse trainer, also taught the boy to ride.

A few years later after their regular six-monthly visit, I had a message awaiting my return to my office, that they wanted to see me again at the end of my clinic. So I went back to meet up with them. I was confronted by the totally unexpected and startling news that the father had decided to name a racehorse after me. He explained that the only basic requirement was that the name had to be unique and on checking he found that there was no horse anywhere in the world named Dubowitz!

After catching my breath, I tried to back-pedal as fast as I could in order to extricate myself from this somewhat threatening ordeal, as I could already envisage the embarrassment of reports on national races 'Dubowitz fails again', 'Dubowitz comes in last', 'Dubowitz down at first hurdle' and so on.

So I told him quite straight that as much as I appreciated this thoughtful gesture, there was no way I could accept it as the GMC, the General Medical Council, would certainly not condone it, as they would look upon it as a form of advertising and flouting the very strict rules of the British system of medical practice. So I politely had to decline.

He was obviously very disappointed, even hurt. So I tried to recoup the situation by saying I would need time to give it further thought. I had indeed not realised what a singular honour it was in Irish racing circles to have a horse named after you, and it was in very bad taste and almost unheard of to turn down such an accolade.

On getting back to my office I told my secretary Val of my plight and dilemma and she instantly came up with a solution. Why not call it 'VictorD' in place of 'Dubowitz'? Brilliant. At least that sounds a lot more victorious than Dubowitz and nobody would recognise the link, and certainly no skin off the teeth of the GMC. I immediately rushed back to the clinic and caught up with the departing family. They were very happy to go along with my alternative suggestion, and we ended the day with smiles of relief all round.

I then went off for my usual one month's annual vacation camping in Yosemite with the family, and was confronted on return by the usual tower of mail (no faxes or emails yet in those days), most of which my very efficient secretary (another endangered species) had already dealt with.

At the top of the pile was a very nice 10 × 8 colour picture of two horses on a race track, and a note at the bottom 'VictorDub is the grey on the left'. I thought it a bit of Irish chutzpah to expand the name, as it was now almost recognisable. But obviously no point in now trying to close the stable door after horse had already bolted.

Further down the pile was a letter with a whole batch of cuttings from the *Irish Times* and the *Irish Racing Times*, with a series of headlines 'VictorDub awaits jury decision'; 'VictorDub

VICTOR DUB SURVIVES AN INQUIRY

EDWARD O'GRADY'S luck took a turn for the better at Naas last evening when Victor Dub, an even money favourite to make a winning debut in the bumper, got home by three quarters of a length from Well Told and then held the race after an inquiry which many thought would probably go th eother way.

By TOM MacGINTY

Victor Dub was inclined to hang towards the runner-up in the closing stages. Mr. Ted Walsh who rode Well Told was of the opinion that that incident made no difference to his horse but a furlong and a half earlier Victor Dub had literally barged his way out of an inside position and badly interferred with Father O'Grady and Instanter.

Although the stewards allowed the result to stand they took a dim view of the winning jockey Mr. Frank Codd's performance and imposed a four days suspension on him.

There is a certain amount of [illegible] horse has lost a race for rather less.

PARNELL DOUBLE

David Parnell who won on Green Ernest the previous night, brought off a double on Musical Score and Sir Shostakovich. Musical Score came from behind in the Clondalkin Race to beat Hunter's Delight convincingly but Sir Shostakovich only just survived in a dramatic finish with Midnight Lace in the Celbridge Handicap.

Declan Gillespie rallied Midnight Lace to such good purpose the two horses were almost inseparable on the line.

"I would have shot myself had we lost. I gave him a crack down the shoulder and had a glance back. I saw nothing in sight ad then suddenlfy a horse's head appeared" said young Parnell who has now ridden 49 winners since he first came to prominence in 1980 and needs only another five in jockeys races to have his allowance reduced to three pounds.

COOL MARTIN

VictorDub (VictorD), the grey on the left, won his first race, but faced a jury enquiry for barging his way across Father O'Grady. A relief I had refused calling the horse Dubowitz faces disqualification' and the like. What had apparently happened was that in his very first major race, VictorDub had headed straight for the finishing line and indeed got there ahead of the field. Unfortunately in his enthusiasm he had crossed lanes and knocked Father O'Grady completely off the course!

Some months later I had a long and rather sad letter from the father, saying that in spite of his excellent pedigree and his great early promise, VictorDub had proved to be totally untrainable, and it was reluctantly decided he had no future as a racehorse and so he was sent to stud instead. I wrote a personal note back expressing my condolences and also noting that although I could detect some similarities in temperament between VictorDub and his namesake, I was certainly unaware of any retired university professors being sent to stud.

12

Remarkable people

This section started with the thumbnail sketches of a number of remarkable people I have had the pleasure to know, who stood out above the normal echelon of society because of their exceptional qualities and achievements. It then expanded to also include some special people, who have had a major impact and influence on my career, and finally an ever-increasing list of close and longstanding friends or academic associates.

On looking back on my career of almost 50 years in clinical paediatrics and neuromuscular disorders, which took off tangentially on a number of occasions from my original objective of family medicine, there are a number of my mentors who stand out in sharp relief for the important role they played in this. What they had in common was the foresight, and might I modestly say wisdom, to take me on trust and give me a more or less free rein. On a 10-point scale, so popular these days in all walks of life, I would probably have scored between one and three out of ten for knowledge and experience, but about nine out of ten for enthusiasm, initiative and drive.

David Lawson

The first was Dr David Lawson, the consultant paediatrician and also medical superintendent at Queen Mary's Hospital for Children, Carshalton, Surrey, who could easily have shaken my hand and wished me well on my further travels after my short *locum tenens* in 1957. Instead he encouraged me to apply for the one-year senior house officer post falling vacant shortly and in parallel with that gave me *carte blanche* to study and investigate any of the long-stay muscle patients under his care, which he was happy for me to continue doing as a research fellow, supported by a grant from the Muscular Dystrophy Group, when the residency year ended. This was my first exposure to paediatrics and opened the door for my whole future career.

What's this—a harem at Queen Mary's Hospital? Things are not what they seem, for these young beauties are really nurses, at the hospital, "wine

FIRE HOAXER MAKES HIS NINTH CALL

INQUIRY LASTED

David and Billi Lawson (centre) at annual Christmas dinner at Queen Mary's Hospital for Children, Carshalton, Surrey, served by a harem of wine waiters, provided by the nursing staff

Tony Pearse

The second important person was Professor Everson Pearse at the Hammersmith, a world leader in the new discipline of histochemistry, who welcomed me to his team of highly motivated and knowledgeable international enthusiasts. This provided for me a highly charged intellectual environment at the Royal Postgraduate Medical School, and a chance to take up the challenge of the steep learning curve of acquiring and understanding what was for me a totally new scientific language. Tony Pearse had an immense capacity for inspiring young researchers and quietly guiding and channelling them, without being in any way overbearing or intrusive. In turn, he was particularly interested in venturing into new clinical problems, which were not in his own mainstream of research, which was more geared to endocrine functions of neuronal cells. I derived so much pleasure and inspiration from Pearse, that I seriously contemplated a career in pathology and muscle research. The opening John Cuming offered me in an academic position in his clinical pathology department at Queen Square was a major stepping stone in that direction, but I rapidly realised my heart was in clinical medicine, so I needed to change course again.

Tony Pearse, Royal Postgraduate Medical School, pathologist and scientist, father of histochemistry

Ronald Illingworth

I could hardly believe my luck when Professor Illingworth offered me a clinical lectureship post in paediatrics after I had not even considered myself eligible to apply, given the specific requirement of a membership diploma of the college of physicians, the requisite gold standard for entry into training as a clinical consultant. A major factor was undoubtedly Illingworth's willingness to take me on trust. I later learnt he had a capacity for taking people at face value, was extremely loyal in his support of his junior colleagues, and would be quite prepared to encourage anyone with initiative and drive. It really was a big jump up the rungs of the clinical ladder to go from one year's experience at a resident level in paediatrics to a position equivalent to a senior registrar level, usually attained after three years in the intermediate registrar grade. In addition, the status of a lectureship in the university provided a certain amount of academic autonomy and security. I guess a number of additional factors must have played in my favour. Firstly, the meeting with Moncrieff, which essentially was a preliminary interview for the post. Furthermore, there were not many people in clinical paediatrics who were actively engaged in a career in research, given the difficulty of obtaining a consultant position at that time, with the large bottleneck of time-expired, fully-trained senior registrars. So the possibility of someone opening up a new field of clinical interest and research outside the current interests of the department must also have been of some attraction to Illingworth.

From my own perspective I also felt a responsibility and challenge with each of these coveted appointments, to take advantage of the opportunities they opened for me, and to ensure I did not fail the people who had taken me on board. These personal experiences also inspired me in turn in later years to adopt exactly the same approach to applicants for junior posts with me and a number of my protégés were able to get into senior academic positions, such as professorships and heads of departments or of specialised units, in spite of not having the usual experience at the time of appointing them, in comparison with other candidates. The same applied to other posts I filled, such as technical assistants in the laboratory, or editorial assistants with the journal. I always felt that people with initiative and drive could readily catch up with the knowledge and expertise of the job, but people ostensibly having the experience but lacking the drive and initiative, are likely to remain relatively moribund.

It has been very exciting over the years, particularly through the World Muscle Society, but also in my subsidiary areas of general interest in paediatric neurology and neonatal neurology, to come into direct touch with some of the leading and dynamic brains and researchers in the field. I had started including a thumbnail of many of them but soon realised this was an open-ended commitment, and I was rapidly heading into the wedding-guest dilemma of not knowing where to draw the line. So I eventually decided not to include them at all in this separate section but to refer to them where appropriate in the general text.

What I consider a very special privilege has been to meet and get to know personally a number of exceptional people, who have stood out above the ordinary echelon of society because of certain additional qualities. This usually entailed excelling and being knowledgeable in an additional area of interest, apart from their professional one, and thus coming within the category of 'renaissance' person, but in addition also having an extra quality which I value even more highly. That is a sense of philanthropy and public service, and encouraging new initiatives, either in science or the arts. There are two individuals in particular that I have been pleased to look upon as personal friends, who fall into this relatively rare group.

Arthur Sackler

Whenever I was within spitting distance of Philadelphia, which essentially meant the eastern seaboard of the USA, I took advantage of the very special facility Saunders Publishers provided me, of the use of their private apartment in West Washington Square, nearby their offices. Those were the days in the 1980s when they were still an independent medical publisher, which had started originally as a family business, and one could drop in to the office of Jack Hanley, the CEO, for a friendly chat and be welcomed almost as one of the family, having already published two textbooks with them. There were two major advantages of this arrangement. I had access to the Jefferson University medical library up the road, which seemed to have every conceivable current journal available on its shelves, and I could physically scan a year's literature in index medicus in the neuromuscular field in a day and then access the articles, photocopy the abstract page, and then go through them in the evening after closing, and abstract essential information and also print out some selected full manuscripts the next day. The other main advantage was that I was completely incommunicado and thus beyond the usual interruptions and diversions one normally has to any effort at serious writing (other than between midnight and 4.00 am). The only person who had my telephone number was Lil, in case of emergency.

It thus came as a complete surprise to me to have a phonecall out of the blue one morning from a Dr Sackler, who told me he had tried to contact me at the Hammersmith Hospital in London, asked the telephone operator for Dr Dubowitz and the lady they put him through to (actually Dr Dubowitz, my wife) gave him my number, as he said he was calling from New York and she presumed it was in connection with the congress I was going to.

Arthur and Jill Sackler at reopening of the Palace Theatre, formerly the Grand Opera House, in Stamford, Connecticut, December 1983

As always the story was a rather circuitous one. He had a young nephew in England with an unusual neurological problem and was thinking of bringing him over to New York for consultation with Sydney Carter at Columbia University Medical College in New York, who advised him to have a chat with me first, as it might perhaps spare the child a trip over. After a very detailed discussion of the medical problem of his nephew, for whom I was pleased to arrange a consultation on my return to England, he asked if there were any chance of my coming to New York. This type of opening gambit from a medical colleague usually produces a protective response in me, in order to avoid being shown around hospital buildings during my visit rather than slipping away to some galleries or other cultural activities. So I started back-pedalling very hard, indicating I would in fact be in New York for an unusual meeting of Thanatologists at Columbia, but the programme was pretty congested and I doubted I would have much residual time.

'Pity,' he responded. 'It's just that the Metropolitan opera are opening their season next week and I thought you might like to come along with me to the premiere!' 'Now you're talking!' I spontaneously responded, but it looked as though I would not be in New York in time for the opera. He then also asked if I was interested in art and I responded that I usually tried to get the Museum of Modern Art to see any special exhibitions or look around their superb permanent collection. He wondered whether I might be interested in a unique collection of terracotta sculptures at the Metropolitan Museum, their first ever, and I certainly was. The only time free from my conference was after 5 pm on the Wednesday. A bit difficult, he replied, as the museum closes at five, but he would see what he could arrange. I had a call back from him later that his secretary would collect me at the end of my session at the conference at Columbia and take me to the Metropolitan Museum where he would meet me.

When I got to New York, I looked at the *New York Times* and other notices on the various galleries and could not find any information on the exhibition, but walking up Madison Avenue and popping into various private galleries, I picked up one of the brochures on what's on in the galleries and came across a notice of the terra cottas, from the collection of Dr Sackler. En route to the Museum I mentioned this to his secretary and asked if it was the same Dr Sackler. Indeed it was. When we arrived at the Met, the portcullis was already half down with a few final visitors exiting. Dr Sackler was there with the curator and I was then treated to a two-hour tour of the museum including the well-known Sackler wing with the Egyptian temple of Dendur, saved from the flooding of the Valley of the Kings with the Aswan Dam programme, the wing of Asian art, which he had also endowed, and finally the superb and most fascinating collection of terra cottas, spanning several centuries from early religious figures through to originals by Rodin and other famous sculptors. He had built this collection up fairly rapidly over a few years after coming across a small terra cotta he liked in a bric-a-brac shop in France, which turned out to be the work of a famous sculptor. That fired his enthusiasm and he continued to search for more works, many of which were not recognised in antique shops, as they were not part of the mainstream of serious collectors.

With my own particular interest in sculpture the collection was of extra special appeal to me. This chance meeting with Dr

Sackler was the start of a friendship over several years and my wife and I met up with him and his wife, Jill Sackler, on several occasions when we were passing through New York. One memorable occasion was the reopening of the Palace Theatre of the Arts, originally the Grand Opera House (1893–1904), in Stamford, Connecticut, a one-time splendid building that had ceased to be an opera house at the turn of the century after destruction by fire, and had become a cinema and then declined in recent years. There was a wonderful evening with champagne and dinner and two full concerts with the American Symphony Orchestra, conducted by Gabriele Bellini, and including the Dvorak cello concerto (one of my favourites), played by Janos Starker, a Liszt piano sonata by Claudio Arrau, and performances of ballet items and songs by international artists. When the festivities started the workmen were still inserting the last seats in the front row of the dress circle. In addition, a special treat for me was an exhibition of sculpture by the still active and productive 86-year-old Reuben Nakian, whose early exhibition in the Museum of Modern Art, Lil and I had the pleasure of seeing during our year in New York in the mid 1960s.

The Royal Academy in London also has a Sackler wing he endowed, with major reconstruction within the buildings. Sadly, he did not live to see the opening, which had an impressive exhibition of Jill Sacker's collection of jewellery she had assembled in recent years.

A really wonderful man, totally human and humane, with a great joy for giving, who had started from humble beginnings, qualified in medicine, was doing research in psychiatry, and made his fortune with publishing medical magazines for free distribution and attracting a lot of advertising revenue. A truly renaissance man, with a deep knowledge of and love for the arts in many different forms, and a great philanthropist. In addition a very modest and unostentatious man. He had a very ordinary and unimpressive motorcar and a dedicated chauffeur, who used to collect and take him everywhere. He turned out to be a bright young Central American lad from a very poor background, whom Arthur was fully sponsoring through medical school. I consider it a great privilege to have known him personally and a feeling of personal loss when he died unexpectedly of a heart attack at 74.

Ralph Kohn

I cannot quite recall how I first came to meet Ralph Kohn, but it would have been in connection with academic activities. In any event, I got to know him well through his help in coordinating a trial of therapy I set up in boys with Duchenne muscular dystrophy, using a product called isaxonine, which was claimed by the French pharmaceutical company producing it to have a specific effect of nerve influence on muscle and had been shown to be of clinical benefit in a number of nerve disorders, ranging from leprosy to diabetes, and also by Eric Barnard, a biochemist at Imperial College in London, to have a beneficial effect in a chick form of muscular dystrophy. It thus seemed worth trying in Duchenne dystrophy.

Ralph Kohn had a remarkable career. Originally native to Leipzig, his parents had managed to escape to Holland during the growing anti-Semitic campaigns of Hitler in the 1930s and then to escape from Amsterdam to Britain on 14 May 1940 a few hours ahead of the Germans invading the city. The family settled

Enjoying a joke with Ralph Kohn at a lecture at the Royal Institution, London

in Manchester and he duly qualified as a scientist in pharmacology and worked on research with some of the greats of the day, including Ernest Chain, a biochemist in Oxford and Nobel laureate for isolating penicillin to enable clinical trials.

After rising to a senior scientist position in the giant international pharmaceutical company of Smith Kline and French, he decided to start from scratch again and set up his own company, Advisory Services (Clinical and General), aimed at providing special expertise in the interface between the pharmaceutical industry and the medical profession, and in particular setting up clinical trials of new drugs, following the very rigid guidelines of randomised controlled studies. He had obviously discovered not only a niche for his own expertise but also a demand for an expertise not previously available. Not only did he set up studies in the UK, but a rapid demand for his expertise and services also appeared in France, Germany and other European countries, which did not have any comparable mechanism for pilot studies of new drugs, and also in Japan. So successful was his company that a few years later it won a coveted Queen's Award for Industry, the first time a Harley Street based, academically oriented, company had achieved such a distinction, based on the export not of a vacuum cleaner or similar commodity, but of expertise. Ralph had a full team of experts, including a medical statistician.

So my first forage into a Kohn-assisted project also included a trip to Paris to meet up with the scientists in the French company involved in the development of isaxonine, with a very productive lunch that went on into the late afternoon, and ended in the mental haze of a vintage Armagnac.

It is always an exciting experience to meet up with a dedicated enthusiast, but very few people have an additional vision, which sees beyond the ordinary. A sharp contrast to many of the ordinary academics in the upper tiers of academia, and particularly the political front of academia, who have a relatively blinkered vision by comparison.

Following on the remarkable success of his company, both academically and also financially, Ralph was able to set up a Kohn Foundation, which has made substantial contributions to not only the world of science, with a number of major endowments to the Royal Society, but also to the world of music, his other major passion. In addition to his versatile scientific mind, Ralph was also blessed with a superb baritone voice and I have had a particularly pleasurable education and entertainment listening to a whole tower of recordings he has made with the celebrated accompanist, Graham Johnston. Whilst working on cutting edge research with Chain in Italy, Ralph also had regular lessons in singing from one of the maestros of the day, and could probably have followed a professional career as a singer.

A major contribution of the Kohn Foundation was to set up an International Song Competition biennially at the Wigmore Hall in London, for aspiring singers under 32 years, which has met with tremendous enthusiasm and a large number of international entries, gradually condensed down by a panel of international judges on the basis of submitted recordings to about 50 semi-finalists who then performed through the course of an intensive week at the Wigmore Hall. It has been a great privilege and a unique experience for Lil and myself to attend the finale on the Saturday evening, with the final four performers at the end of the week of eliminations.

Muscular Dystrophy Group of Great Britain

The Muscular Dystrophy Group played a very important part in getting my own research career in muscle off the ground in the 1950s, with a research fellowship to pursue my histochemical studies in normal and diseased muscle. I later also served on the scientific research committee for several years. I had the privilege of meeting Professor Nattrass in the early years, who had been the main initiative behind the formation of the Group and struck me as a very sensitive and humane individual. Over the ensuing years there were two people who stood out for their personal dedication to the Group and its activities. The one was the President, Richard (Dickie) Attenborough, the famous actor and later film director, who had a tremendous personal dedication to the activities of the Group.

Interestingly, his initial interest in and subsequent total commitment to muscular dystrophy, had been inspired by exactly the same experience as originally fired me a few years earlier. He was invited by the then secretary of the Muscular Dystrophy Group, Mrs Duval, a friend of the family, to host an event at

Queen Mary's Hospital for Children in Carshalton, Surrey, in aid of muscular dystrophy research. He was so moved by the plight of these cheerful adolescent boys confined to their wheelchairs, and realised how fortunate he was when he watched his own son kicking a ball on the village green later that day, that he felt a commitment to promoting the work of the Group, later becoming their president. Of all the charitable work he did, it always remained his prime charity.

I was impressed by his genuine commitment when he paid us a pastoral visit to our unit in Sheffield in the late 1960s to get a first-hand impression of what was happening at the different centres, and again after our disastrous fire at Hammersmith in 1988, when he personally came to express his shock and support, and launched a public appeal on behalf of the Muscular Dystrophy Group.

The other person who always impressed me with his empathy for the families as well as their cause was Paul Walker, who was the executive director of the Muscular Dystrophy Group for several years. He seemed to have a very personal interaction with many of the families coming to the annual conference of the Group in the Kensington town hall, and indeed some families regularly stayed at his home. He was also very supportive of the Jennifer Trust for Spinal Muscular Atrophy and was happy and enthusiastic to chair their scientific conference each year, and I still have a vivid recollection of the animated lunch we had together with some of the families at his last conference in 1999, a few weeks before his sudden death.

Parents of Prominence

In the course of my work in the muscle field, it has also been a privilege to meet a number of parents of affected children, who had the initiative and drive to see beyond their own personal tragedy, and to initiate efforts to promote interest and support and research in the specific muscle disease involving their own family.

Anita Macaulay

When I fist met Anita Macaulay at my muscle clinic, I had the difficult task of gently breaking the news to her that her delightful firstborn daughter, Jennifer, who had been progressing so well in the first weeks of life, had been struck down by the severe form of Spinal Muscular Atrophy (SMA type 1; also known as Werdnig-Hoffmann disease), one of the most severe genetic neuromuscular disorders. Apart from the severe weakness of the limb and trunk muscles, these infants also have weakness of the respiratory muscles, so any mild chest infection can be life threatening. About 80% of them do not reach their first birthday and it is exceptional for any to survive beyond two years. When Jennifer died, Anita felt not only the tremendous grief at the loss of her daughter, but also a sense of total isolation, as she did not know anyone personally with a similar experience that she could share her grief with. So at Jennifer's funeral she resolved to start a support group for the parents of infants with spinal muscular atrophy. This was the start of the Jennifer Trust, which initially provided personal support from parents who had had a child with SMA for the parents of newly diagnosed infants. But with the tremendous drive and determination of Anita, it gradually grew into one of the largest muscle-oriented charitable trusts in the UK after the Muscular Dystrophy Group, dedicated not only to the initial goal of family support but also to funding research in Spinal Muscular Atrophy. Their annual weekend congress, in the environs of Stratford-upon-Avon, has a day dedicated to scientific

Paul Walker and Anita Macaulay at annual conference of Jennifer Trust for Spinal Muscular Atrophy

The Jennifer Trust is a national support group. It was founded in April 1985 following the death of Jennifer Macaulay from Werdnig-Hoffmann Disease at the age of 7 months. It provides information, understanding and friendship to those in need.

A quarterly newsletter 'Holding Hands' is produced and an Annual Conference Weekend is held offering the opportunity to meet professionals, and others in similar situations in both formal and informal surroundings. J.T.S.M.A has a network of Area Contacts, both for the childhood forms and for adults, who provide 'local support and advice' and are experienced in SMA and aware of the wider issues.

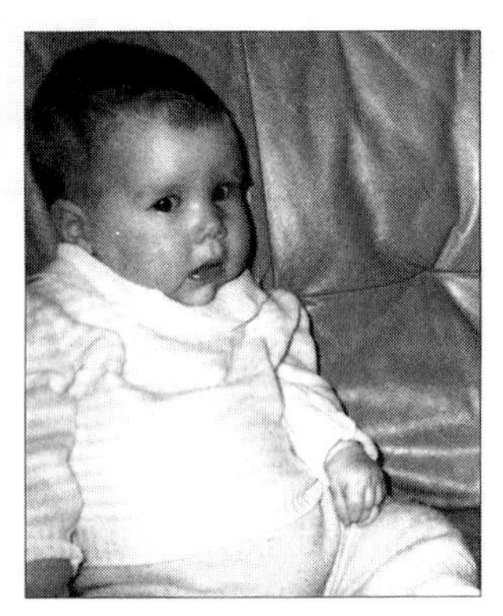

'I founded The Jennifer Trust for SMA to give support today before research finds answers tomorrow.' Anita Macaulay.

Jennifer Macaulay after whom the Jennifer Trust was named

contributions on advances in basic research as well as clinical management of these infants, and also the milder variants of SMA due to mutations in the same gene. There is also opportunity for informal discussions with the scientists and clinical professionals. The rest of the weekend is devoted to social activities and interaction for the children and the families.

Elizabeth Vroom

I first met Elizabeth Vroom some ten years ago through a mutual friend and colleague, Linda de Vries, who had spent some time as a postgraduate on our unit, specialising in neonatal neurology. She had been a close friend of Elizabeth through medical school, and having also had some exposure on our unit to muscle disorders, was concerned that Elizabeth's two-year-old son Justus might have muscular dystrophy. Hence the referral to my clinic. The diagnosis of Duchenne muscular dystrophy was confirmed and Justus subsequently was also one of our first young Duchenne boys to receive treatment with a new schedule of corticosteroids and to show a remarkable improvement. Elizabeth had trained in dentistry, which ran a largely parallel course to medicine in Holland, and had established a very successful practice in children's orthodontics.

From the time of the diagnosis, it was obvious that Elizabeth was not only determined to get the best possible management and support for her son, as a mother, but also to try and get insight into the disease from a scientific viewpoint. Before long she found herself doing battle on several different fronts. In the first place, she devoted time and attention to Justus on a day-to-day basis to ensure that he lead as full and as normal a life as possible. A far greater battle was against the conservatism and completely negative attitude of the medical profession, which was particularly exacerbated by the Dutch neurologists with expertise in the neuromuscular field, who were completely opposed to the use of steroids (without any personal experience of it) and had written to the main Dutch medical journal that there was no concrete evidence of its being of any value and because of side effects it should not be used. So Elizabeth started a campaign of public awareness of the disease, which had such a devastating impact on the affected boys and their families, by personally giving interviews for popular magazines, followed by appearance on television. Before long she had also established a parents support organisation for providing a forum and support for affected families. And it was not long before this blossomed into the major Parents Project organisation, comparable to a similar organisation that had evolved in the United States, which also started appealing for funds to support research directed at the treatment of muscular dystrophy. Her almost single-handed efforts proved to be very successful, mainly through her personal contact with a wide variety of individuals and organisations, both in the arts and in industry. As a result of personal contacts with the Royal Dutch Ballet Company she was able to organise a charity performance by the company, together with a special dinner, with all proceeds going to the Parents Project research funds. The ballet and the dinner were fully subscribed. At a later repeat of the ballet concert, the choreographer produced a novel ballet on Duchenne dystrophy, with three dancers, one of whom gradually showed the progressive loss of muscle power of the Duchenne dystrophy. A subsequent initiative was to commission, as a donation to the Parent Project for Duchenne, a lithograph from ten leading Dutch artists, with a limited edition of 20 copies of each, which were then boxed as a set, and auctioned. All were sold.

Elizabeth Vroom, founder of Parents Project for Duchenne in Holland, with a campaign poster

Justus modestly displays his Order of Oranje Nassau medal, achieved in the Dutch Queen's honours list 2001

It has filled me with amazement and admiration over the years how Elizabeth has managed to come out on top on all fronts and in all her parallel endeavours. And on the face of it, it all seems to be so effortless. But anyone who has organised anything is fully aware that when things seem to be going absolutely smoothly, there is always a vast amount of invisible effort and input behind the scenes to ensure the success and the smooth running and to keep all the cogs in the system well lubricated and functional.

Justus himself was no ordinary person either. He had an unusually high and incisive intellect and could always be expected to come out with the most unexpected remarks or insight into particular issues. Thus, after seeing the performance of Duchenne dystrophy by the Royal Dutch Ballet, he was able to point out that the affected dancer did not really have Duchenne dystrophy, as there was a particular manoeuvre he was able to accomplish, which would not have been possible for an affected boy. Perhaps the choreographer should have consulted him at the time. At a personal level Justus always had everything he could possibly have wished for and aspired to and Elizabeth spared no effort. Apart from regular holidays to exotic places, it also entailed a move from a four-storey town house in central Amsterdam, where Justus achieved the ability to go up the three flights of stairs unaided after being on corticosteroids, which I witnessed personally, to a more practical street-level, one-floor apartment, where Elizabeth had an indoor swimming pool installed in one of the rooms, complete with hoists and ancillary gear. That must certainly have entailed a lot of spadework getting around the normal ground rules of the bureaucracy.

A truly remarkable lady, and well-deservedly honoured in the Queen's Birthday Honours in 2001, by the award of a knighthood in the Order of Oranje Nassau (name of the Dutch Royal family), not only to Elizabeth herself, but coupled with Justus.

13

Extramural: the arts

Growing up in a small country town in South Africa was pretty well devoid of any cultural activity and there was no particular effort at school to either encourage or promote either musical or theatrical activity. I do distinctly recall that we did have one session per week in the junior school devoted to singing, but any potential I might have had was nipped in the bud during one of these group singing activities, when the teacher went round from one individual to another and silenced all those singing in tune. Eventually I was left singing solo. He then announced, 'There's the nightingale! Now will you please remain silent so that the others can go ahead singing in tune'. My mother apparently had a good voice in her youth and both my sister and I had piano lessons for a while but did not show any aptitude or talent. There was also no musical appreciation and the only travelling orchestras were the *boere orkes* (boor orchestra) groups playing popular music and folk songs. I did not develop any appreciation for classical music until I got to university. The one hobby I did pursue from an early age was photography and enjoyed doing my own developing and printing of black and white pictures.

First, and last, theatrical (acting) experience

My only endeavour at anything theatrical was in my final year as a medical student, when a group of my medical contemporaries put on a production of Tennessee Williams' *The Long Goodbye.* Another medical student, Fred Danziger, and I had the role of the two furniture removers, and as I recall my whole speaking contribution was one line with a handful of words, which I practised with care to ensure an appropriate American accent. On the night we produced a near disaster, when we missed the door we were supposed to carry a cupboard through and almost brought the whole set down. I realised there and then that the stage was not for me.

Fred and I met again by an amazing coincidence some 10 years later. I was flying for a day from Melbourne to Canberra to visit Eccles' physiology department in Canberra and we were double-booked on the same seat. We subsequently met up again in New York and it transpired he was also a classical music and hi-fi buff, so gave us a lot of useful tips on buying some economical equipment and also taking advantage of special offers of recordings at Sam Goodys.

I almost become a cellist

During his senior school years, David was quite enthusiastic about playing the cello and, apart from being in the Hampstead Garden Suburb Saturday morning Youth Orchestra, he also had additional lessons on Sunday mornings at Primrose Hill. The young teacher, herself a budding concert cellist, who had trained with Fournier, was keen for parents to also join in to encourage the children. She refused to take no for an answer from me, when I told her I was completely tone deaf and was unable to produce a single note, and told me that everyone was potentially educable! The only problem was that I did not have a cello and she offered to lend me one, which her father had once picked up in a junk shop and which she didn't need. She duly brought it along the following week with a pot of glue in order to re-seal the front of the cello, which had come away. I gradually learned to produce a few notes on the cello and to learn to translate the position of notes on various lines to the corresponding strings of the cello. I quite liked the cello itself, partly for its mellow tone and also for the nice carving of the rosewood pegs, which I admired from a purely sculptural point of view.

We were faced with a bit of a crisis when we got back from an extended absence on holiday and had offered our house to a young paediatrician and his family from Gibraltar, who had worked on our Hammersmith unit for some time. It transpired that his children had been using the bed in David's room, which was 'officially' out of bounds, as a trampoline and had also managed to crush my cello, which was left for safety behind his door. As I felt extremely embarrassed about this, I offered to have it repaired when I went to the next class with our teacher and preferably to buy it from her, rather than have it on loan. She agreed to this and quoted a nominal charge, as she did not consider it of any substantial value. She also recommended a Mr Hillman who was a good string instrument repairer in my area. I accordingly took the cello to him and asked if it were possible just to get it functional again by replacing the collapsed crushed sides of the cello, and getting the sound post back in place. He took one disparaging look at it, quoted a minimum of £200, and said it wasn't worth spending any money on it at all and continued to make various derogatory remarks about it, which rather upset me, given that I thought it had a good tone. He then also measured the neck and said that this was obviously replaced by someone at some stage, as it was too short!

Feeling rather deflated about the whole course of events and seeing also an end to my budding cello career, I consulted my friend, Richard Edwards, a close physician colleague with a special muscle interest at the Hammersmith, who had been a member of the Welsh Youth Orchestra as a cellist in his earlier days and came from a very musical family. He told me that I should pop around the corner from the Hammersmith Hospital to Scrubs Lane, where there was a very nice violin maker, William Shepherd, who also did some repair work. I accordingly did so soon afterwards, and well remember coming into the workshop with my cello and finding him busy on the telephone. He indicated for me to take my cello out of the soft bag, which I was reluctant to do for fear of being fobbed off, as I had been before. I accordingly waited till he was finished and then explained my sorry story before letting him look at the cello. I was amazed to note that when he pulled the cello out, that his face seemed to light up and his first comment was, 'This is a nice cello! I think it may be a Banks!' 'What is a Banks?' I sheepishly asked. 'He was a well-known British cello maker at the end of the 18th century.' He then measured the neck and said with some excitement, 'I think it is still the original neck! They always made them shorter in those days.' He then looked at the cello and said there would be no problem at all to repair the sides but that was the least consideration. He was much more worried that there was some woodworm in the back of the cello, presumably as a result of it not being played for an extended period of time, and that would need some considerable work on it. I already visualised the zeros in my head, adding onto the original cost. My first question to Shepherd was whether he felt it was worth repairing. 'What do you mean, worth repairing?' he responded. 'We have to repair it. We have a responsibility and obligation to these old instruments to maintain them and in a sense we don't own them but are only custodians of them and need to ensure that they survive our generation and can be passed on to the next.' What an amazing difference in attitude to what I had had with Mr Hillman! I gingerly and somewhat anxiously asked him for an estimate of the cost. 'I think we should be able to manage to do it for about £100,' he responded. I was almost totally bowled over. I then asked him about his violin making activities and he explained to me the very intricate processes in shaping the front and back of the violin, which started as 2 triangular wedges with a thick central part and had to gradually be paired down to a very thin centre, in order to achieve perfection of sound. I asked him whether he could give me a call as soon as he had my cello open so that I could see the inside of it. A few days later he phoned me and had opened it and it was ready for me to come round but also had some bad news. I rushed round the same day and apparently there were 2 additional problems. Firstly, he said, you wouldn't believe but some idiot had gone and stuck down the front of this old cello with impact glue and it was almost impossible to get it off, without doing some damage to the delicate front of the cello, but had eventually managed after very patient and careful separation. The second problem was he had found some woodworm on the inside of the front as well and would have to remove it. This would entail cutting away a segment of the front and replacing it with a matching segment of the same wood and providing a perfect fit, which should be practically invisible. Of interest also inside the cello, apart from seeing its well-carved shape, was a card of a cello repairer who had last done a repair on the cello in 1884. One additional repair that would be necessary was to replace the pegs, which were rather worn and somewhat loose. I expressed my sadness as I was rather attached to them. 'In that case we shall retain the pegs, and block up the holes and bore new ones.'

'How much extra would you like for all this additional work?' 'Don't worry; I think we can manage within the original estimate'. He refused to up the cost, as he felt he had an obligation to maintain this old cello. I did manage to provide something in addition when he was telling me how difficult it was to get the good quality Italian rifflers, similar to ones I used for my own wood sculpture, and that Tiranti in Warren Street, the main artists' suppliers that all sculptors used, only allowed one per customer at a time. So I made several trips to Tiranti in the ensuing weeks to build up a collection of rifflers of different shapes and sizes for him.

After David left for Cambridge and took his own late nineteenth century full size German cello with him, I continued to have lessons locally but just did not have enough commitment to practise on my own and the time for my leisure activity was gradually taken over almost totally by my exponential interest in sculpture. I still feel very guilty whenever I look at my Banks and feel I am a rather bad custodian and perhaps I really ought to start playing it again, however badly, just to keep the woodworm out, or otherwise find a better home for it. Sadly William Shepherd died unexpectedly of a stroke a few years later and another committed custodian of old instruments has passed on and his workshop is no more.

Collector's instinct

Since my childhood I have always collected things. In my schooldays I was interested in postage stamps and eventually specialised in South African stamps and became specially interested in different printings of the regular stamps, and also looking out for printing errors and documented aberrations.

When I came to England, I became fascinated with old glass and particularly the cotton twists of the late eighteenth century, and built up a collection. We were also interested in old silver and later in Sheffield, the birthplace of Old Sheffield Plate, became specially interested in this area, the poor man's silver ware with the same finesse of craftsmanship. Lil had a special interest in Oriental rugs and was knowledgeable on various designs and knots and other characteristics. We both had a feeling for old things and particularly good craftsmanship, be it a piece of modern jewellery or a piece of antique furniture. We also had a tendency to acquire all manner of artefacts from the remote corners of the world we visited, and each piece always carried its particular story for us, related to its source. Small wonder my brother always remarked that our home was really a museum.

Interests in art

I first developed an interest in art in 1951 during my student days in Cape Town, when I got an urge to do some watercolours of some of my favourite places I used to regularly visit, such as the view from Chapman's Peak of Hout Bay, and the view looking south to Kommetjie. I also did a number of my favourite places in Beaufort West that year, such as the town dam, the striking pillars alongside the mountain pass road a few miles north of the town, and a view of the Dutch Reformed Church at night. It then seemed to go out of my system until a home visit in July 1953 when I did a large watercolour of the location (African township) with its endless rows of orange-brick, terraced houses clustered into Blocks, each with an alphabetical notation. This was my favourite painting and I gave it as a present to my aunt Mary, for her kindness to my parents. I eventually managed to retrieve it after she died in Johannesburg a few years ago through her daughter, after it was left in the apartment and no one had claimed it.

My art activities then remained completely dormant until the 1960s in Sheffield, when I got an urge to model portrait heads of the boys. So I registered with the evening adult education classes at the Sheffield College of Art in Psalter Lane and apart from doing some of the sitters at the classes, I also managed to capture both David and Gerald in some modelling sessions at home, when they were four and two years. I cast the clay model myself in plaster and have retained just the original copy of each and been reluctant to recast it in bronze resin. I also had a go at doing Michael but just couldn't capture him.

They then closed the evening classes for head modelling as the fulltime day students were demanding the use of the facilities in the evening as well. I really felt quite deprived and decided to switch to the only remaining class, which was stone or wood carving. We had an excellent teacher. who was a monumental

Beaufort West 'Location' (African township). Watercolour painting I did in 1953

Contemporary photographs of children in the township

Fetus. Ancaster stone

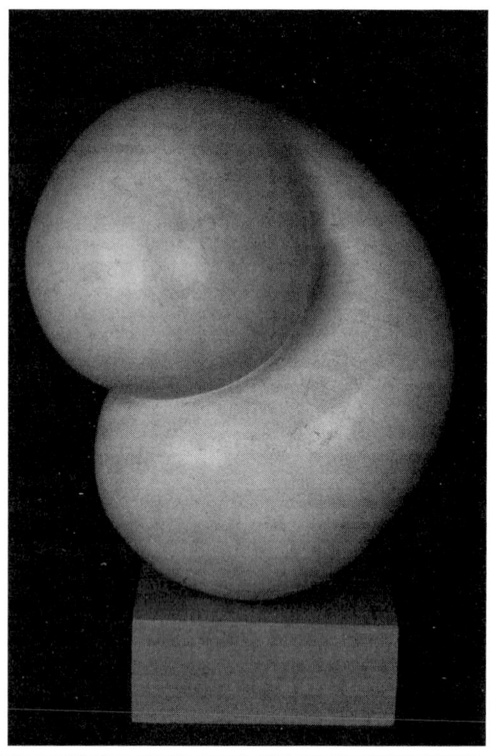

David (left) at four years and Gerald at 18 months. Plaster cast

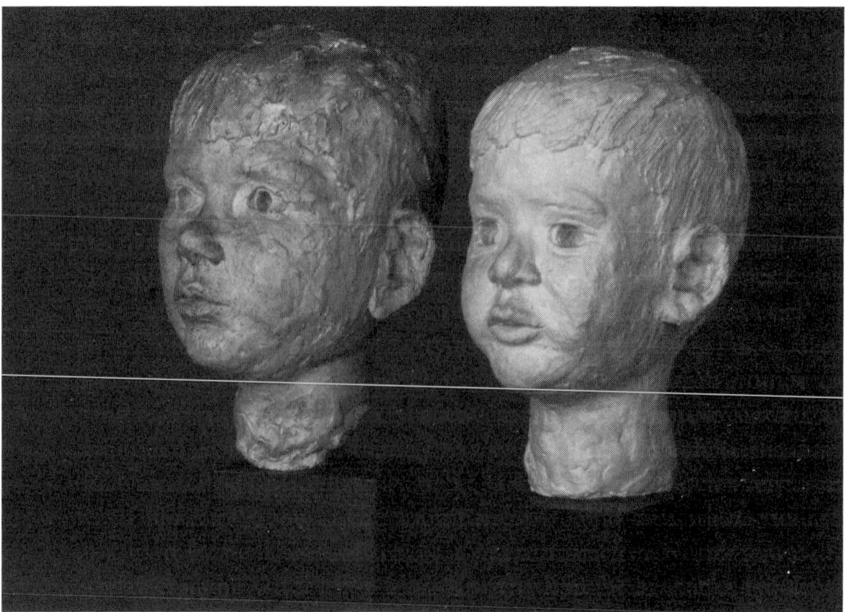

stonemason by profession, but also a very good teacher. It was an interesting exercise carving a wooden bowl out of a slab of mahogany and learning to cope with a convex and a concave shape. I managed to complete one further woodcarving and two stone carvings before we moved to London. I then joined the classes at the Hampstead Garden Suburb and have been attending the evening classes on a nominal weekly basis since but owing to my frequent travel commitments, find myself getting to the classes very intermittently.

One of the first pieces I completed in London was a carving of a Victorian billiard table leg I found on a skip near our home. It was a very solid and dense oak with a very bulbous shape. So I managed to carve out of it a muscle belly arising out of a spiral base, and called it *myogenesis*. I donated it to the Jerry Lewis Muscle Laboratories when they opened in 1974. Some years later I searched for it and found it gathering dust in a corner of one of the labs. So I thought I could give it a more deserving place at home and quietly walked off with it, unmissed by anyone. It was a wise move as it was one of the few things that survived our devastating fire in 1990. I was happy to return it to the new labs a few years later, on the occasion of the official renaming on the laboratories as the Dubowitz Neuromuscular Centre, some time after I had fully retired in 1996.

One of the early pieces I was engaged in for an intractable time was a beam of oak, about nine inches square and five feet long, which Richard Edwards got from a demolished building. I spent the best part of about seven years on it converting it into twins, juxtaposed head to head and rotating away from each other. My teachers, Len Wilton and John Brown looked upon me as a bit of a dilettante, but changed their view after I managed to get to their one-week, annual Easter course for the first time one year, having put it as my main priority and deciding to skip the annual paediatric congress that year. I was actually flying back from a conference in Italy on the Monday morning the course started and rolled a piece of plasticine I had with me into a cylinder and then rotated it on itself and eureka! I had a fetus. All I needed was a block of stone of the appropriate size and dimensions and of a hard enough texture to get a smooth surface. Nothing was available at the school but John Brown thought he had a block of Ancaster stone, that I might find suitable and gave me the key

Exhibition at new BUPA building in central London

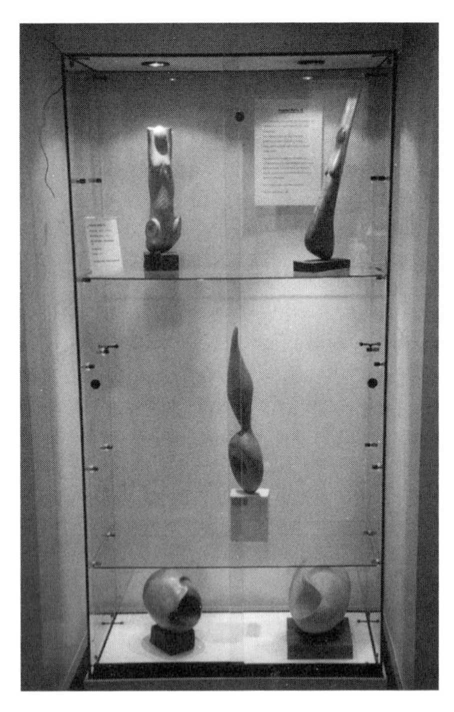

L. *First cry*. Yew wood
R. *Myogenesis*. Oak

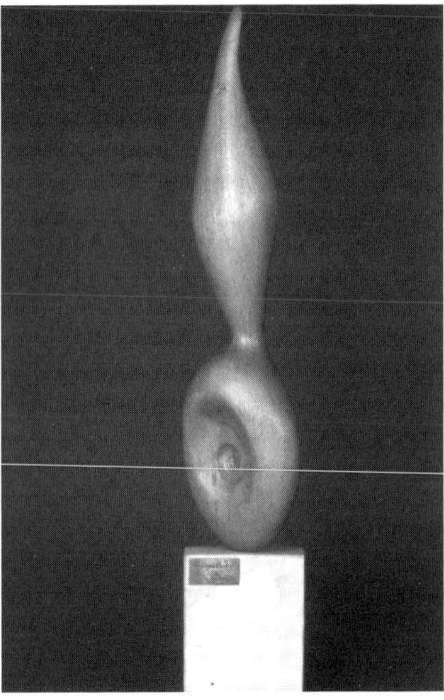

of his house in Barnet to go and collect it. It was perfect and I could visualise the fetal form in the stone and all I had to do was release it. For the first time I knew what the Zimbabwean sculptors were referring to when they say they look at the rough stone until it talks to them. After working solidly at it from nine to five each day, I completely finished it down to the final wet and dry sanding to get it completely smooth, by the Friday evening. My finger tips were down to the pulps from the sanding and my classmates were very impressed by the blood oozing from them, when I held my hands up at the end o the session. It remains one of my favourite sculptures and certainly one of my most exciting creative experiences.

I continued doing both wood and stone carving, mainly semi-abstract but with some overtones of human form. I thus did a cry in stone and later also a different version in yew wood. I have also been picking up pieces of flint stone or other stones, which have proved an inspiration for many of my subsequent sculptures. One of the few portrait forms I have done was *Cry Freedom*, inspired by a remarkable picture by Peter Magubane in *Time* magazine in December 1985, when flying home from a meeting in Washington. It showed a mother grieving the loss of her son, killed by the apartheid police in the Mamelodi township near Pretoria, during one of the protests of the black school children against the enforcement of the education programme with Afrikaans as the major language. Her expression was an amazing combination of grief together with anger and protest, with her clenched fist raised aloft but not entirely facing forward in protest but half rotated. I initially started on a rough clay model to get it into three dimensions, with a view to carving it in wood, but got so taken with the clay model that I took it to completion and had it cast in bronze resin. I did a limited edition with one for each of the boys, one for my brother and the one additional copy I gave to Dickie Attenborough, as a token of appreciation after the release of his poignant film on Steve Biko, *Cry Freedom*. The other somewhat similar emotional type of representation was inspired by a picture of a bronze relief sculpture of Kathe Kollwitz called *Lamentation*, which I transposed to a section of old pine beam I had from the demolition of an old school building. I think it turned out fairly faithful to the original that inspired it, but somehow the woman acquired a much more African appearance.

World

SOUTH AFRICA

Declarations of Defiance

An activist and a union leader speak out

More than 40,000 people packed the soccer stadium in Mamelodi, a black township outside Pretoria, to attend a funeral rally for twelve blacks killed during a clash with police three weeks ago. Diplomats from the U.S. and ten other Western countries were among those who had come to pay their respects to the dead, including a two-month-old baby who suffocated from tear-gas fumes. While police looked on from a hill above the stadium, the mourners sang freedom songs, waved the black, green and gold flag of the outlawed African National Congress and cheered speeches by both white and black antiapartheid activists.

Most of the mourners had gone home by the time a gold-colored BMW drove up to the stadium. But the remaining 8,000 or so people quickly recognized the woman who emerged from the car, and they escorted her into the stadium shouting, "Winnie! Winnie! Mother of the nation!" To their surprise and pleasure, Winnie Mandela, wife of jailed A.N.C. Leader Nelson Mandela, addressed the crowd. "This is our country," she told them. "As you have had to bury our children today, so shall the blood of these heroes be avenged."

With that, Mandela, 51, defied the government restriction that has forbidden her to speak in public for nearly 25 years. A leading antiapartheid activist in her own right, Mandela has endured arrests and solitary confinement. She was banished eight years ago to Brandfort, a remote area of the Orange Free State. But since her home was firebombed by unidentified arsonists in August, she has become increasingly defiant, leaving Brandfort without permission, traveling throughout the country and meeting with the press.

So far, Pretoria has seemed reluctant to move against her. But last week's speech represented perhaps her boldest act, and could prompt the government to retaliate. Two days after her speech, Mandela, reportedly suffering from exhaustion and the recurrence of a minor heart problem, was admitted to a private nursing home. It seemed unlikely that the government would act before she was released.

The sort of defiance that Mandela displayed seemed to be in the air last week. The newly formed Congress of South African Trade Unions (COSATU) also flouted the government by calling on foreign-based companies to divest themselves of South African holdings. "While Western companies argue that this will

Winnie Mandela addressing the Mamelodi rally

bring suffering to blacks, COSATU says that black people have been suffering since 1652, when the Boers first came to this country," said Elijah Barayi, president of the group. It was one of the most radical calls to action made publicly by the head of a legally recognized black organization since the A.N.C. was outlawed in 1960.

Black unions have been legal in South Africa only since 1979. At first they restricted their activities to work-related issues, and their efforts met with varying success. Last year 40,000 black miners staged their first legal strike and won wage and benefit increases from South Africa's mining companies, which have generally been receptive to reforms. In September, however, the miners' union was forced to suspend a strike after only three days when less conciliatory mine operators threatened to dismiss the strikers and evict them from company-owned housing.

Over the past year, however, as violent unrest in the country has increased, members have pressed the unions to become more overtly political. COSATU, the result of four years of painstaking negotiations among the leading black unions, is the most powerful manifestation of this burgeoning political consciousness. Although the new solidarity is still fragile, the giant federation of 34 multiracial unions claims some 450,000 members in the country's most vital industries and clearly has the potential to be a major force in South African affairs. Its leaders have already openly committed themselves to an activist role in the antiapartheid struggle. "We are no longer going to be passive," said Barayi. "COSATU is going to govern this country."

The federation's ambitious agenda includes the call for foreign divestment and nationalization of major industries, the release of Nelson Mandela, the withdrawal of government troops from the black townships and the abolition of the pass laws. Barayi said the federation would lead a campaign for blacks to burn their passbooks publicly if the law is not revoked within six months. That threat prompted grim reminders of the last widespread protest against the pass laws, which ended with the deaths of 67 people after police opened fire on a demonstration in the black township of Sharpeville in 1960. The A.N.C., which had initiated the campaign, was outlawed at the same time.

The Reagan Administration applauded the formation of the federation but frowned on its support for divestment. "We agree that pass laws and apartheid ought to be dismantled," said a State Department spokesman, "but we strongly disagree with the call for divestiture." Officially, the South African government adopted a cautious attitude toward the new superunion. Indeed, declaring that the "revolutionary climate in South Africa is fast losing momentum," State President P.W. Botha lifted the five-month-old state of emergency in eight of the 38 areas where it had been imposed. Those areas were mostly rural settlements and had been for the most part untouched by racial unrest, which has claimed more than 900 victims this year. Privately, officials made it clear that unless COSATU leaders control their radicalism, they too could be subjected to detentions and other restrictions.

—*By Janice C. Simpson.*
Reported by Peter Hawthorne/ Johannesburg

Over the coffin of an infant, mourners display grief and anger

Meanwhile, a new call for foreign-based companies to divest.

36 TIME, DECEMBER 16, 1985

Time magazine report on funeral of 12 black youths killed in clash with police in Mamelodi township near Pretoria. Lower picture by Peter Magubane of mother grieving loss of her son

Cry Freedom. Bronze resin. Inspired by picture of mother alongside her son's coffin, showing combination of grief and anger and protest

Soon after I came to London I also joined the Medical Art Society, which was originally established in the mid 1930s, had an annual public exhibition of its members' work, and also arranged various painting weekends and other travel activities. Its early patron, the Baron ver Heyden de Lancy, was a graduate in both medicine and law and also had an interest in the arts. He provided a bequest to the society to provide two prizes each year for the most prestigious painting and three-dimensional work. I won the prize on three occasions, for my stone *fetus*, for my *torso*, carved from a piece of pine wood I salvaged from the wood burning sauna in Finland, and which I worked on in-flight to

Left: Itinerant wood sculptor. Right. *Lamentation*. Pine

Tokyo in 1979, and for my *fish*, carved in alabaster and inspired by a small pebble with a hole through I picked up on the beach near Sandbanks.

Whilst on one of my peripatetic visits to Bologna, my friend Luciano Merlini took me out to the country residence of an academic dental professor, Martani, whose remarkable sculpture garden on the open hills Luciano had noted during a recent marathon run he did which traversed the property. The following year I organised a weekend visit of the Medical Art Society to Bologna, including a day with Martani and also a visit to various other interesting places in Bologna, such as the anatomy department with its famous wax models of human anatomy.

I served a three-year term as president of the Medical Art Society from 1997–2000, and negotiated an arrangement with Dr Anne Grocock, the executive director of the Royal Society of Medicine, to have our annual exhibition at the RSM.

Our society also had an annual lecture, usually given by the art historian, Laurence Bradbury. During my presidency I presented him with a hand-painted silk tie produced by Lil. The following year he wore his tie for the lecture, and I was wearing a Lil tie

John Blandy (in foreground) MAS president congratulates Peter Lavender on winning annual prize for painting

Annual MAS dinner. In centre is Pat Mortimer, chief organiser of annual exhibition

Visit of MAS group to open air sculpture park of Professor Martani, nr Bologna, Italy

Retrospective exhibition in RPMS library on my retirement
John Heckmatt and Charlotte Thompson viewing photographs *Children around the world*

Display of sculptures

Robert Balasz (foreground) with Pauline and John Brown and Barbara and Sam Tucker

Comparing Lil ties with Laurence Bradbury, art historian, annual lecturer to MAS

as well, so we were able to compare the artwork. He jocularly told Lil that at least she would be able to say that her ties have been on display at the Tate.

At the time of my obligatory retirement in 1996, the librarian at the Royal Postgraduate Medical School did a retrospective of a series of my sculptures, together with some selected photographs from a series of Children around the World, and a display of my published books. She also organised a very convivial preview evening.

14

Medicine: world passport

We have been very fortunate over the years to combine our academic activities with our passion for travel and on selected occasions with family holidays. This was partly because many of the invitations I had to conferences or as visiting professor or to give named lectures or to receive a particular award were in places of special interest. I have selected a few of these travelling experiences to illustrate the wide range and variety of opportunities.

Dubowitz two times rule: stopover in Bombay

In the early seventies I formulated an important personal philosophy on academic travel, which I called the 'Dubowitz two times rule'. This arose out of an invitation I had from Anil Desai, a senior neurologist in Bombay with a muscle interest, to stop over and visit his department en route to an international muscle congress in Perth, Australia. This embraced a lecture to the neurologists and a clinical meeting for discussion of patients. He also offered me hospitality in his home. I readily accepted. Soon after I had a further letter from him that the paediatricians had got wind of my visit and were keen for me to spend some time with them as well. And to cap it all the pathologists requested a session for discussing some interesting muscle biopsies. I had already planned a three day stopover in Bombay so I wrote to Anil that I would be happy to give the six lectures or discussion sessions, but as I was only stopping over for three days, and could not possibly miss the opportunity of a side trip to Auranghabad to visit the famous Buddhist cave temples in Ajanta and Ellora, with their incredible stone carvings, I would have to fit these into one and a half days. And so it came to pass that I flew into

Bombay, spent the night with Anil, and flew out again first thing the following morning to Auranghabad, and had an exciting visit to both the cave temple sites, returning on the following day and completing my academic commitments. One additional engagement arose on the flight to Auranghabad, when I found myself alongside the regional minister of health, who was a consultant to the local hospital in Auranghabad and prevailed on me to do a wardround with his resident staff at 8 pm that evening. It turned out to be a very interesting experience with a large number of unusual patients with complications of tuberculosis and other diseases one did not meet with in the UK.

So in future years I often quoted my Dubowitz two times rule, 'Half the time is for you, but the other half is for me!' when my hosts gave the impression that nothing would please me more than seeing the inside of hospitals or lecture theatres throughout my stay. On several occasions I also took the precaution of reading up about local interests ahead of my visits, so that I could counter the remark, such as from Joe Volpe on the occasion he wanted to fit in an extra afternoon wardround during a short side visit from Washington to St Louis, Missouri, 'There is nothing really to see in St Louis', 'What about the fine arts museum on the university campus?' And so he acquiesced to get his wife, who was a volunteer guide there, to show me around and I had the unique opportunity of seeing one of the finest collections of pre-Columbian art in the United States, not to mention the services of a superb guide.

Similarly, in response to my hosts in Salt Lake City, who wanted to fit in an extra lunchtime meeting, in addition to the pre-breakfast, breakfast, morning and afternoon activities in my one-day stopover, as part of my Bilderback lecture commitment in Portland Oregon, 'I thought I would skip lunch as I am very keen to visit the museum of American Indian art and history, which I note is on the university campus and within walking distance!'

These experiences also established a new concept for me that in any city anywhere there is always something of unique interest, if only one scratches below the surface and looks a bit off the beaten track. Thus for example, I discovered that Pittsburgh has the finest collection of dinosaurs in the USA, and in Durban, South Africa, a local pharmacist with a passion for photography had assembled a remarkable collection of historical cameras.

Perth and Papua New Guinea

I attended the International Muscle Congress of the World Federation of Neurology in Perth in 1971 on my own, as it was impractical to arrange for Lil and the four children to accompany me. After Perth, I visited Melbourne and Sydney, and then did a side trip on the way back to New Guinea, where Audrey Bishop, who had started our muscle tissue culture programme in Sheffield, was now domiciled in Goroka, with her husband, a teacher of science teachers, who was seconded there by UNESCO. In addition to visiting various remote villages around Goroka, I was also able to fit in a round trip in a light aircraft, piloted mainly by Australian pilots, to the Sepik area, to take in a canoe trip on the Sepik River and to acquire some interesting woodcarvings and other artefacts. Two flight experiences still stand out in my mind. Flying over the dense New Guinea jungle, I was in the front seat alongside the pilot and asked him why the fares within New Guinea were so high, equivalent to more than a first class fare on a mileage basis. 'Because the insurance is so high,' came the terse response. From time to time light aircraft disappeared without trace into the jungle. I also recall the pilot requesting us to be back before 3 pm. If we were unable to take off from Sepik by 3 pm we were likely to encounter fog around Goroka and would be unable to land and have to detour via Mt Hagen. And that is exactly what happened and it was quite eerie travelling through the fog with no clear visibility, at about 10,000 feet, knowing some of the peaks in the area were higher than that. A further hair raiser was having to land for refuelling at Onkalai airport, said to be the steepest in the world, with an incline of about 18 degrees. The pilot has to swoop down into the valley, and then head up the airstrip to the top, in order to be able to take off again. The takeoff was even more hairy, as the plane goes headlong down into the valley and has then to bank sharply as one seems to be heading straight into the facing mountain. As the pilot was in the midst of this tricky manoeuvre, one of the two elderly Americans in the rear seats leaned forward, in a state of obvious anxiety, tapped the pilot on the shoulder and

Visit to Papua New Guinea 1972
Onkalai airport with steep gradient into the valley below

Highland girls in traditional dress plus incongruous brassieres

Local chief at a sing-sing festivity

said, 'I say sonny, did you have a happy childhood?' I have often recalled this episode when going on sightseeing flights in single engine Cessna aircraft around California with either David or Gerald, both of whom are keen pilots.

West Indies

In addition to being an external examiner for the final examination of students at a number of medical schools in the UK, such as Newcastle, Leeds and Liverpool, I also had a few invitations further afield, such as The West Indies, Hong Kong, and Malaysia. The visit to the West Indies in 1976 was a particularly rewarding one, as the authorities had decided for the first time that it would be more expedient and economical to ship the few examiners from one centre to another, rather than bringing all the students together in Kingston, Jamaica. So I had the opportunity of visiting Barbados and Trinidad in addition to Jamaica. There was the extra bonus and pleasure of having as co-external examiner Professor Harold Ellis, the eminent London surgeon and teacher and delightful company. The Barbados visit, apart from the magnificent beach alongside the hotel, provided another interesting experience. There was a Synagogue Street in the town suggesting there must have been a Jewish community. It turned out there had been a fairly large community at one time, and a fairly orthodox one, comprising mainly emigrants from Eastern Europe at the turn of the nineteenth century, bound for South America, who had decided to stay in Barbados during a stopover. The old synagogue had long since been converted into a storage shed, but there was still one custodian left, mainly caring for the extensive cemetery. The gravestones were unusual and something I had not previously seen. All the male ones had skull and crossbones on, whilst the females showed a tree, of differing maturity depending on the age at death, felled by an axe. In Kingston I also had a unique experience, at least for me, although pretty commonplace in those days in a crime-ridden Jamaica. I was giving an after dinner talk at a reception arranged in the postgraduate facility on the university campus. Halfway through my presentation, there was a shriek from the hostess in the kitchen alongside. She had been held up at knifepoint by a robber, who fortunately made a hasty exit through the kitchen window when several people from our table rushed in. With a bit more forethought the robber could have had quite a good haul if he had held up all the diners instead and asked them to empty their pockets.

My first visit to Yosemite

The Royal Postgraduate Medical School had an excellent reciprocal arrangement with UCLA (University California, Los Angeles) for visiting professors, initiated by the Dean of the UCLA medical school, Melenkov, who apparently held the record for the longest serving Dean in the USA, and covered financially by UCLA in both directions. Each year one clinical department was nominated by UCLA and in 1975 it was the turn of paediatrics. As it was during term time and impractical to take the family along, I spent a month there on my own, conveniently parked on campus in a university facility for visiting firemen. A few weeks ahead of my arrival my host, Bob Neerhout, asked me if I would like to join them for the annual meeting of the California Chapter of the American Academy of Pediatrics, at the Ahwahnee hotel in Yosemite National Park, shortly after my arrival. He warned me that although he would be happy to register me as his guest for the meeting, I would have to cover my own residential expenses and the Ahwahnee did not come cheap! I obviously could not miss such an opportunity and promptly accepted. I was greatly relieved a couple of weeks later when I had a further request from Bob Neerhout. One of the keynote speakers had taken ill and was unable to come; would I be prepared to fill his slot. The Academy would cover all my expenses. The beauty and grandeur of Yosemite is mind-blowing and I can still recall the immense thrill I had when seeing the spectacular Yosemite Valley as one emerges from the Wawona tunnel. I religiously still stop at the lookout every time I visit Yosemite, and take yet another photograph of the spectacular valley.

As we arrived a day ahead of the meeting I took a leisurely walk for most of the day around the valley floor and admiring the splendour of the various waterfalls, Yosemite Falls, Vernal and Nevada, which in spring were in full flood. On the third morning, which was the day of my own presentation, I woke up

First visit to Yosemite National Park 1975 Margaret and Bob Neerhout

Spectacular view of Yosemite Valley as one enters via Wawona tunnel

Tenaya Lake, Yosemite. Dan hooks a rainbow trout

early with an acute crisis, which I feared might make my lecture impossible. I had acute laryngitis and completely lost my voice and could manage no more than a whisper. And the cost of the Ahwahnee was considerably more expensive than I had anticipated, in the region of 200 dollars per night! But I eventually found a solution. During the lunch break I tested out the microphone system and found that if I held the mouthpiece against my larynx, my whispering voice could be amplified and was perfectly audible. In addition frequent sips of water helped to keep my parched throat moist. This solution won the day, and I suspect some of the audience in the back may not even have been aware of my plight.

I wrote to Lil about the splendour of Yosemite and thought it would be an ideal place for a family holiday. So we waited patiently for an opportunity, which did present itself some years later.

First visit to Yosemite of the family

In 1980 I had an invitation as visiting professor to the Oakland Children's Hospital in association with the University of California San Francisco and Stanford, for a one-week visit, with a fairly extensive academic program. They were able to provide me with a full economy airfare, plus my accommodation and a modest honorarium towards incidental expenses. The major expense for the family was of course the additional airfares for Lil and the four boys. But after some shopping round I discovered a solution. Pan Am, which at that time was one of the major transatlantic carriers (some years ahead of the tragic Lockerbie disaster which crippled and finally extinguished it), was offering a special family package. If one booked one listed fare, one could take one's family on low cost standby fares, and they would guarantee a flight during a nominated week, but only allocate the actual flight the week before departure. This was fine and the arithmetic worked out. As I had a fixed commitment of lectures, I booked a non-changeable, non-refundable, apex fare for myself, and with the balance of my full fare allowance was able to cover Lil and three of the children with standby fares, and only had one additional fare to cover. The arrangement also panned out very well, as the flight they were allocated was on the Friday, at the end of my week of academic commitments, so we only needed one night's collective accommodation in San Francisco. Accommodation in Yosemite Valley is limited and gets booked up many months ahead. The Curry Village tented accommodation was the most economical and on the face of it looked the most suitable for us as well, so we asked our friend and paediatric colleague living in San Francisco, Charlotte Thompson, who had a special interest and expertise in children with disability, to make reservations for us for a few days as soon as booking opened. In line with my usual annual arrangements for vacation, I took a full four weeks leave and we planned an extended trip to various additional national parks after Yosemite, motoring on east across the Tuolumne meadow of Yosemite park and the Tioga pass, and then south to Bryce and Zion and on to the North Rim of the Grand Canyon. We also borrowed some camping equipment in case we were unable to get formal accommodation.

Yosemite proved a great success but the accommodation in Curry Village was an instant disaster. The tented cabins were in fact fixed wooden cabins with a tented roof and no cooking facilities and no space to move around. Not for the Dubowitzes with four active children! So we survived it for one night and then moved over to one of the campsites in the valley, pitched our tents and had a blissful few days of campfires and barbecues and hikes along various trails. The rest of the trip was also most exciting, except for the long distance travelling, most of which we did by night. We had originally also thought of taking in Yellowstone Park in the final week, but that was impossible so headed back through Yosemite. We staked a claim for an unoccupied campsite for the night, with a paper bag with our name over the number post, at the large Tuolumne campground with over 200 sites. The following morning we discovered the small Tenaya Lake campground with only 30 walk-in sites on the water's edge. So in subsequent years we headed straight for Tenaya Lake and stayed put there. Some years later this idyllic campground had to be closed, because of the fragility of the environment and the difficulty of providing adequate water and toilet facilities. Having discovered the excellent hiking opportunities in Zion National Park we also returned there on a number of future occasions as the main centre for our camping holiday.

While the children were still at school we were able to combine a number of holidays with a well-timed conference or lecture visit. Once the boys embarked on their own careers this was more difficult, although we have continued to meet together for holidays right up to the present time.

Tokyo-Sydney-Cape Town; vital visas

In 1979 we flew from London to Tokyo on the first leg of a 'round the world ticket', starting in Tokyo as guest speaker at the annual meeting of the Japanese Society of Child Neurology, then going on to Sydney for the meeting of the International Child Neurology Association (ICNA) and finally to South Africa for my 25th class reunion, and the 150th anniversary celebrations of the foundation of Cape Town University, and a special medical faculty week of academic activities, to which I had been invited to contribute.

When we arrived at the new Narita airport, some distance outside Tokyo, Lil was refused entry, as she did not have an entry visa on her Australian passport. We had been totally oblivious of the need, had not been alerted by our travel agent, and indeed had not checked ourselves. Lil was now virtually imprisoned in the airport, admittedly within the relative comfort of the Airport Hotel, pending being sent back to the UK on the next available flight! To compound matters it was a Sunday so all government offices were closed. Fortunately our host, Dr Masaya Segawa, came all the way out to the airport to meet us, and when I explained to him our plight, he was tremendously helpful, and also very apologetic on behalf of the authorities. He immediately telephoned his father, an eminent and highly respected paediatrician, who in turn phoned the interior minister, whom he knew personally, and within a short while Lil was given a reprieve, was allowed to stay within the confines of the airport hotel, a series of visa application forms were filled in (in triplicate), and Lil was assured that an emergency visa would be processed as soon as the visa department opened on Monday morning and would be despatched by special courier to her as soon as it was ready, hopefully by Monday afternoon. Meanwhile, we decided that I should go ahead on my connecting flight that afternoon to Fukuoka in Kyushu Island, in the far west, the first stop of a preconference lecture tour to be followed by further stopovers, by bullet train, at Nagoya and Kyoto, before

Carving a pine wood torso in flight to Tokyo, 1979

returning to Tokyo. This was punctuated by one further problem when going through security for the flight to Kyushu. I had a large Chinese leather attaché case, purchased at low cost in Sheffield, which held all my lecture slides and on this occasion I also took along a small wooden sculpture I was working on plus a chisel. No problems going through security at Heathrow, but they now opened my bag and held up the chisel and asked me what I was doing with a dangerous weapon in my case? I had fears of being impounded at the airport and joining Lil! When I showed him my pine sculpture of a torso, he smiled and was more relaxed. He then told me they would have to confiscate the chisel but if I signed for it they would put it in a special bag to be carried by the crew of the aircraft and I could retrieve it in Kyushu.

The professor of neurology in Fukuoka, the main town in Kyushu, was a most gracious and hospitable person and also a camera fanatic, who seemed to acquire every new model, and like me, being an Olympus enthusiast, insisted I should get one of the recently launched new pocket XA cameras, the first in a new generation of high-quality pocket-sized (literally) cameras, and gave me the address of an outlet in Tokyo with a personal note, as there was a waiting list.

My lecture was scheduled for the Tuesday morning, and Lil in the late afternoon, with various clinical presentations between.

Lil pitched up just in time for her lecture, rapidly loaded her series of slides into a carousel, and rushed them to the projectionist, who then dropped the carousel with the slides falling out all over the place. It took Lil a full 20 minutes to re-sort them. We had a very entertaining couple of days in Kyushu with a good mix of academia and sightseeing.

Our stopover in Nagoya was relatively short but we had a few days in Kyoto to also allow a daytrip to the ancient city of Nara. The Japanese are extremely hospitable and generous but also have a fairly rigid protocol to adhere to. This often seems to involve the choice of what they consider the best option for European visitors. We were accordingly accommodated at the Holiday Inn in the newly developed 'English quarter' of Kyoto. Our hearts sank further as we came up the escalator of the complex to be confronted by a McDonald's on the first floor. We tried to politely suggest to our hosts a transfer to a Japanese ryokan, which we were keen to experience, but they explained there was only one ryokan in Kyoto of sufficiently high standard for foreigners, and that one was fully booked. We eventually prevailed on them to transfer us to a downtown ryokan for the tail end of our stay, as we were keen to see some of the local activities in the downtown area. Our host soon had second thoughts on the wisdom of the decision, when we were waiting to register in the lounge area and two completely inebriated Japanese businessmen, who had obviously had a much extended lunch meeting, came stumbling down the stairs followed by attendant geisha girls. The ryokan proved superb, with constant individual attention in our own apartment, with our private hot tub facility, sleeping on tatami mats and eating our breakfast in traditional style.

A highlight of our visit to Tokyo was a visit to the home of Masaya Segawa's father in central Tokyo. He was a wonderful old man, steeped in traditional Japanese customs and had a magnificent moss garden, which was his special pride. He also had a teahouse in the garden for the traditional tea ceremony.

The Japanese also had a very rigid protocol for exchange of presents and we had been advised ahead of our trip that a very acceptable gift for a senior academic was a bottle of Johnny Walker black label, and for more junior members the red label. One of the embarrassing experiences one faces is that whatever personal gifts you bring for your hosts, they will reciprocate with a gift that is often more elegant, beautifully wrapped and bearing the name of one of the leading stores. We also discovered that one of the usual gifts for visiting lecturers was one of those superb hand made traditional Japanese dolls, in full dress, complete with glass display case. I hinted to our host that we were already heavily laden with baggage for our extended trip and would have difficulty transporting it. But to no avail. Shortly before our departure we were duly presented with a hand painted special Kyushu doll, complete with glass case, and an assurance that they had also arranged for it to be safely packaged for us and that the Japanese airline had confirmed that there would be no problem for us to take it as hand luggage!

We duly arrived in Sydney and spent a few days over the weekend ahead of the congress with Lil's family in Melbourne. Over dinner with Lil's longstanding family friends the Bechers on the Friday evening, Lil was relating her experiences at Tokyo airport, when Ushi responded that she could cap it with an almost identical experience when she visited South Africa. Lil's face blanched visibly and she had a few moments of stunned silence. 'You are not telling me I need a visa for South Africa?'

This now posed a major problem for us. We were due to fly to South Africa the following Saturday after the week's congress in Sydney on the only weekly direct flight from Australia to South Africa with South African airways and had been waitlisted for over three months before we could get seats on this crucial leg of our round trip. If we could not make that flight there was no alternative to aborting the whole South African excursion. This called for some drastic action.

So on the Saturday I obtained the telephone number for the South African Consulate in Canberra, and repeatedly dialled the number, fully realising it was a pretty fruitless exercise as they were certainly shut over the weekend. However, on the umpteenth attempt someone unexpectedly responded with a heavy South African accent, 'Good afternoon. I am not here! Can I help you?' Typical South African sense of humour. Turned out to be the trade attaché, who was doing some paperwork in his office and happened to be passing by the incessantly ringing phone. I engaged him in an extended conversation, with my best Beaufort West accent, explained our predicament, and he advised to call immediately after the offices opened on Monday morning and speak to the person in the visa section. Fortunately the person I spoke to on Monday morning was helpful and sympathetic and offered to do all she could although it was extremely unlikely to get a visa within a week as it had to be sanctioned from Pretoria and usually took 3 to 4 weeks! She suggested I call in personally as soon as possible at the South African Airways office in Sydney, and ask them to put the passport, together with a duly completed visa application, in the diplomatic bag on the next flight to Canberra and mark it for her personal attention. So far so good. That covered the greater part of the first session of the congress. I telephoned her in the afternoon to confirm the safe arrival and reiterated my extreme gratitude for her understanding and help in the stressful circumstances. I then had a friendly chat with her each morning to review progress and all seemed to be going smoothly until the Friday morning, when she said all was ready and she was just awaiting the final confirmation from Pretoria and hopefully would have that by the end of the day. I then pointed out that we were due to fly out of Sydney the following morning and if the passport was not on the 2 pm flight from Canberra to Sydney it would not arrive in time before the South African Airways shut up shop for the weekend. 'Oh! I had not thought of that.' She promised me it would be on the flight. I then took a final walk to the South African Airways offices, told them the passport would be on the 2 pm flight from Canberra, and that I would be calling in personally in the afternoon to collect it. They assured me they would look out for it in the diplomatic bag. All's well that ends well.

Apart from this time-consuming and somewhat enervating exercise, we had two additional more pleasant experiences. One was a presentation at our congress by Paul Pilowsky, eldest son of Marlene and Issy, whose birth we had celebrated shortly after our arrival in Sheffield in 1961. This was his first presentation at an international meeting of his sophisticated neuroscience research, and he gave a very polished and confident talk.

The second was an invitation from a paediatrician, Heather Jeffery, who had worked with us on our neonatal unit at Hammersmith some years earlier, and was doing research on sudden infant death syndrome (SIDS) with the professor of physiology, John Hoh, who had a special interest in laryngeal muscle. She had been looking at the laryngeal muscles of infants coming to autopsy after unexplained sudden death, and had found pathology in some of them, suggesting a congenital myopathy. Would I be able to spare half a day to come out and have a look through all the samples under the microscope? Whilst potentially interesting, I just could not see my way clear to going all the way out to their department for a half-day detour to look down a microscope. So the Dubowitz two times rule swung into action and I expressed my regrets that I would have to decline the invitation and perhaps we could arrange to have sight of some of the slides through the mail. I then had a further phone call from John Hoh personally whether he could perhaps tempt me with an afternoon's sailing in Sydney harbour after our academic activities in his department. As they say, every man has his price. So we selected the least interesting day of the congress, were duly collected at our hotel in the early morning and after a very interesting session of reviewing all the muscle samples, we had a brunch at John Hoh's house and then set sail in his yacht, ably crewed by four very efficient and attractive young physiology research fellows, whom he obviously chose not only for their intellectual prowess but also for their good looks and potential sailing skills.

We duly flew out of Sydney on the Saturday morning even more heavily laden than on arrival. In addition to the portable Fantz box for the assessment of visual function in newborns David had constructed for us, plus the Japanese doll, I had also acquired an irresistible New Guinea wooden sculpture in a shop in Sydney specialising in New Guinea artefacts and arranging appropriate fumigation and certification. This was an almost full-length two-dimensional human torso, garnished by genuine human hair and moustache, with a practical function of being suspended as a clothes hook inside their hut. It still graces our entrance hall.

In Cape Town we had a very interesting time, both academically and socially. In addition to the formal activities, we also did some comparative neurological assessments on the newborn babies of the three main population groups, Black, White and the mixed Cape Coloureds. The African babies were mainly well nourished and comparable to the White, whereas the Coloured babies were small, mainly due to the poor nutrition of the mothers, and also had a different neurological pattern of behaviour. Lil was also able to undertake some comparative assessments of schoolchildren in a Black township, in a Coloured school and on a cohort of White children and discovered an advanced verbal function in the Black babies, with ability to repeat up to five or seven digits with ease, beyond the normal range for their age. The poorest function was the white infants, probably reflecting much less verbal input from their nannies, than the constant contact of the Black babies with their mothers. She also discovered that the Black children, whilst using their own language for all modalities of speech, were taught to count in English. The teacher explained this was because of the complexity of the Xhosa language for numbers, which were descriptive, so for example, three might be a cow with one leg raised. She also discovered there was no distinction between certain colours in the Xhosa language, so that both blue and red were referred to as 'imauve'. When we discussed this with Professor Pat Smythe, the paediatrician, he was totally unaware of this, and initially a bit incredulous, until he checked for himself with his housemaid and got the same response. No provision had been made at all for this type of distinction in the standard intelligence tests, which were applied to all children, irrespective of their racial background.

The Himalayas

We had a further opportunity of visiting Tokyo in 1990 in conjunction with another meeting of ICNA. We were due to go immediately afterwards, by a rather circuitous route, to a meeting of the Central and South American Pediatric Neurology Association in Uruguay. This had originally been scheduled for Colombia, but with the instability of law and order there, had been postponed and relocated. At relatively short notice and after we had already tentatively fixed our travel schedule, they postponed the meeting again and decided to relocate to Brazil. I then decided enough was enough and bailed out. I then offered Lil a choice of where to go instead, as we had already arranged our leave.

In 1988 Lil had had an unexpected urgent heart bypass operation after relatively mild symptoms. She had come through

Start in Pokhara of our 12-day hike to Annapurna Sanctuary, 1990

Lunch break and rest en route

Annapurna Sanctuary
L. top: Camping en route; L. lower:Taking a break, with Machapuchare, the sacred 'Fish Tail' mountain, in background; R. top: 'High tea' at high altitude. Annapurna South in background; R. lower: Lil and I reach Annapurna South base camp

it very well but felt she was now on borrowed time and had drawn up a list of places she would still like to visit. Top of the list was the Himalayas. So with an agency in Bristol we set up a personal trek through a trekking company in Kathmandu, and duly flew from Tokyo to Kathmandu after our congress and then on to Pokhara, whence we did a 12-day hike to the Annapurna sanctuary and up to the Annapurna South base camp. We had a superb guide, Kumi, who had been with an expedition to Everest, plus an excellent cook, and a full complement of porters, who always went ahead to set up the next camp. It proved to be one of our most exhilarating and enjoyable trips and also gave Lil renewed confidence in her survival.

Further forays in Japan

In conjunction with the festschrift for Professor Yukio Fukuyama in Tokyo and the four-yearly muscle congress of the World Federation of Neurology in Kyoto in 1994, we also took an extended trip by bullet train, to Hokkaido Island in the north. We had an interesting experience in contrasts, as we initially stayed in a newly built luxury hotel arranged by a neurologist friend of King Engel from Sapporo, whom we met in Kyoto. He offered to make all the arrangements for us. It proved to be the ultimate in luxury, with two king-size beds and a full length window facing east and giving a panoramic view of the adjacent valley and the peaks beyond which were snow capped and like mini Mt Fujis. In addition there were two separate bathrooms with walk in hot tubs and the same panoramic view, should one wish to relax for the day in the bath. Only concern was whether we would have enough money to cover the cost and Lil encouraged me to go down to reception the second evening, prior to departure the next day, to get an estimate of the cost, so that we could possibly make some contingency arrangements. I was stunned to find the cost was less than we had paid for our somewhat mundane hotel in Kyoto, and exactly the same as we were paying for the youth hostel accommodation at Osahidake we had booked ourselves for the second leg of our Hokkaido visit, to the eastern part in the region of the volcanic mountains and sulphurous geysers. Our neurologist host had some special connections and had managed to arrange an almost complimentary stay for us. In addition we had the hospitality of a paediatrician from the eastern area, who was also at the congress and drove us around some of the remarkably photogenic countryside. We were struck when hiking up the volcanic mountain area by the vast number of groups of people of all ages, doing the trek, colourfully bedecked in individual cap or shirt colours to allow cohesion.

On our bullet train trip back we made a stop for a day to visit Misonokuchi, the hometown of the legendary potter, Shoji Hamada, a long time associate of the contemporary doyen of British pottery, Bernard Leach. The town had become a haven for potters, many of whom had trained with the master potter.

Tokyo again; Mount Fuji

We had long had a desire to do the classical hike up Mount Fuji and our opportunity finally came in 1999 in conjunction with an invitation I had from Komei Kumagai, a paediatrician who had spent some time in London as doctor for Japanese residents. I had met him through some referrals to the paediatric department at Hammersmith and invited him to join our wardrounds. He was currently president of the Japanese Society for Child Neurology and invited me as a guest speaker to the conference. When I mentioned our interest in Mt Fuji to our longstanding friend and colleague, Makiko Osawa, who had succeeded Fukuyama as head of the paediatric department, she offered to make all the necessary arrangements for us and as she had not personally done the Mount Fuji trail before, she took the opportunity, in remarkable Japanese efficiency, of doing a preliminary visit herself to check out the trail, up to station five, and arrange the appropriate accommodation en route, and then offered to accompany us on the trip itself. It fully came up to all our expectations including the traditional early morning rises to see the sunrise from a suitable vantage point. We had an extra bonus at the tail end of our circuitous trip, visiting the remarkable Hakone sculpture park, beautifully laid out on the side of a hill, and with a generous selection of all the international modern sculptors. It must surely be the largest and one of the most impressive sculpture parks in the world.

From top Festschrift for Fukuyama 1994; Mount Fuji, 1999; Room with a view, Toya, Hokkaido, 1994

Scandinavian countries

We have had numerous opportunities of visiting the Scandinavian countries over the years, starting with the west coast of Sweden whilst still in Sheffield in the 1960s, and several visits to Helsinki in the 1970s, which we were able to couple with family holidays at the summerhouse of Hannu Somer on the Saimaa Lake. There have also been a number of exceptional invitations of special interest.

Arvo Ylppo Award

Arvo Ylppo, who was born in October 1887, was the doyen and dynamo of Finnish paediatrics, and his career went back to before the First World War, when he worked at the famous Kaiserin Augusta Victoria Children's Hospital in Berlin. When he turned 70, the Finnish paediatricians decided to honour him by the establishment of a five-yearly award of a gold medal and lectureship to a paediatrician who had made a substantive contribution in relation to the newborn. I had the distinction of receiving the award on the occasion of his 95th birthday in October 1982 for my contributions on the neurology of the newborn and the floppy infant. In keeping with the Dubowitz two times rule, Lil and I were happy to accept an invitation to stay a few extra days on either side of the special day itself, and were able to savour the full Monty of Finnish hospitality, resplendent with multiple saunas and dinners. At 95 Arvo, who was a fairly diminutive size, in contrast to his immense academic stature, had to be restrained from still wishing to pursue the Finnish tradition of plunging straight into the icy waters from the hot sauna. A Finnish magazine, equivalent to *Time* magazine, had a picture of him on the cover swinging from the branch of a tree. He always prided himself that at 70 he was still able to put his hands flat onto the ground without bending his knees, and had fathered a son, by his second wife Leah, also a paediatrician. I had a vague recollection of having met Ylppo at an early meeting of the British Paediatric Association and indeed on scouring the archives of the Association I was able to find a picture of the two of us at the meeting in Scarborough in 1964, when he was a mere 75 and I was less than half his age. One of Ylppo's protégés, Niilo

Receiving gold medal award from Arvo Ylppo on his 95th birthday in 1982, with Professor Niilo Halman, Helsinki, one time president of International Pediatric Association

At dinner with Ylppo and his wife Leah

On ballroom floor with Leah and Arvo Ylppo and Helena Pihko

Halman, succeeded him to the chair of paediatrics and also attained international pre-eminence as president of the International Pediatric Association.

Lil and I were able to attend the celebrations again at his 100th anniversary lecture given by Abe Rudolph, another South African expatriate, who was now an eminent neonatologist in the USA. Arvo died in January 1992 at 104 years. They have continued the five-yearly tradition and we attended the award lecture again in 2002 to commemorate the 115th year of his birth.

Count Folke Bernadotte Lectureship

In 1985 Lil and I were jointly awarded the Folke Bernadotte lectureship, which entailed a lecture visit to all the main academic medical centres in Sweden. Bernadotte, a Swede with family ties to the Swedish king, had gained international recognition through his work in World War 2 as head of the Swedish Red Cross. A diplomat fluent in six languages, he was appointed mediator of the UN General Assembly in 1948. He brokered a ceasefire between the Jews and Arabs and tried to implement his own solution to the Middle East of a union between the warring parties. This was unacceptable to either side, and during a visit to the area, he was assassinated by a Jewish underground group.

We started our visit with a flight to Upssala, and then up to our first port of call, the medical school at Umea in the far north east of Sweden. This provided us an opportunity of a side trip to Lapland, where we were treated to a wonderful few days of cross-country skiing and motorised trips in the remote parts, in addition to seeing local muscle patients. We then tracked back to Upssala, where we met up with our longstanding friend and colleague, Ingrid Gamstorp, and then on to Stockholm, Lund and finally Gothenburg where we were royally hosted by Bengt and Gudrun Hagberg and their colleagues. At each centre we had a very stimulating time, both academically and socially, and were able to combine a few formal lectures with numerous interactive clinical sessions with patients and doctors.

The Faroe Islands

The Scandinavian paediatric neurologists, a relatively small and friendly society, met each year on a different island, which is not surprising, given their passion for and constant proximity to water. On the occasion I was their guest speaker, they met in Torshavn on the remote Faroe Islands, which are equidistant between Norway, Iceland and Scotland, and probably easier to get to by boat from Scotland, than via connecting flights through Norway or Denmark. A desolate, treeless landscape, with a beauty of its own, and a thriving fish-farming industry in its crystal-clear waters.

Spitsbergen

However, the Scandinavian neuropathologists managed to cap this one, with an invitation to a conference in an even more remote location, in Svalbard, Spitsbergen, which is just below the 79th parallel. One does not appreciate how far north it is until you fly about 1000 km from Oslo to Tromso, the most northerly city in Norway, and then another 1000 km to Svalbard. It had a fascinating history with the combined interests and outposts of both the Russians and the Norwegians in this remote arctic island.

In order to take advantage of this unique opportunity to visit the Arctic Circle, we were faced with a difficult dilemma. There was one excursion after the congress of a short trip to the pack ice, which was barely affordable. Then there was a much more attractive option of a week's trip in an icebreaking boat, converted to take 20 passengers, with an extended visit to the various places of historical interest of explorers heading for the North Pole, with numerous excursions ashore. This was way beyond our budget and in a different bracket to anything we had ever spent on the family or ourselves in any of our trips. But it was extremely tempting. One also had to see it in the context of prices for everything in Norway already being inflated in recent years.

I kept phoning the travel agents in Tromso and speaking to a very patient and helpful assistant for more and more details. The day before we finally had to make our decision, I phoned her again and had a prolonged discussion and finally asked, 'Given the high cost, do you really think it is worth it?' She was silent for a few moments and then responded 'I cannot answer your question sir, but all I can say is you cannot take it with you'.

Visit to Arctic Circle. Disembarking on the pack ice

Very wise words; I instantly confirmed our booking. We never had a moment's regret. It turned out to be one of the most interesting and spectacular trips we have taken, enhanced by a very knowledgeable guide, a law student interested in history, who had been on the trip for three successive years.

We had one special experience when we crossed the 80th parallel, which was in broad sunlight at 2.30 in the morning. Suddenly the boat's horns went off at full blast and our guide came round with a bottle of champagne to toast the important event, comparable to the ceremony one used to have of crossing the equator by boat in days of yore.

I then told him that for Lil and me it was a double celebration, as it was also our 35th wedding anniversary. A few minutes later the horn went off again and an announcement on the tannoy system that a second round of champagne was on its way to celebrate our wedding anniversary. The following morning our guide brought us two bottles of wine as a gift for the occasion and said it was the best wine he could find in their very extensive cellar of vintage wines from around the world. I suggested we open it later in the day and celebrate it together but he persuaded me to keep it for a special occasion. It was not till we looked a bit closer at the bottles in our cabin that we realised another amazing coincidence, which had not caught the eye of our guide. The wine was a limited 1986 vintage of Prieure Lichine, to celebrate the 35th anniversary of the union of two French vineyards. When we showed it to our wine guru son, Michael, he instantly recognised it and was able to show us a picture of the very label in the Sotheby book of wines. Michael thought it was almost ready for drinking but would be even better in five years, or ten years, and if we decided to keep it for our 50th anniversary, it would probably be at its peak.

North America

Following on my early visit to Yosemite, the USA became a happy stomping ground for many of our annual family camping holidays and I also had many solo visits to individual society meetings. There were a number of special events, which opened the way for subsequent new vistas.

Bilderback lecture

In 1979 I was the first non-American invited to give the annual Joseph B Bilderback lecture in Portland, Oregon, to honour Bilderback who was the founder of the American Academy of Paediatrics. As it was my first visit to the region, I planned to allow a full week in Portland. It was, however, not long before I had to invoke my Dubowitz two times rule, when I found myself saddled with no less than 27 different commitments in the way of lectures, not only within the university and hospital, but also to outside groups such as the Oregon Pediatric Association, plus clinical rounds, and informal meetings with the resident staff. So I discussed this with my host, Bob Neerhout, who agreed the best option was to give me a complete day free. So on the Wednesday I had a memorable day with his wife, Margaret, an accomplished artist and sculptress, who took me on an outing to the Oregon coast and specifically to visit one of the huge woodpiles of logs of all shapes and sizes, brought down by flooded rivers, that washed up on the coast during the winter storms. I could not resist carrying a few small pieces home, which I was later able to carve. I often thought what a wonderful retirement one could have, just camping on the beach and spending the rest of one's days carving away at the huge redwood and other logs in situ.

I also had a unique experience whilst loading my slides for my Bilderback lecture into carousels at the back of the lecture theatre, when a paediatrician who was chatting to Bob Neerhout and myself dropped dead alongside us. He was apparently lifeless and Bob Neerhout instantly started thumping his heart with external cardiac massage, combined with mouth to mouth breathing. Minutes later the cardiac crash team arrived from the main teaching hospital up the road. The following morning we visited the lucky paediatrician, sitting up in bed having a hearty breakfast. He had apparently had two previous heart attacks superadded on severe diabetes. When I lectured again in Portland some years later I walked in with my preloaded carousels and opened my lecture with the story and that I was not taking any chances of loading my slides at the lecture again.

There was also an arrangement between Portland and the medical schools at Salt Lake City and Seattle to share any visiting professors. So an additional few days were added on to my travel schedule. My first stop was in Salt Lake City, where I had a very full day of academic activities, which I already mentioned earlier in relation to my two times rule, and I also added on an extra day to spend with my friends from our Sheffield days, Peter and Kati Vamos, who were on a sabbatical there.

The other leg of my whistle stop Bilderback tour was Seattle, which was of some interest to me as it was my first time there. In spite of the very full programme over the two days, I do still recall the excellent luncheon the hospital residents arranged for me at an American Indian restaurant, where they barbecued whole salmon in a traditional manner. This short visit was also to have a later spin-off, as my host in Seattle, Beverly Morgan, moved to the chairmanship of the paediatric department in Irvine, California, and orchestrated an invitation to get me out as visiting professor to the various medical schools within the University of California at various centres. This in turn was to open up yet new vistas for us, and have a major impact on Gerald's future life and career.

With Joe Volpe and Phil Dodge in St Louis for the Phillip R Dodge lecture in 1989

Phil Dodge Lecture

I first met Phil Dodge at the Massachusetts General Hospital in Boston in 1966 at the tail end of our stay in New York. We next met up again in 1968 during a stopover in St Louis en route to the international paediatric congress in Mexico. Lil was having a rough time with morning sickness in the early stages of her pregnancy with Daniel. Phil treated us royally with a luxury suite in the Queeny Tower, a residential facility associated with the children's hospital for families and patients, and also visiting academics. We met up with Phil on many further occasions over the years, both at meetings in the States and also on his intermittent visits to England. I felt particularly pleased and privileged to give the Phillip R Dodge lecture in St Louis in 1989 to honour Phil Dodge's long-term chairmanship of the department of paediatrics in St Louis and unparalleled role as the doyen of paediatric neurology in the United States, who had at one time or another trained almost all the present generation of paediatric neurologists.

Canada

We have visited Canada on many occasions over the years, the first being to the Toronto Hospital for Sick Children during our time in New York. It coincided with the annual ball game

With Bill Gibson in the Burkhart Gardens, Vancouver Island, Canada, in 2000

between residents and staff and an associated barbecue at the home of the chairman of department some way out of town. In 1968 I participated in the International Congress of Neurogenetics in Montreal and met up with Fred Andermann, the head of neurology and his wife Eva, a geneticist, whom we were to meet up with again on many occasions in the future.

My 1988 Bernard Sachs Lectureship of the American Child Neurology Association, to commemorate the founder of child neurology in the USA, was held that year in Halifax, Nova Scotia, another first timer for Lil and myself, and as guest lecturer of the Canadian Congress of Neurological Sciences in 2000 in Victoria, Vancouver Island, Lil and I had our fist visit to Victoria followed by an extended trip up Vancouver Island, before returning to Vancouver by ferry. I had never realised how big the island was. We also had an opportunity of meeting up with Bill Gibson, now Vice Chancellor at the University in Victoria, who had been so helpful with the establishment of the Jerry Lewis Muscle labs at Hammersmith. He and his wife were very hospitable and gracious, and insisted on taking us out to some of the special sights, such as the Burkhart Gardens. I was very pleased to have a further invitation to the Canadian Congress of Neurological Sciences in Ottawa in 2005, our first visit to this interesting city.

Beijing, 1985. A city of cyclists

China

We have had two opportunities of visiting China. The first was in 1985 as an excursion from Hong Kong on a combined visit to Beijing, Xian and Shanghai, through the local Chinese tourist office. As each booking forms a group by itself, we were fortunate to have only two other fellow travellers, the wife and daughter of a Canadian pharmaceutical representative working in Hong Kong. This gave us a lot of latitude with our driver of the minibus and expert guide and enabled us to visit some medical facilities not normally available. At that time Beijing was still a city of cyclists, who formed a dense phalanx across the road at every intersection, with hardly a motorcar in sight, and there were many fascinating back alleys in the old quarters of the city.

In 2002 we had another visit to Beijing for the International Child Neurology Congress, which was now completely transformed into a concrete jungle, with the disappearance of all the little back alleys, and not a cyclist in sight in the busy motorised traffic. We took the opportunity for a five day trip up the Yangtze through the three gorges, just a few months ahead of the damming up of the Yangtze and the flooding of numerous towns on its banks by the 60 metre rise in the water level, and the massive rebuilding and rehousing schemes under way ahead of the flooding. It was fascinating to go ashore in many of these towns and to see the scale, as well as the amazing pace, of the rebuilding programmes.

South America

There was a time when we had not yet visited South America, which was rapidly resolved when we had invitations to Caracas, Venezuela, Santiago, Chile, and Bariloche in the Argentine Andes, within about a year. We took advantage on each occasion of some extended travel and visited Canaima with a trip by motorised boat up (and down) the rapids up the Canaima River up to the Angel Falls, the highest in the world. Whilst in Chile we planned to do two circuits, on special visit-Chile airpass round trip fares, one in the north and the second in the south. But we had not bargained for the actual size of the country, which stretches in length the same distance as from Edinburgh to Algiers in North Africa. So we were only just able to complete the northern loop with an extended visit to the Atacama Desert and a side trip to La Paz in Peru, including an extended hike including over a 16,000-foot mountain pass and a visit by boat to Lake Titicaca. From Bariloche we were able to do a circular trip into southern Chile, going out overland by bus and returning by boat and land connections through a series of spectacular lakes and former volcanic mountains, resembling Mount Fuji.

My first solo visit to Brazil in the mid 1970s for an international congress on rehabilitation in Rio De Janeiro, to be followed by an extended academic and sightseeing programme to all the main centres, generously supported by the local branch of the British Council, was cut short by an attack of tachycardia shortly after my arrival in Rio and a decision to fly back again. In a later visit to Brazil for a special millennium meeting of the South American Neurological Associations in Salvador in 2000, Lil and I were able to take advantage of the unique opportunity for an extended visit to a number of special places, including the Pantanel, the Amazonas and Iguaçu Falls, on a fairly economical airpass with the Brazilian airline, in addition to a visit to Sao

Paulo for some academic chit-chat with Mayana Zatz and Mariz Vainzof, who had established a genetics centre with a special interest in muscle diseases, of international repute. This visit also sowed the seeds for the selection of the Iguaçu Falls as the special venue for the 10th anniversary meeting of the World Muscle Society in September 2005.

Accompanying spouse

I always had aspirations of one day going to a congress as an accompanying spouse, having often envied the congress companion attendees, who were able to visit all the cultural and other activities of real interest, whilst their better halves were confined to barracks in the lecture rooms. I did actually take the opportunity to play truant at the meeting of the European Society of Pediatric Research in Lausanne one year, when I thought the ladies' programme with a visit to a cheese factory much more educational than any of the four parallel sessions at the meeting. My opportunity eventually came when Lil had an invitation to assess low-birthweight newborn infants in New Guinea and subsequently in the malaria research centre at Shoklo in Thailand.

Newborns in New Guinea

In 1987 Lil had a communication from Paul Garner, a physician from the London School of Hygiene and Tropical Medicine, who had been working in New Guinea for some time on the nutrition of women during pregnancy. He had also become interested in the low birthweight of the newborn infants and recently a visiting Swedish psychologist had been applying the Dubowitz Score for assessing their gestational maturity at birth and concluded they were premature. This seemed to be in conflict with his own observations of the infants, which suggested they were fairly mature but only underweight, possibly due to poor nutrition of the mothers. He had some detailed discussions with Lil and was keen to get some advice. We commented it was difficult to offer any opinion without personally assessing the infants and to his surprise suggested we would be happy to come out and assess them if someone would cover our airfare. An

Husband and wife team hit the jungle trail

New Guinean tots put to the test

Wading knee-deep through rivers in sweltering tropical heat to study new born babies in remote jungle villages of Papua New Guinea is a far cry from paediatrics at Hammersmith Hospital.

But, with the renowned Dubowitz Score (see story left) penetrating even the exotic Melanesian island, Victor and Lilly Dubowitz last December found themselves on a rewarding fortnight's visit.

Advice

They were invited to the deprived Wosera region of the northern Sepik province where an English doctor, Paul Garner, has been running a programme on new born babies during the past year.

He wanted advice and interpretation of his data using the Dubowitz Score, a particularly useful method of assessing the age of a newborn in primitive societies where mothers do not keep a record of their menstrual cycle.

"Everything was well organised for us and we were able to assess 30 newborn infants, mainly in huts in isolated villages with no midwifery or medical support," says Professor Dubowitz.

Others were assessed in maternity units at local hospitals.

"Fortunately Dr Garner had formed a close relationship with these communities, who are normally very suspicious of any unexpected and unexplained interventions. He was able to communicate very well with them in the local pidgin."

Dr Garner had trained a New Guinean field worker without medical background, called Monassah, to do Dubowitz Scores on newborn babies.

The infants observed were of low birthweight — an average of 2.5kg, compared to 3.5kg in this country.

The question was whether the babies were mature and merely small-for-dates, or whether they were premature as had been suggested in an earlier study by a Swedish psychologist.

Mature

Dr Garner, who works for the New Guinea government subsidised Institute of Medical Research, believed it was the former.

Dr Dubowitz found excellent correlation between her assessment of individual babies and Dr Garner's assessment of the same infant.

"We concluded that these babies, although small, were all mature — but with a couple of unusual features such as relatively poor head control and immature ear structure," she says.

• Dr Lilly Dubowitz tests the reflexes of a newborn baby.

The couple, whose visit was funded by the Wellcome Trust, also carried out a neurological assessment of these babies and found they fitted into two groups.

One group behaved like full term babies of normal weight, while the other behaved like small-for-dates — hyperactive, hyperalert and hyperresponsive.

The latter resembled small-for-dates infants the Dubowitzes had previously studied in England and South Africa.

"As the local people habitually chew betel nuts, together with lime — which is a mild stimulant — we wondered whether some active constituent might cross the placenta or be in the breast milk and have some effect on the behavioural pattern of the infants," says Professor Dubowitz.

"Nutrition on the whole seemed good and there is a plentiful supply of fruit an[d] vegetables which are locall[y] grown and they also eat a lo[t] of different greens, some o[f] which have a high protein con[tent].

"Meat is rarely eaten an[d] fish only occasionally."

The biggest eye-opener fo[r] them was observing five t[o] six-month-old infants studie[d] by a Canadian nutritionist.

"These babies had remarkable acceleration of thei[r] development," says Professo[r] Dubowitz. "They were able t[o] sit unsupported and quit[e] steady and had remarkabl[e] hand co-ordination and man[ipulation], both equivalent t[o] the average nine month in ou[r] society."

The Dubowitzes think it' because the babies have muc[h] more contact with thei[r] mothers and the fact tha[t] they are constantly carrie[d] around on their mother' back, in a handwoven bilu[m] bag. A similar phenomeno[n] has been obserbed in Eas[t] Africa.

"The visit overall was extremely interesting and scientifically rewarding," says D[r] Dubowitz.

"We would welcome future opportunity of under[taking] a similar short ter[m] field study there."

In particular, the coupl[e] believe it would be fruitfu[l] doing comparative studies [of] larger and plumper babies [in] another area or betwee[n] hospital and village base[d] babies.

Visit to Papua New Guinea in 1987 to assess newborn babies for gestational maturity in remote villages in Sepik area, with Paul Garner

• Dr Lilly Dubowitz and her host, Dr Paul Garner, take the plunge en route to a remote Melanesian village.

Dubowitzes score a hit

Victor and Lilly Dubowitz met at a picnic in Virginia Water, Surrey, in 1960.

"I was attracted by the excellent Hungarian salami sandwiches she made," he says.

With a very busy work programme, the couple wasted little time and were married soon after.

They have usually collaborated in work, most notably in the Dubowitz Score, a gestational age chart which became States soon after its publication in 1970.

A system of assessing the age of a newborn baby independently of the mother's dates, it developed from Professor Dubowitz's personal interest in the 1960s which was subsequently evolved by his Hungarian-born wife.

Typically, the Americans have converted the eponym into a verb, the initial Dubowitz Score having become, "Have you done a Dubowitz "Have you Dubowitzed the baby."

South African born Professor Dubowitz (he comes from a small country town called Beaufort West, home of Professor Chris Barnard) is director of the Paediatric Department and co-director of the Jerry Lewis Muscle Research Centre at the medical school.

He joined Hammersmith Hospital in 1972, while Dr Dubowitz came three years

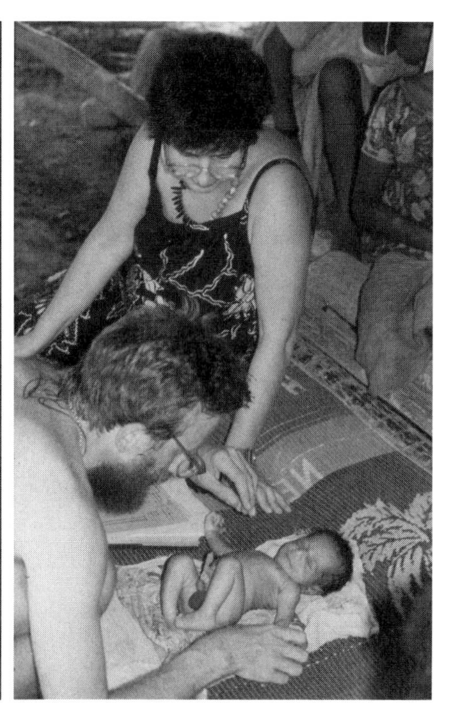

Lilly and Paul wading across a river to a village, to examine a newborn infant at entrance to the hut. Below: Lil assessing a 6-monther, with villagers looking on

application to the Wellcome Trust was successful and we accordingly headed off to New Guinea in 1987 for several weeks. We initially visited the general hospital in Madang, where the local population had better nutrition than in the remote Sepik area, and were able to assess some of the newborn infants there before flying on to the Sepik area, where they had a basic medical facility in a Catholic mission station in Kunjingini. The most precious commodity was electricity, available four hours each day from their generators.

The local paramedical assistants at the clinic were a great help in tracking down the pregnant women to their own small villages and we were eventually able to go and assess the newborn babies *in situ* in their huts, where their deliveries took place. It turned out that most of the infants were indeed at term and fully mature but undersized, probably as a result of poor nutrition of the mothers, who also did all the agricultural hard labour in the fields, while the men, when not hunting, spent their time at leisure in their meeting houses. It also seemed unlikely that the malaria, which was endemic in the area and affected almost all the mothers, was a factor, as the parasite does not cross the placenta from mother to fetus. Some of the abiding memories of that visit are the gathering of all the local villagers to watch the assessment of these newborn babies, usually on a sheet laid out outside the door of the hut, as it was too dark inside. I captured some of these moments on film and also the assessment of some of the older infants.

This visit opened the door for a number of further invitations for Lil to Malaria Research Centres in Thailand, Kenya and Malawi.

Toddlers in Thailand

Lil was invited by François Nosten, working with Médecins Sans Frontières in Thailand, and also the special Wellcome research group on malaria, to assess newborn infants in relation to the general problem of malaria in the mothers, at a Karen refugee camp at Shoklo, near Maesot in Northeast Thailand, on the border with Burma. On one of her visits my coast was also clear and I was able to go along. So while she was actively assessing the babies, I was able to indulge in my photoholic addiction and

Karen refugee village at Shoklo, on the Thai border with Burma

Family relaxing in shade under their hut

Local village school

Hill village in Northern Thailand. Infant being carried by older sibling, and by grandmother

take unrestrained pictures, either of the babies, or of the local infants in their school and other environments. I had a fun morning sitting in on the infant school and observing at first hand their enthusiasm for their lessons and also their decorum and discipline. It was quite remarkable to see these four- and five-year-olds being taught the basic reading and writing skills in three languages, with Thai and English in addition to their mother Karen tongue.

We were subsequently also able to organise a visit to various hill villages in northern Thailand plus a raft trip. It was of special interest to see infants being carried around by either their mothers or grandmothers or older siblings, who were at times hardly bigger than the infant.

Sadly, the Karen camp has finally had to close a few years back, when the marauding Burmese troops coming over the border, who had regularly harassed the Karen refugees from Burma in the past, now started harassing the hospital staff as well, which made it unsafe for the good work to continue and the whole team and facilities, organised by Médecins Sans Frontières, had to relocate to another place.

The lecturer's nightmare; leaving one's slides behind

A recurrent nightmare amongst academics is finding at the start of a lecture one has forgotten one's slides or brought the wrong set for the occasion. This happened to me on three occasions.

The first was in the 1960s, during a visit as guest lecturer in Jakarta, hosted conjointly by a local neurologist and the paediatric department. I stayed in the quarters of a hospital called the Friendship Hospital, built by the Russians, and was chauffeured around by my neurologist host. The morning I was giving a one-hour lecture on muscle diseases to the paediatric department, he duly collected me for breakfast and then drove me to the children's hospital. I got out of the car and as I was about to retrieve my leather bag with all my slides from the trunk of his car, he drove off, completely forgetting he had put them there. I met up with the paediatric professor, told him my plight and we then spent the next hour trying to track the neurologist down, but without success. The audience by this time was assembled in the lecture theatre so I had no alternative but to improvise. So with a good supply of chalk I then provided an hour's illustrated lecture, on the main muscle disorders of childhood, covering both the clinical and the pathological. I was rather surprised how one could build up visual images by careful description, aided with some freehand drawings.

The second occasion was some years later when I was giving the annual guest lecture as part of a visiting professorship at Edmonton, funded on an annual basis by oil revenues of the state of Alberta. It seems to be par for the course for me that I never get round to thinking about the lectures I have to be giving till the day before my departure, and as I was giving a comprehensive broadly based lecture on muscle disorders, I selected a series of slides, to cover about 50 minutes, with double projection.

I also took along a whole series of additional folding slide holders covering some additional aspects for subsidiary talks, which formed part of my comprehensive collection of about 6 or 7 folders of 80 slides each. As always I tried to combine my academic visits with some collateral travel, so Lil and I flew into Vancouver, hired a car and had a spectacular journey through the Rockies via Banff and Jasper and eventually reaching Edmonton a day ahead of my lecture.

A special dinner reception was arranged for that evening so by the time I got to our hotel I was just about ready for bed. I rapidly scanned through my packets of slides for the preselected main one for my lecture, only to find it was not there! I had brought all the remaining ones with various additional slides but not the comprehensive preplanned series. As this was a lecture open to all the local and regional paediatricians and other disciplines, there seemed no possibility of doing a Jakarta! So I set about preparing an alternative series of paired slides to substitute for my missing set.

By about 4 am I had just about completed the task. The only major one missing was a picture of a classical Duchenne dystrophy. So the following morning I met up with Mike Brooke, the senior neurologist whom I had known for many years since our early meeting in Denver and deciding to do a muscle pathology book together, and told him I seemed to have lost a couple of key slides of Duchenne dystrophy and could he lend me a couple for my lecture. He readily obliged, I gave my 50-minute lecture with double projection as planned and to this day I doubt anyone locally appreciates that it was a substitute *ad hoc* series of slides I had assembled for the auspicious occasion. I have learnt that an important principle in any lecture, is never to start with an apology! 'I am sorry but I left my main slides at home . . .' is not going to endear you to your audience and more than likely will just turn them off.

The next occasion was a somewhat similar crisis, with a completely different and somewhat novel solution. This was the 5th annual meeting of the World Muscle Society in 2000, and being our special 5th birthday meeting as well as the millennium, I felt we needed something special for the occasion. I planned the meeting in the Kruger National Park in South Africa, with the help of two very enthusiastic paediatric neurologists in Johannesburg, John Rodda and Gail Scher, and a superb congress organiser I had a met a few years earlier at a paediatric congress at the same venue, Barbara Lilienfeld. We had had an earlier visit to plan the details and had also arranged for our regular banquet of the society, a special outdoor barbecue. When we arrived for the actual meeting Barbara informed me that as a special treat and surprise she had arranged for us to have our banquet at a local shangaan village, with the local chief in his full leopard skin regalia in attendance. Our annual three-day meeting is structured with a selected topic of recent interest and growth within the field with a series of invited keynote speakers on each topic in the morning, and the rest of the time devoted to presentations, mainly by posters, of ongoing research and encouraging the young researchers to present their data rather than listening to the old icons. The first morning the topic was 'Advances in the muscular dystrophies', with five invited speakers covering different aspects. The programme committee asked me if in addition to my usual opening of the congress and words of welcome, I could provide an overview on 'What is muscular dystrophy?' for the benefit of our non-medical research colleagues. I duly prepared a series of double projection slides, pairing the clinical with the pathological to fill a 20-minute slot. I had this securely packed in my regular leather attaché case I always carry with me with my slides. I also needed to prepare a separate set of slides for another contribution I was giving, which I did the night before we flew out.

The first day of the congress most of the 250 participants were arriving with a special informal reception in the evening. The congress proper opened the following morning.

I got to my room about midnight and planned to have a quick look through my slides for the morning; only to discover that I had only brought the second pack along and had left the introductory lecture on my desk at home. A major crisis. No possibility of an alterative set of slides. No possibility of an illustrated blackboard presentation in the absence of a blackboard. The situation seemed deadlocked with no apparent solution. As I was about to call it a day, I had a sudden idea, and scribbled down a few notes on a card of paper.

The following morning after my usual introductory words of welcome, I started my presentation on 'What is muscular dystrophy?' with a commentary. 'I have bad news for you, but also good news. The bad news is I discovered at midnight last night that I had inadvertently left my folder of slides for this lecture on my desk at home, when finally checking the contents of my bag the night before departure. The good news is that we have a special treat for you thanks to Barbara, and shall be having our annual banquet at the local Shangaan village with the chief, together with his special entourage of singers and traditional African dancers in attendance. I felt it appropriate to pay a courtesy visit to the chief on arrival yesterday to tell him how much we valued his hospitality and to explain a bit about our society. I told him we were concerned with muscle diseases such as muscular dystrophy. He then asked me 'What is muscular dystrophy?' And I then proceeded to explain to him, in plain English. And that is what I now intend to do. I then gave a 20-minute talk, without slides, on the topic, covering all aspects and referring by name to various colleagues in the audience, who had made seminal contributions to the clinical aspects, the pathology, the biochemistry and the genetics of the muscular dystrophies. Several colleagues afterwards commented, 'Why do you bother with slides? It's so much more intelligible without!'

Cape Town 50th reunion; return to roots

In December 2004 we had a 50th reunion of our 1954 medical class and in addition to the usual social and culinary activities, they also introduced for the first time a regraduation ceremony, with the usual pomp and glory and gowns and hoods. In addition the public orator gave a thumbnail comment on the subsequent career of each individual. There was also an additional 'academic session', perhaps to allow the local people to claim tax rebate, at which individuals could present details of their activities. There were still around 80 survivors of our original 120 graduates, and 40 attended, coming from all corners of the globe, in addition to the local sedentary ones. What was remarkable was the diversity of activities of our class and also the high number who were still in active practice, one way or another, in their seventies.

I also took the opportunity for an extended trip into the eastern Cape Province, and in particular to visit, for the first time in my life, Aberdeen, the birthplace of my father and grandmother, and the wedding place of my grandparents. I was able to add the details to the first chapter. I also revisited Beaufort West which is hardly recognisable any more. The original tree-lined main street has lost all its trees and is now a busy route for a constant stream of heavy trucks in both directions, being on the main road from Cape Town to the north. My father's shop and our adjoining house were converted into the first night club in the town, after the end of apartheid, and a pool table now stands where my bed used to be. I think my father, who always had a good sense of fun, would have approved of the new facility.

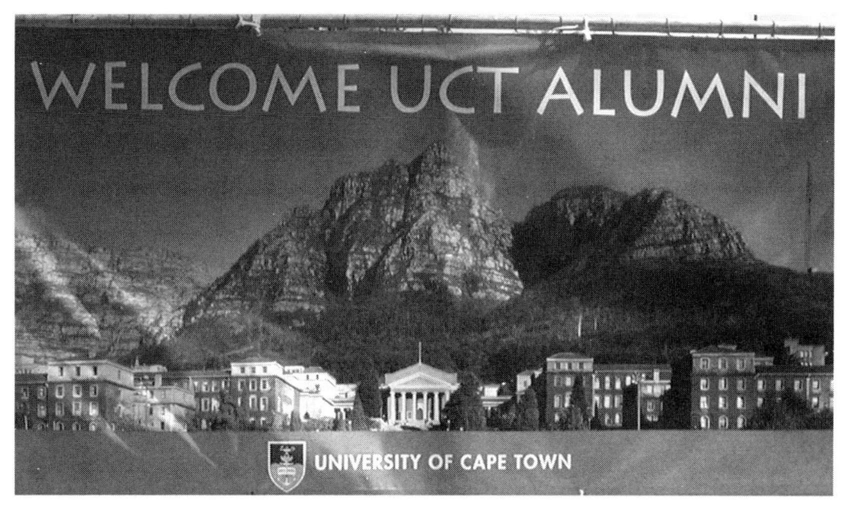

Welcome banner University of Cape Town

50th anniversary reunion and regraduation, UCT, December 2004

Mossie and Marlene Silbert, myself, Simmy and Sybil Bank, David Stein behind

Beaufort West 2004. Donkin Street now a busy trucking root

My father's shop now a night club, with the adjoining house gutted and integrated. A pool table now stands on the spot of my childhood bed

15

Changing face of medicine

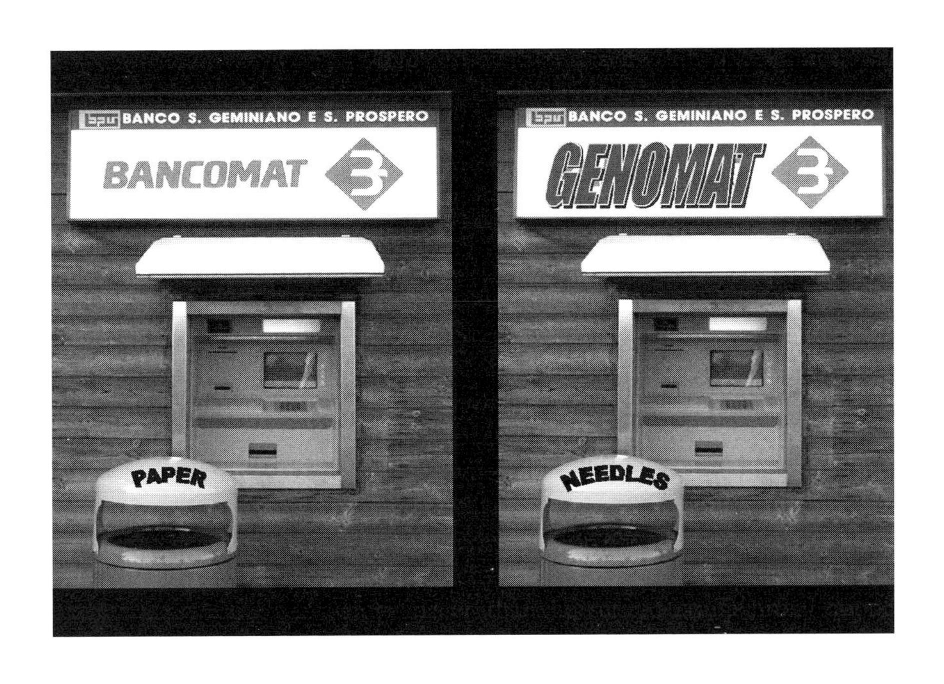

During my residency year at Groote Schuur Hospital in Cape Town, I had already become aware of the importance of a social dimension to the very intensive workload, when one regularly worked through the night, in addition to the previous and following day, when on take and call for emergency admissions. The intermittent relaxation afforded by short breaks in the nurses' office on the ward and being provided some of the traditional toasted banana sandwiches somehow managed to provide an important dimension in making one's work pleasurable and not exhausting.

At Queen Mary's Hospital for Children things were even better, as we had a very dedicated staff looking after the doctors' mess and providing refreshments at all times, in addition to the excellent daily menu and Sunday roast we had from the patients' kitchen. There was also a tremendous spirit at Christmas time, when there were some four or five Christmas dinners in the course of about a week. One was for the doctors and nurses at which the catering and admin staff officiated with the services, another for the admin, waited on by the doctors and nurses and another for the domestic and ancillary staff at which doctors also officiated in addition to other staff. This made for a tremendous amount of rapport and goodwill between the different tiers of staff.

At the doctor's Christmas dinner, Mike Harris and I decided to provide a bit of entertainment and put on a floorshow. Dressed up in nurses' uniform, one in pink stripes, the other in green, designating different levels of seniority, we sang a series of verses to the tune of 'Darkie Sunday School' with a refrain after each verse for audience participation. There was a stunned silence when we announced that in keeping with the solemnity of the occasion, we thought it appropriate to have some hymn singing as an interlude and would shortly be handing out the scripts of the hymns. We then circulated individual sheets with the refrain of our songs on, printed on the NHS firm transparent toilet paper, which was hallmarked either 'Government Property' or 'On Her Majesty's Service'.

The following is a small selection.

Refrain: (to tune of Darkie Sunday school)

Green stripes, pink stripes, everybody come
Join Queen Mary's Hospital, you'll have a lot of fun
Take a swig of lucozade, and sit upon the floor,
And we'll sing you smutty stories, like you've never heard before.

Queen Mary's is an institute, of credit and renown
It is a children's hospital, not far from London town
It cares for toddlers big and small, and infants in the arms
And gives us nurses every chance, to advertise our charms.

The matron is our mother; she is so good and kind,
She listens to our problems, and troubles on our mind,
If anyone should dare to breathe a single nasty line,
We'll get our lynching party out; they stand by all the time.

Some sisters here from GOS are full of pomp and pride,
They think they run the hospital, without them it would slide,
They may have trained with VIPs, or with the House of Kent,
We have no time for snobbery, on nursing we are bent.

The Chairman of Establishment, a lady straight and true,
Decides on the appointments, and tells us what to do.
'Do you like the children?' she asks, she almost sobs.
We hate the little buggers, but we badly need the jobs.

I had the sudden inspiration to start writing these verses and to incorporate some of the ongoing characters at the hospital into them. Thus it was commonly known how caring the matron (senior nurse) was for her junior nurses, who often referred to her as their mother. She also used to have a standard question when sitting on the medical appointment boards for the junior medical staff 'Do you like the children?'

Many years later in 1974, I felt the whole system was dealt a body blow when the then Secretary of State for Social Services in Harold Wilson's labour government, Barbara Castle, announced that doctors should no longer scrounge free coffee on the wards and nurses were strictly banned from providing any such luxury. I thought it was an excellent example of bureaucratic politicians having absolutely no concept of all the additional activities doctors and others provide in a purely voluntary way and as a token of goodwill to the whole system. So it marked the end of the extra hour or so I regularly spent on the ward each week, having a cup of coffee with the senior nurse and trying to help resolve many of the day-to-day problems in the running of the unit.

During that same Government, there were efforts to bring the salaries for academics with consultant status into line with their health service counterparts, who always got increments ahead of the academics, who then had to negotiate for parity. This was finally resolved some years later by putting the clinical academics on the clinical salary scale and not aligned to the university scales.

At the junior level there were also efforts to get an overall reduction in the hours worked per week and a rise in the basic salary. Eventually the minister for health came up with a payment system for units of work ('units of medical time') rather than a flat salary, so there were units for routine duties and separate units for out-of-hours duty and so forth. This might have seemed reasonable for the residents but almost overnight it wiped out a tremendous resource which had been provided, without cost, for the health service, in the highly motivated clinical trainees, who came from abroad for postgraduate specialised experience in our unit, particularly in relation to newborn care. They were only too happy to provide on-call cover at night as part of our rota, without fee, in order to keep up their clinical skills. Once everything related to fee for service, the residents became reluctant to give up any of their paid sessions to the volunteers from abroad. There was also a new development which from the beginning I found ominous. Once the system became more rigid and hide-bound, and the residents had a fixed contract in relation to their hours on duty, various bureaucratic rules were introduced, such as a complete embargo on doing any additional duties beyond their on-service hours, even on a voluntary unpaid basis. This usually meant that if a resident was on duty through a night, he was obliged to go off duty at a stipulated hour, and was debarred from attending the consultant's round in the morning to discuss the cases he had admitted during the night. This was obviously a major disadvantage to both the service for the patient and the education of the resident. One could already envisage a shift system gradually evolving, where the residents would come on and go off at a fixed hour and simply hand over to the next shift to take over, even in midstream. Out of the window goes all the personal interrelationship of doctor and patient.

Inevitably each generation will adapt to the circumstances of the times, and be able to look forward rather than back. So here are a few examples of resident life from the next generation, through the experiences of two of our sons. I think a classical example of the predictable aftermath of this creeping antisocial indifference of the administration towards the residents came a couple of decades later when one of our sons was a junior doctor at Northampton General Hospital. During the nights on call, when they were obliged to be resident, the bed linen was only changed once a week and the only way the doctors could ensure clean linen for the next occupant was to strip the bed and put all the linen in the washbasin and fill it with water.

A somewhat similar experience was repeated when on medical take and emergency call one weekend (Friday night till Monday morning) at a teaching hospital in west London. The residents were informed by the nursing staff on the ward that they had received a message from the administration that there was no food available for the on-call staff for the whole weekend. So all the residents for the different specialties got together and drew lots on who was going to protest to the senior administrator on call. The resident who drew the short straw phoned the administrator on call, who responded 'That has nothing to do with me!' After a bit of further pressure on the seriousness of the situation and the image the hospital might get if there were some unfortunate headlines in the Monday morning daily newspapers, he then suggested that perhaps they could just pop out for a Chinese takeaway. When it was pointed out that the resident was the only trained person on call for cardiac emergencies and carried the 'crash' bleep, he suggested one of his colleagues could go out and get the takeaway for him. It took a formal letter of protest the Monday morning to the senior consultant to take some steps to remedy the totally unacceptable situation and to take it up officially with the (non-resident) senior administrator.

And the bureaucrats wonder why the junior staff are constantly complaining these days and demanding shorter hours. It's not so much the pressure of work or even the EU rules and guidelines but simply that the whole goodwill has been knocked out of the system and doctors are treated like any other employees, rather than a caring profession with a direct interpersonal relationship with their patients. It becomes difficult to go whistling to work in such a hostile environment.

A proliferation of bureacrats

The Royal Postgraduate Medical School, established in 1935, was the only multidisciplinary medical school in the country devoted entirely to postgraduate education. It was also unique among hospitals with academic links with medical schools, in that the clinical professors who were heads of the academic departments were also the Directors of Clinical Service. This was a special arrangement, the so-called 1951 agreement, whereby the University provided the senior medical consultant staff from its academic ranks, whereas the junior hospital staff were all provided from the National Health Service budget. This did not pose any particular problem for the academics, as one could organise a clinical service of excellence in about 10% of one's available time. But all that gradually changed and the tail gradually started wagging the dog with increasing ferocity.

The 1970s saw a tremendous escalation of bureaucracy within the health service under government 'expansion' schemes, with the creation of three tiers of control and funding, at District, Area, and Regional level, each of which had its separate boards. A vast army of new administrators was created, who seemed to be very busy moving bumf either vertically, up and down, between the different levels of control, or laterally, to left and to right, within one level. A collective noun for bureacrats could be 'a proliferation', as they seem to be self-generating.

To add to the vast amount of paperwork this generated, one also started receiving regular family trees, which mapped out the gradual expansion within the hospital as each administrator needed a deputy and new tiers of people were appointed for responsibility for all the subsidiary activities on site. And yet there was still only one of me. I guess one would just have sunk into the quicksand of bureaucracy and disappeared without trace, if one did not have a superb PA to shield one from the constant onslaught and to filter off all the immaterial.

As with politicians, who from time to time find themselves doing U-turns, new developments gradually turn out not to live up to expectations, and after a few years, politicians suddenly realise the reality, which has been obvious to everyone else from the outset, that the system and its vast expenditure have not produced commensurate improvement of service at the patient level, and the whole system goes full circle back to square one. So the extra tiers of administration were gradually pared off and in the 1980s we saw the emergence of a new breed of young career hospital managers, who were from the same yuppie brigade who were rapidly ascending the ladders of commerce in the wider world.

And so our paediatric department saw the appointment of one of this new breed, who had collective responsibility for the lesser half of the hospital covering paediatrics, obstetrics and geriatrics and a few additional services. He duly appeared at our weekly (or more frequent) meetings with a very impressive leather case, somewhat reminiscent of the Chancellor of the Exchequer, but without the embossed coat of arms, and displaying a leather-bound personal organiser book, wrapped in a soft protective cloth. Despite endless discussions on urgent needs and preparing priority lists, very little came to fruition and much more energy was directed by these managers to saving money rather than spending it. And there seemed to be a spiralling ongoing programme of saving funds and reducing budgets to meet performance targets. In one particular year, when most hospitals found themselves beyond their budget, there was widespread constraint on services to save money. And there was no question that the major goal of hospital managers was to manage the budget and produce savings rather than to focus on patient services. And the health service in turn provided brownie points and financial rewards for efficient managers able to rein in their budget.

This was well reflected in an informal chat I had with our manager at the annual open day get-together around Christmas time, when the hospital played host to all the staff over snacks and cocktails for the afternoon. I usually ensured that I got along to these events for the last half hour or so after completing my day's activities. No sooner had I exchanged greetings with my manager than he started complaining about the doctors being uncooperative and not pulling their weight, in the interests of the hospital. I was puzzled and asked him to explain what exactly he meant.

'Well,' he explained, ' the situation is that we have been trying our best to save funds in order to keep within our budget; we have closed wards, we have closed operating theatre sessions; and yet there has been no fall in the patient throughput and the doctors are still seeing too many patients.'

I looked at him in stunned silence and disbelief for a few moments and then gave him a possible solution. 'I think you have really got the wrong end of the stick, Paul,' I said. 'If you really want to save money the first thing you have to do is to get rid of the doctors. Then you get rid of the nurses. Then you will inevitably have a fall in patient numbers and you will save a lot of money.'

He seemed to reflect on it for a few moments, and then came back, in all seriousness 'You know I think you are quite right. Can you suggest some of the services that we don't really need at Hammersmith.' A few moments pause for further reflection. 'For example, do we need orthopaedics in an academic hospital?' 'Of course, we don't need orthopaedics,' I egged him on, 'it could readily be done elsewhere.' His mind was obviously ticking over. 'That could save us £300,000 per year!' 'Now what about my muscle clinic, Paul?' 'That should be fine.' 'But what do we do if we want to pursue our regular programme of rehabilitation of boys with muscular dystrophy and then keep them ambulant in callipers, after surgical release of their ankle tendons by the orthopods?' 'That is a bit of a problem.'

While this appeared almost like pantomime at the time, on now looking back with some hindsight, perhaps I was the one who was being naïve and this was all an orchestrated effort of the hospital administration to cut back services in order to save funds and help the government of the day to achieve its goals for the NHS. Not long afterwards there was a concerted effort by the hospital administration to close the physiotherapy department of the hospital in the interests of rationalisation and economic expediency, notwithstanding that it was a major service department.

Musical chairs; bureaucracy calls the tune

But this process was coming right from the top and the then current conservative government, with Virginia Bottomley as

Minister of Health in the driving seat, was pressing hard to combine various London hospitals in the interests of rationalisation, and setting up working parties with Fellows of the Royal Society and knights of the realm, in order to advise her. There was a campaign to close St Bartholomew's Hospital in the city, with a tradition of serving the city over many centuries, and of fusing Guy's Hospital and St Thomas' Hospital and trying to move the major services to the St Thomas' site, where most members of parliament sought medical attention.

There was also a major campaign to fuse the Hammersmith Hospital with Charing Cross and to move the whole complex to the Charing Cross site, mainly it was surmised for the political reason that the local area was a marginal Conservative seat. Two separate independent working parties, at an unspeakable cost, who had looked into all the logistics of the move, came to the same conclusion that as all the major research and state of the art equipment and personnel were based at Hammersmith, it would be much more logical for the clinical services of the Charing Cross Hospital to be moved to the Hammersmith site. So, after some three years of major site appraisals and meetings with academics and disruption of the academic activities of many staff, and causing a tremendous sense of insecurity amongst them, the minister, in her wisdom, decided the best solution was the status quo, and let us just all go back to square one, as if nothing had happened.

But the whole protracted process had major implications for our own department. The rationalisation programme also moved to academia and a concerted plan was evolved to rationalise the large number of independent medical schools in the capital from thirteen to four by a process of fusion and amalgamation. And so it came to pass that four medical schools in west London, the Royal Postgraduate Medical School, St Mary's, Charing Cross, and Chelsea Westminster, were brought together under the collective umbrella of Imperial College, world renowned for its pre-eminence in science and technology, boasting several Nobel laureates, and equivalent to America's MIT. Imperial had already absorbed some of the preclinical departments in biochemistry and physiology from St Mary's into its orbit, but had not previously had any clinical schools. So the independent medical schools ceased to exist, although they did retain their individual campuses. Academic rationalisation soon followed with the appointment of one nominal head of a specialty such as paediatrics at one of the campuses to take administrative responsibility of the whole.

There was now a combined force of academic and clinical rationalisation, with Professor Michael Levin at St Mary's being the nominal academic head of paediatrics across the four campuses. There was also a decision to close the in-patient paediatric services at Hammersmith and to concentrate them at St Mary's. Of course once the announcement was made, there was a mass exodus of nurses from the children's wards, seeking alternative posts, and the wards actually had to close several months ahead of schedule. A feather in the cap for the efficient, cost-saving bureaucrats. There was also a master plan to move our whole neuromuscular unit, together with its clinical and academic staff, and also the associated laboratories geared to investigation and research, to newly provided facilities at the St Mary's site.

We are now more than five years on and no additional facilities have been provided at St Mary's, and the muscle unit has still not moved, and remains in isolation at the Hammersmith site, without a general paediatric in-patient facility. And discussions have now been opened for at least re-establishing some degree of in-patient service at Hammersmith for the immediate needs of the Muscle unit.

But the effects are far more far reaching. The whole department has come full circle in little over 25 years, since my appointment to the newly-established faculty chair of paediatrics at the Royal Postgraduate Medical School at Hammersmith. My main brief at my appointment had been to expand the general paediatrics at an academic level in addition to the well established neonatal unit. We now once again have an isolated, highly efficient, neonatal unit functioning in an even more complete vacuum, without a general paediatric service.

And as for my own post, it is interesting to look back on the various hidden agendas that arose after I took early retirement within the university system. One of the suggestions was to fuse obstetrics and paediatrics under a combined academic umbrella, and thus conserve the cost of the paediatric chair, presumably for more urgent needs in the medicine monolith. There was an overture to attract into such a post, Charles Rodeck, the

Professor of Obstetrics, with whom we had a lot of common interests in fetal medicine and prenatal diagnosis. But he had his own agenda and shortly after moved to the obstetrics chair in University College Medical School.

After many years of constant efforts to get the well established Queen Charlotte's Hospital with its isolated obstetrics and neonatal facilities to move into the fold, it finally moved in recent years onto the Hammersmith site, into a new most impressive state-of-the-art building, but still retaining a peculiar autonomy as functioning not as a department of obstetrics within the school and Hammersmith Hospital but as an autonomous Queen Charlotte's Hospital on the Hammersmith site.

Soon after my retirement, through the concerted efforts of the Dean of the school, David Kerr, and Mike Silverman, longstanding reader in the department and expert on respiratory medicine, who was appointed as interim head of department, the school managed to scoop one of its largest awards of several million pounds to establish a chair of neonatal neurology research. It also included a senior lecturer position, and support for a laboratory and personnel, in order to further this important and growing area of neonatal paediatrics, which was already well established at the Hammersmith. The appointee was David Edwards, a bright young researcher who had established a niche for himself in neonatal research at University College Hospital. This was an exciting new initiative and an excellent appointment and had the makings of a major new force in neonatal neurology. It also seemed absolutely essential that his position in research be protected, and that he were not overburdened with administration. As I saw it, he needed complete protection from it, equivalent to the sort of firewall one needs these days on broadband internet access to keep all those threatening viruses out.

Mike Silverman was certainly very conscious of this. But after a second year in a temporary position as head of the department, he gave the then Dean, Colin Dollery, an ultimatum that either they appoint him to the definitive chair, or he would like to step down into his previous position, dropping all the administrative commitments, and get on with his respiratory research programme. That is exactly what happened. The next temporary appointee was David Harvey, senior lecturer in the department, based at Queen Charlotte's, who had originally trained in Peter

Tizard's department at the Hammersmith and had been running the neonatal unit at Charlotte's since the time of my arrival at Hammersmith in 1972. Mike Silverman's post was also not refilled after he moved to a chair of paediatrics in Leicester. The department was now essentially back to a neonatal unit plus the muscle unit, with the loss of the specialised respiratory unit and also paediatric haematology which was shipped off to St Mary's.

David Harvey proved a good administrator and very compliant from the Dean's point of view and was then appointed as Director of Services for Paediatrics. Gradually more and more administrative responsibility started falling on David Edwards, until he was appointed Head of the Division of Paediatrics, Obstetrics and Gynaecology. He fairly jubilantly informed me some time later that he had just been appointed Director of Services for Paediatrics and Obstetrics. And the final nail in the academic coffin has recently been announced with the disappearance of individual disciplines such as paediatrics and obstetrics, and the fusion into divisions, with individual staff members within a department having a choice on which division to align to. So the neonatal unit has remained with obstetrics and the muscle unit has moved to medicine. And not a trace of paediatrics on the site of the one-time vibrant multidisciplinary Royal Postgraduate Medical School. *O tempora! O mores!*

Academic musical chairs

Meanwhile, back at the ranch, the muscle unit had also been caught up in the pangs of reorganisation.

A number of concurrent and sequential events had a dramatic influence on the future of our neuromuscular unit and I am sure reflect similar experiences in many other units in the same maelstrom. The early 1990s saw the coalescence of the four West London medical schools, RPMS, St Mary's, Charing Cross and Chelsea-Westminster into Imperial College and the demise of the independent schools. A special dissolution party and 'celebration' was thrown by the RPMS at the time of its demise – a remarkable combination of a lavish festival and a wake. In parallel with these events, the Medical Research Council, which is the primary governmentally funded research body in the country, was trimming its budget and rationalising its commitments and decided to close the Clinical Research Unit, that had been running for many years on the Northwick Park Hospital site. As anticipated, many of the research teams voluntarily started seeking greener pastures and by the time of the closure there were only a small number of selected research groups that the MRC was still supporting.

A new initiative was then embarked on between the MRC and the Wellcome Trust, an independent body supporting medical research, originally set up by the pharmaceutical company Wellcome Burroughs, and currently having a budget for research comparable to the MRC, to establish a new research centre on the Hammersmith site, jointly funded by the two bodies. This came to fruition and a new building was erected. A director was sought for this and after the usual head hunting process, Kay Davies from Oxford, a senior MRC research scientist, was appointed to the post. I personally was very happy about her appointment and fully supported it, as she also had a longstanding interest in neuromuscular disorders and we had worked collaboratively over the years on a number of clinico-genetic programmes. She made it conditional for her appointment that she would also be the director of the muscle research laboratories and this also seemed reasonable, although it was a departure from my longstanding efforts to integrate clinical and basic research and not to drive a wedge between them, as Arthur Buller, a physiologist, had favoured when secretary of the Muscular Dystrophy Group, by establishing two separate granting committees, one for basic research and the other for clinical service. It did also mean giving up the one office I had included in the new building for the director, that I envisaged would continue to be a clinical scientist.

The Dean of the Postgraduate Medical School was also very pleased with her appointment and within a short space of time she was given a personal professorship within the school and also appointed as vice-dean for research, which essentially gave her executive control of all research within the school in addition to the MRC/Wellcome unit of which she was director. Being very energetic and productive, she very rapidly set up collaborative genetic programmes with many of the clinical research groups within the school and all seemed to be progressing very smoothly.

But then the minister of health, Virginia Bottomley, put a spoke in the wheel, with a governmental drive to amalgamate Charing Cross and the Hammersmith Hospitals on one site, and a lightly-veiled threat to move to the Charing Cross site. This caused a tremendous upheaval amongst the academics and a sense of insecurity in the prolonged process of appraisals and site visits by expert committees set up for the purpose, and indeed many people did leave for other positions. More seriously, Kay Davies found her time more and more eroded by committee meetings she was obliged to attend for the appraisal process, which in turn reduced her available time for her research programme. I was able to monitor this closely by her infrequent visits to and conspicuous absence from the muscle laboratories. And after some two to three years of growing frustration, she decided to resign and move back to Oxford, where they created a professorship for her within the Department of Biochemistry on the retirement of the geneticist John Edwards, and she subsequently was appointed to the established chair of anatomy in the university.

Meanwhile our personal research projects in the neuromuscular field continued and my successor in the clinical department, Francesco Muntoni, pursued them with renewed vigour. He had been appointed, after my obligatory retirement at 65 years, into a lectureship post but was rapidly promoted through the ranks of senior lecturer and reader to a personal professorship within the university.

A major problem then arose because the Dean had a blinkered view that our neuromuscular unit couldn't possibly survive without Kay Davies and there was a recommendation to appoint her as honorary director of the unit and she would continue to administer and direct it by proxy from Oxford. More amazingly, the board of the Muscular Dystrophy Group were prepared to support this. So I personally lobbied the officers of the research board of the Muscular Dystrophy Group that the only sensible and practical solution was to appoint Francesco Muntoni as director of the unit and I was confident that he would ensure both the high standard of basic research within the unit and also an excellent clinical service involving diagnosis as well as management and treatment. And this finally prevailed and nobody has had any cause for regret. The unit has gone from strength to strength and the scientists within it have discovered a whole new group of genes within the muscular dystrophies, and the Department of Health has designated it as one of the national centres for referral of the group of congenital muscular dystrophies, which has been one of the special interests of the unit almost since its inception.

The problem for the future is the chaos caused by the fusion of paediatric services between Hammersmith and St Mary's and the closure of the in-patient paediatric services at Hammersmith, and the patent failure of the administration after five years to yet provide the additional facilities at St Mary's for the smooth transfer of the neuromuscular unit to the St Mary's site. Just as every executive in industry has his price, so every academic has his frustration flashpoint. The same bungling that eventually took Kay Davies to the end of her tether came very close to overstretching the tolerance and resilience of Francesco Muntoni.

Summary dismissal from the medical faculty

On the night of 1 December 2003, I was just finishing off for the night at about 2 in the morning and sending off my last batch of queued emails when the following email appeared in my inbox, timed at 01.00, 2 December.

> **Notification of removal from the Faculty of Medicine website**
> Dear Professor Victor Dubowitz,
> You are receiving this e-mail because your name has recently been automatically removed from the Faculty of Medicine website (names which no longer appear within the College's HR system as being members of the Faculty are automatically deleted from the site). This means you no longer have Faculty of Medicine member access to intranet areas of the site, and your Personal Page has been removed.
> If you believe your name has been removed in error, please contact Ms Rosie A Shaw (*r.a.shaw@imperial.ac.uk*) who will be able to help you further.
> If you have now left the Faculty of Medicine, we wish you all the best for the future.
> FACULTY OF MEDICINE WEB TEAM

I was frankly puzzled as I had an official appointment as emeritus professor in the medical faculty, which I had understood was for life. I was also extremely concerned that I would instantly be deprived of my email facility, which would be disastrous for my ongoing journal activities as well as my day-to-day communications worldwide.

So I immediately sent off a letter to Rosie Shaw, with a copy to David Edwards, head of paediatrics, that there had obviously been some error as I had emeritus status and the only possibility that crossed my mind was that I had been given a titular position in the department of Senior Investigator, which carried a small remuneration, and gave me the kudos of quoting the title and the department the right to include my publications in the annual department list. This was for a two-year period and indeed due to end at 30 November. I also wrote a separate letter to David Edwards asking him to extend the appointment for a further year if this was the easiest way of rapidly circumventing the bureaucracy. There was no further word through the next day but my email still remained active. That evening we had our muscle unit annual Christmas informal get-together party at a restaurant, with the usual joviality and conviviality. In the course of the evening I related to Francesco this unusual email I had received. 'Don't tell me about the bloody email!' he responded in his usual direct Italian manner. 'I also had one and I immediately send a reply "Please f**k off. I have no time for these practical jokes." '

The following morning I had still had no response so I wrote off again to Rosie Shaw and asked her in the first place to confirm she was a real humanoid, and not just a computer generated automaton, or possibly a virus. I added I was still concerned at my summary dismissal from the medical faculty but somewhat relieved to hear from a colleague that he had had a similar letter. Later that day I finally had a response, starting with an apology for the delay, but she had been a bit busy that morning sending out 7000 emails to the entire medical faculty who had had a similar letter. She was particularly sorry in addition that I had been omitted from the list of 7000, because indeed I was the only genuine case, as my contract as senior investigator had ended at this time. She was concerned that the system had not picked up that I actually had a position in addition of emeritus professor.

I wrote a pretty vitriolic letter back saying that while I was relieved to hear she actually existed, and could sympathise with her own predicament, I looked upon this as a serious case of academic abuse, comparable to any other form of battery, and demanded an official letter from the faculty of my reinstatement as emeritus professor.

I sent the correspondence for a laugh to my sons and one or two close friends in the academic circuit. The best response came from my eldest son, David, who is on the medical faculty at the University of California at San Diego, 'I must say that pissing off 7000 academics at one go is pretty impressive! As they say, to err is human, but to make a real cockup you really do need a computer. Guess you must be very proud to be back on the faculty of your prestigious institution.'

Clinical practice in the 21st century

The Italian muscular dystrophy association established a telethon in 1990 and I served on its foundation multidisciplinary research awards committee for several years, and later on its advisory committee, together with Peter Goodfellow from the UK and Jean-Louis Mandel from France. They were instrumental in attracting a large amount of funding from the Italian public in their annual telethon lasting some 32 hours.

The name telethon is a truncation of the words TELEvision and maraTHON and was created in the USA in 1966 when Jerry Lewis, the well known comic actor of screen and stage, started a marathon performance over the Labour Day weekend at the beginning of September each year, to raise money for research into muscular dystrophy, and it rapidly became an annual tradition.

In 1987 the French muscular diseases association AFM introduced a similar annual telethon in France, and went a stage further of patenting the name, so that no other charity could repeat the exercise! They very generously allowed the Italians to use their Telethon trademark.

The Italian telethon was able to promote and fund a vast amount of research in the muscle field and rapidly became an important player on the world stage. I regularly attended their annual conferences which had a large number of poster displays on ongoing research across the muscle field and later a broader genetic field, and also a symposium on a selected topic with a panel of invited experts. At the 1999 meeting in Rome, they had the fascinating topic of Clinical Practice in the 21st Century, chaired by Kay Davies, the well-known scientist in molecular genetics. I was struck by the fact that all four speakers were covering new developments in technology or gene therapy and there was no clinician in sight, which seemed a bit paradoxical to me. So I asked Kay if she could allow me a 5-minute slot at the beginning of the scheduled half hour discussion time at the end, to make a few comments, and she promptly agreed. In the event the speakers all overshot their time, in particular one scientist was so impressed with his new microarray technology that he ground on and on, with one example after another. Eventually they filled not only all the time allowed for discussion but were already encroaching on the lunch hour break and the audience were becoming palpably and audibly restive. It looked as though Kay was about to wrap up the session and break for lunch, with no discussion, so I waved my hand frantically. She took the cue and generously announced that no session on a look into the clinical practice of the next century could be complete without the view of a clinician, and who better, et cetera. So I rushed up to the podium, asked the audience's indulgence for just another three or four minutes, and commented that having listened to the four presentations, I had become convinced there might indeed be no need any longer for clinicians in the 21st century and that the traditional medical doctor, much like the traditional witch doctor of Africa, might be an endangered species. I then showed a series of self explanatory slides, with the opening remark, and image, that I envisaged that in parallel with every Bancomat, the well know Italian cash withdrawal machines, there would also be a GENOMAT for the automated diagnosis and management of muscle diseases (see p. 459).

I was very relieved during the buffet lunch hour by the large number of the audience, many of whom were clinicians, who came not to criticise me for invading further into the lunch hour, but to thank me for bringing a breath of fresh air and a bit of light relief into the very terse scientific session.

Clinical Practice in 21st Century

- Italian Telethon Annual Congress

- *Chairperson:* KayDavies Ph.D.
- Four presentations by molecular scientists

Clinical Practice in 21st Century

- Welcome to the automated molecular / biochemical muscle diagnostic service
- Insert your fee
- Choose 1. molecular or 2. Biochemical
- Insert forearm into slot for blood sample and muscle biopsy
- Note your reference number; *gssu 021* wait for results; current delay 40 min

Clinical Practice in 21st Century

- Welcome back. Insert fee and ref. no.
- Results: exon 7 deletion in *SMN* gene
- Diagnosis : spinal muscular atrophy
- Prognosis : variable; from bad with early death to mild with minimal disability
- Didactics: As you are attending yourself you are probably over 2 years & walking therefore better prognostic group

Clinical Practice in 21st Century
Therapeutic Options

Insert fee ; select one of these options:

- 1. Gene therapy (new genes)
- 2. Biochemicotherapy (new proteins)
- 3. Immunotherapy (knockouts)
- 4. Traditional medicine (20th Century)

Insert internet personal contact chip ID

Clinical Practice in 21st Century

- If you wish to see the doctor press here
- Indicate urgency 1, 2, or 3
- Current waiting time (priority 1) : 3 years
- Thank you for using the automated muscle diagnostic service
- Goodbye and Godspeed
- *GSSU inc.*

Clinical Practice in 21st Century

- Footnote:

- *GSSU : God Shall Save Us*

Postscript

Looking back over the past 50 years I feel extremely privileged to have lived through some of the most dramatic advances in the history of mankind, both in medicine and in general.

Large-scale immunisation programmes have virtually eliminated the common childhood illnesses, which were still a scourge and fear of my own childhood, such as diphtheria, poliomyelitis, measles and whooping cough. There is a distinct danger of these diseases coming back again if one loses the herd immunity by the misguided anxieties of potentially rare complications of immunisation terrifying parents by intense media attention. Unfortunately they are still a scourge in underdeveloped countries.

Another triumph has been the virtual disappearance of the complications of streptococcal sore throat such as rheumatic fever and associated heart disease. At Queen Mary's Hospital for Children in 1957 there was still a whole ward full of children at long-term bed rest for rheumatic heart disease.

The advent of chemotherapy and sophisticated techniques of radiation has had a major impact on cancer, although there is still a long way to go in some of the commonest adult cancers such as breast and prostrate. In childhood leukaemia I have personally experienced the remarkable change from seeing as a medical student a 16 year-old-girl with acute leukaemia, who died within six weeks of the onset, whereas now we can expect complete remission in most cases.

The tremendous advances in molecular genetics and the encoding of the whole human genome have heralded a new era for potential treatment of genetic diseases, including all the crippling neuromuscular disorders of childhood. Despite all the fanfare and tremendous hype over the past few years in relation to gene therapy, this still remains a goal for the future.

In parallel with all these advances in medicine for the benefit of mankind, it has been sad to witness the continuing savagery of man to his fellow man. We have witnessed in our lifetime two of the most brutal and barbaric butchers of all time in Hitler and Stalin, murdering millions of innocent citizens. Yet, despite the posturing of the United Nations and the lip service of the powerful nations to never allowing the holocaust to recur, we continue to witness genocide in one country after another. And civilians continue to be caught up in one conflict after another and to be mere statistics, or collateral damage, in the various campaigns with the ever more sophisticated modern weapons of destruction. The memory of the first atomic bomb on Hiroshima 60 years ago, which wiped out 140,000 people in one day, needs to be kept alive.

It is also paradoxical that half the world should be fighting obesity, whereas the other half are battling against famine. And whilst the AIDS pandemic does not respect any geographical boundaries, it is again the poor countries as in Africa that have fared worst with inexplicable political posturing and denial, and inadequate access to potentially beneficial treatment.

To end on a more positive note, I feel reassured that in spite of one's obvious anxieties for the future, each generation has had to cope with comparable challenges and has in turn found the most expedient solutions.

Index

Page entries in italics denote illustrations